# GRAVITY

To Sue

Live Long and Prosper!

5th February 2016

Nicholas Mee

Other titles by Nicholas Mee

*Higgs Force: Cosmic Symmetry Shattered*


Multimedia CD-ROMs

*Higgs Force Interactive*

*POLYTOPIA*

*Art and Mathematics*

*Life, the Universe and Mathematics*

*Symbolic Sculpture*
John Robinson and Nicholas Mee

*The Code Book* on CD-ROM
Simon Singh and Nicholas Mee

*Maths Lesson Starters*
David Benjamin, Justin Dodd and Nicholas Mee

*Nubble!*
Edgar Fineberg, Jack Berkovi and Nicholas Mee

*Connections in Space*
Nicholas Mee, John Barrow, Martin Kemp and Richard Bright

*Key Concepts in Chemistry*
Debra Nightingale and Nicholas Mee

# GRAVITY
## Cracking the Cosmic Code

**Nicholas Mee**

Virtual Image Publishing
www.virtualimage.co.uk

Published by
**Virtual Image Publishing Ltd**
www.virtualimage.co.uk

ISBN (HB): 978-1-9015794-8-2
ISBN (PB): 978-1-9015794-9-9

*British Library Cataloguing in Publication Data*
A record is available from the British Library

First Published 2014

# Contents

The colour plates can be found between pages 218 and 219.

# INTRODUCTION

## *Can You Feel the Force?*

I aim to convince you that you have never felt the force of gravity – strange, but true.

Newton's analysis of gravity provided the critical impetus that kick-started the modern scientific age, yet Newton's theory of gravity is still widely misunderstood. School pupils are often taught that there is no gravity in space, and this is why astronauts feel weightless. This misleading statement is passed on to pupils despite the fact that the main motivation for Newton's theory of gravity was to explain the motion of the planets around the Sun through space.

Clearly, it is absurd to suggest that there is no gravity in space. The Moon remains in orbit. The whole solar system is bound together by gravity. Indeed, the hundreds of billions of stars that straddle the night sky as the Milky Way are whirling around in a gravitational embrace that forms our galaxy. Gravity diminishes with distance, but never completely disappears. The galaxy, which has a diameter of 100,000 light years, is held together by the gravitational attraction of the stars and other matter that it contains.

So why do astronauts feel weightless, while the rest of us, who are bound to the Earth, are weighed down by more than our responsibilities? The first thing to note is that gravity affects all objects in the same way. We know when an object is acted on by a force because, in accordance with Newton's definition, its velocity changes. In other words, it accelerates. The force of gravity is special, because it produces the same acceleration for all objects. This means that all objects – be they atoms, electrons, chairs, elephants or spaceships – fall in the same way under the force of gravity.

We can appreciate what makes gravity special by considering a different force. Take the electromagnetic force, for example. It is clear that electromagnetism affects different materials in different ways. A positive electric charge will repel another positively charged object and will attract a negatively charged object, but it will not affect an uncharged object. As the mass of an object increases, it becomes more difficult to change its motion. We express this observation by saying that a more massive object has more inertia. For this reason, the electromagnetic force will produce a bigger acceleration on a lightweight charged object than on a more massive charged object.

What is different about gravity? According to Newton's theory, gravity acts on the mass of an object. Mass plays a similar role in gravity to that played by electric charge in electromagnetism. The size of the gravitational force felt by an object depends on its mass – the greater the mass, the bigger the force. However, it is also true that the greater the mass, the greater the inertia, which means that the greater the mass of an object, the more difficult it is to change its rate of motion. It is a unique feature of gravity that mass plays this dual role. It increases the size of the force, but it simultaneously decreases the size of the response to the force. The result is a perfect cancellation of these two effects. So the acceleration of an object due to the force of gravity is independent of its mass. In other words, all objects undergo the same acceleration due to gravity, whatever their mass. This was first demonstrated by Galileo about 400 years ago.

The result is that the trajectory followed by an object, when acted on solely by the force of gravity, is the same irrespective of its mass. Earth-dwellers often find this quite hard to accept, which is why the Apollo astronauts felt the need to offer an explicit demonstration.[1] After the completion of a moonwalk, the commander of Apollo 15 David Scott, held out a geological hammer and a feather and dropped them simultaneously in front of a video camera. In the absence of any atmosphere, the hammer and feather fell without any air resistance; the only force acting on them was the Moon's gravity and, sure enough, both fell with the same acceleration and reached the Moon's surface together.

What would it feel like to fall towards the Moon's surface along with the feather and the hammer? We would fall at the same rate as these other objects and hit the ground alongside both. Even more importantly, all the parts of our body would be accelerated in exactly the same way. Our head would fall with the same acceleration as our kneecaps. Our feet would fall with the same acceleration as our boots, with the result that we would not feel anything at all – we would be weightless. There is nothing special about gravity on the Moon. What is special about the Moon is that it is airless and, as there is no air resistance, the only force acting on us would be gravity.

If we found ourselves in orbit – on a visit to the International Space Station, maybe – we would again be in a situation where the only force acting on us would be gravity. Our spacecraft and ourselves within it would be accelerated towards the Earth, but our orbital motion would ensure that we continue to loop the Earth. We would again feel weightless, because every part of our body – every atom – would be simultaneously undergoing the same acceleration.

To see why this would make us feel weightless, we can do a quick 'thought experiment'. Rather than performing a real experiment, we can just invent a hypothetical scenario and deduce what its physical consequences would be. Imagine that gravity affects all materials in the same way except gold. In our spacecraft in orbit, we are wearing a gold ring. Because the acceleration of the gold is different from the acceleration of our body and, most specifically, of our finger, we can feel the gold ring tugging on the finger as gravity attempts to pull it away from us. Our finger has to produce a force on the ring to resist this pull, or the ring will be ripped from our finger. What we feel is the force produced by the finger that prevents the ring from escaping. If gold really were affected by gravity in a different way from all other substances, then we would feel nothing apart from this tug on our finger (we might also lose our gold fillings). In short, if the only force acting on us is gravity, such as when we are in orbit, then we feel weightless.

Now we need to plant our feet back firmly on the ground. If, as I am asserting, we cannot feel the force of gravity, what is it that we feel when we are on the Earth, as we usually are? When we are standing on the ground, gravity is not the only force that is acting on us. We can be sure of this because forces produce accelerations – so, if only a single force were acting on us, we would be accelerating, and if this force were gravity, we would be accelerating towards the centre of the Earth. In fact, there is another force acting on us that exactly balances the force of gravity – the force that prevents us from falling through the floor. This is what we feel. (If a hole opened up beneath us, there would no longer be an upward force resisting gravity and we would accelerate downwards. Now the only force acting on us would be gravity and we would feel weightless.)

It might seem strange that the ground is always conveniently able to produce an upwards force that exactly balances gravity, but it is quite natural if it is considered in the right way. When we stand on the ground, we compress the material that we are standing on, and this pushes the atoms that it is composed of slightly closer together. The outer electrons in the atoms resist being pushed together and repel each other due to their electric charge. This, ultimately, is the origin of the upwards force on us, and it is electromagnetic. The electromagnetic force is so much stronger than gravity that many materials, such as metals or stone, are barely affected by the downward pressure of our weight. Other materials, such as blancmange, where the intermolecular bonding is much weaker, are significantly distorted.

However, this is not the whole of the story. We do not just feel the upward force in our feet or whatever part of our body is in contact with the ground. If we had the consistency of jellyfish, then our bodies would spread into a thin film, with all parts in contact with the ground. Fortunately, we have bones, muscles, tendons and ligaments that enable us to resist the pull of gravity. These components give our body structure and transmit forces throughout our bodies. When we stand still, the forces are balanced at all points within us, and there is no overall force on any part of our body. In order to balance the forces, there is tension in our muscles and tendons. Our nerves can detect this tension, and this is what we feel as our weight. But all the forces within our body are ultimately electromagnetic in origin, being due to the interactions between the electrons and protons in the proteins and other molecules that compose our body.

## Spaghetti Bolognese

I have argued that you have never felt the force of gravity, and this is true. However, despite these arguments, it is still, in principle, possible to feel gravity in certain extreme circumstances. Gravity diminishes with distance. As Newton demonstrated, gravity obeys an inverse square law, which means that if we double the distance between two objects, the gravitational attraction between them falls to a quarter; if we treble the distance, the force is reduced to a ninth of its original value, and so on. This means that as we stand on the Earth, the gravitational force on our feet is slightly greater than the gravitational force on our head, simply because our feet are about two metres closer to the centre of the Earth. However, the Earth's gravity is so feeble that we will never notice this effect.

On the other hand, if we were to venture too close to a very dense object, such as a black hole, which has an extremely intense gravitational field, our predicament would be very different. The parts of our body that were closer to the black hole would feel a stronger gravitational force than those parts of our body that were further from the black hole, simply because they are more distant and because gravity diminishes with distance. For instance, if we were to fall feet-first into a black hole, then our feet would be almost two metres closer to the black hole than our head. Near the black hole, the gravitational attraction of the black hole will increase significantly over a distance of two metres. The result would be that the force pulling our feet towards the black hole is greater than the force pulling our head towards the black hole. If our feet are not to be accelerated away from our head, then our muscles and tendons must take the strain and exert a force to keep our body together. Of course, this is a battle that we cannot win. As we fall towards the black hole, we will be stretched like spaghetti, eventually producing a very messy Bolognese before falling into the black hole.

Fortunately, it is very unlikely that anybody will ever find themselves close enough to a black hole to perform this experiment. This stretching action of gravity has a dramatic effect on the Earth, however. It produces the tides, as Newton explained. For this reason, it is known as tidal gravity.

This book is the story of gravity and the heroic efforts to make sense of this mysterious feature of all our lives. We will take a look at Sir Isaac Newton's theory of gravity and its publication in his masterpiece, the *Principia*, the book that launched the modern scientific age. Newton's theory ruled for over two hundred years until it was superseded by a very different theory based on the curvature of space and time. Albert Einstein was the author of this revolutionary theory. One mind-bending result of Einstein's theory is that there are regions of space that operate like one-way trapdoors from which nothing can escape, not even light. These objects are black holes. We will investigate their properties and the ideas of Stephen Hawking, who showed that they might not be totally black after all. The final puzzle that physicists face is how to marry gravity and quantum mechanics. Many believe that success in this endeavour will bring about the ultimate 'Theory of Everything'. As we will see, string theory purports to take a big step in this direction. But first we must travel back in time and look for the origins of astronomy.

Chapter One

## THE COSMIC PUZZLE

It only takes two facing mirrors to build a labyrinth.

Jorge Luis Borges, *Nightmares*

### *The Universe Set in Stone*

Westminster Abbey is the last resting place of Sir Isaac Newton, the greatest scientific figure of any age, who transformed our understanding of the universe. If we walk past Newton's tomb towards the High Altar, we will find that the desire for a compact and unified description of the entire universe did not begin with Newton. In front of the High Altar is the Cosmati Pavement,[1] which dates from the reign of Henry III in the 13th century. It is a remarkable representation of the medieval cosmos in the heart of London. The pavement is constructed from an array of stones and tiles set in a very orderly but complex design, formed of squares and circles bound together by ribbons of stone. The pavement represents a medieval vision of the universe.

At the heart of the design is a quincunx, formed of four smaller roundels with a large fifth roundel at the very centre. Each of the four inner roundels contains a different design: one contains a circle, one a hexagon, one a heptagon and one an octagon. The central roundel contains a large beautiful circular piece of chaotically veined marble.

**Figure 1** The Cosmati Pavement in Westminster Abbey.

The full meaning of the Cosmati pavement is unknown. But there are clues that offer insights into the medieval mind. Originally, the ribbons of stone connecting the large roundels carried a message in metal lettering. Only a few of the letters remain, but some of the indentations can still be seen, and there are historical records giving the full cryptic Latin text. Around the innermost roundel, at the heart of the design, the message was:

> Here is the perfectly rounded sphere which reveals the eternal pattern of the universe.

So, the innermost text states that the pavement is intended to represent the fundamental structure of the cosmos.

Around the border, the text said:

> In the year of Christ one thousand two hundred and twelve plus sixty minus four, King Henry III, the City, Odoricus and the Abbot set in place these porphyry stones.

This is an unusual numerological record of the date of the pavement's construction. The year 1268 has been converted into 1212 + 60 − 4. This may be because of the cosmological significance of the numbers 12, 60 and 4 and their relationship to time periods. There are twelve months in a year, sixty minutes in an hour and four seasons in the year.

The longest message was around the four inner roundels, where it once said:

> If the reader thoughtfully reflects upon all that is laid down, he will discover here the measure of the primum mobile: the hedge stands for three years, add in turn dogs, and horses and men, stags and ravens, eagles, huge whales, the world: each that follows triples the years of the one before.

This inscription gives a measure of the time span of the universe. It can be unravelled as follows:

> A hedge lives 3 years.
> A dog lives 9 years.
> A horse lives 27 years.
> A man lives 81 years.
> A stag lives 243 years.
> A raven lives 729 years.
> An eagle lives 2,187 years.
> A whale lives 6,561 years.
> The universe will last for 19,683 years.[2]

In short, the time span of the universe will be $3^9$ years (three to the power of nine, or three to the power of three squared). The doctrine of the Trinity gives the number three a profound significance in Christian theology. This probably accounts for the role of the number three in the puzzle.[3]

**Figure 2** The Cosmati Pavement during conservation work.

Until recently, the Cosmati Pavement was only uncovered for important state occasions, such as the coronation of the monarch. But, following a major conservation programme, it is now permanently on view to the public.

## *A Fortress of Logic*

Much of the Cosmati design derives from the ideas of the Greek philosopher Aristotle, who was one of the great figures of antiquity. Aristotle lived in the fourth century BC. He was a highly original and penetrating thinker with encyclopaedic interests, who established the bedrock for many of our philosophical and scientific disciplines. Aristotle aimed for nothing less than a complete understanding of the entire physical universe. Aristotle's ideas about physics and astronomy are contained in two of his works, known as *The Physics (On Nature)* and *De Caelo (On the Heavens)*. Aristotle's physics was developed from a few simple notions based on his intuitions about how the universe works.

Five planets have been known since ancient times: Mercury, Venus, Mars, Jupiter and Saturn. Each is easily visible to the naked eye and each can be clearly distinguished from the stars that form the background landscape of the night sky. While the relative positions of the stars remain fixed from night to night, the position of each planet gradually changes. The planets remain within the band of stars that we know as the zodiac, but each follows its own trajectory across these background stars. For this reason, the word 'planet' derives from the Greek for 'wanderer'. In ancient times, the planetary system was believed to reach as far as Saturn and no further.

Aristotle held the common sense view that the Earth is positioned at rest at the centre of the universe. In his view, each of the planets occupied its own sphere surrounding the Earth. He believed that all substances in the sub-lunar region below the sphere of the Moon were composed of various combinations of four elements: Earth, Air, Fire and Water.[4] This was the region of change and transformation, corruption and decay. The Heavens, which consisted of the spheres of the Moon and beyond, were composed of a fifth transcendental element known as Aether. The four terrestrial elements were partially separated into layers according to their density. Earth formed the innermost layer, which was surrounded by a layer of Water, composing the world's oceans. Surrounding this, the atmosphere formed a layer of Air and, beyond that, according to Aristotle, was a layer of Fire. The earthbound elements were assumed to have completely different properties from those of the fifth and cosmic element.

The next feature of Aristotle's great scheme was the idea of natural motion. He believed that in the vicinity of the Earth, the natural motion of the elements was in straight lines: downwards for Earth; upward for Fire; and horizontally for Air and Water. And when an object reached its natural place, it would stop moving. Any other movement of the object would be forced or unnatural motion, which could only occur if it were pushed by an animate force such as a human hand; and when the pushing ceased, the object would grind to a halt.

This may have seemed perfectly reasonable to Aristotle and his contemporaries, but it is one of the most serious misconceptions in the history of physics. It is based on everyday experiences of living in an environment where friction and air resistance are almost inescapable. Aristotle knew of ships and horse-drawn carts, but he had never travelled in a car, so he never experienced the feeling of being thrown forward when the brakes are applied sharply. In our high-speed modern lives we have all become accustomed to the effects of inertia. We know that our motion remains constant and in a straight line, unless we are acted on by a force. It simply isn't true that a force is required to maintain movement. As we will see, understanding inertia was one of the critical steps in the birth of modern science.

Aristotle claimed, in complete contrast, that the natural motion of the aetherial substance that formed the heavens was circular – and that, due to its natural circular motion, there could be no change in the eternal cycling of the heavens. Aristotle believed that the heavens were perfect and incorruptible, whereas all terrestrial matter, because of its tendency towards linear motion, was subject to dissolution and decay. In order to fit in with his scheme, Aristotle assumed that any changeable or temporary features of the skies, such as a comet, must be produced in the atmosphere; hence, the connection between meteors and our name for the study of weather – meteorology. The only trace of what we would consider gravity in the scheme was the tendency for heavy objects to fall towards their natural place at the centre of the universe, which Aristotle identified with the Earth. Aristotle also believed that heavier objects fall faster than light objects.

Motion in the heavens had no counterpart on Earth, so there was no sense in which the motion of the planets was controlled by gravity. Beyond the sphere of the Moon were the spheres of Mercury, Venus, the Sun, Mars, Jupiter and Saturn; with the planets arranged according to the rate at which they move across the sky among the background stars. Beyond Saturn was the sphere of the fixed stars. According to Aristotle, the planets were contained in crystal spheres that rotated and guided the planets around the Earth. The outermost sphere beyond the fixed stars was the *primum mobile*. This was the source of the motion of all nine spheres of the heavens. And, because in Aristotle's view, nothing could move without the action of a mover, it was necessary that it should be turned by the hand of God – the prime mover. The spheres were packed together sufficiently closely for the motion of the outer ones to be transmitted inwards to keep the whole cosmos in motion.

Aristotle constructed his physics from the ground upwards on shaky foundations such as these. Unfortunately, his ideas about forces and motion and the relationship between them do not genuinely represent the way the universe works. Even so, the brilliance of Aristotle's deliberations dazzled and misled Western thinkers for thousands of years. Aristotle had constructed an intricate and coherent tower of logic that offered a very appealing description of the universe, providing a consistent answer for virtually any question that might be posed. This fortress of logic would prove to be almost impregnable for later thinkers.

However, it was all utter nonsense. The entire model was constructed by supposedly watertight logical arguments, but the foundations on which it was built were derived from Aristotle's personal intuition, and not from experiment, which effectively meant that the entire edifice was built on sand. In the words of the 20th century philosopher Bertrand Russell: 'hardly a sentence in either [of Aristotle's books on physics] can be accepted in the light of modern science.'[5]

Nonetheless, Aristotle's ideas enchanted Western thinkers for many centuries.

### The Divine Comedy

Following the translation of Aristotle's scientific works from Arabic into Latin in the twelfth century, his extremely coherent, but totally erroneous, view of the universe was adopted by the Church and elaborated with all the trappings of medieval Christianity. Like Aristotle's original system, the Earth was considered to be stationary at the centre of the cosmos, surrounded by nine concentric crystal spheres. The spheres were supposed to be inhabited by a nine-fold hierarchy of angels, whose function was to turn the spheres at just the required rate. In mirror image fashion, the Earth was imagined to contain nine concentric levels of Hell, with Lucifer's throne at the centre. The universe that emerged from this synthesis was like a great gothic cathedral. It was certainly filled with beautiful paintings, but it was also covered in hideous gargoyles. Nevertheless, it holds an undeniable poetic appeal.[6] It was one of the most unified visions of reality ever devised.[7]

The medieval universe found its ultimate expression in the epic poetry of Dante Alighieri's wonderful *Divine Comedy*, completed in 1321. In the poem, Dante travels through the cosmos, visiting every corner of the Christian universe. His journey begins in the underworld – The Inferno. Guided by the Roman poet Virgil, Dante travels down through the nine concentric rings that constitute the pit of Hell and witnesses the torments of every category of earthly sinner until he reaches the realm of Satan himself. After traversing the depths of Hell, Dante emerges to climb the nine tiers of Mount Purgatory before ascending into the Heavens, where he passes through each of the nine celestial spheres. Plate 1 shows a mural of Dante from Florence Cathedral.

The Divine Comedy is suffused with symbolism and mysticism. It is filled with numerological references. The overall structure of the poem is based around the numbers three and nine. The poem is divided into three parts, corresponding to the three regions of the cosmos – Inferno,

Purgatory and Paradise. Each of these parts is divided into 33 sections or cantos which, along with the first introductory canto, makes a total of 100. The geography of each of the three regions is divided into nine – the nine circles of Hell, the nine tiers of Mount Purgatory and the nine celestial spheres of Paradise. The incidents in the poem also occur in threes. Even the sins and the sinners are organised in threes. There are three rivers of Hell and three mouths of Satan. The poetry itself is written in an intricate rhyming scheme devised by Dante and known as *terza rima*, which interlocks the lines of the poem in threes. This can be expressed symbolically as (aba, bcb, cdc ....), where a, b, c, etc. represent the rhyming sounds at the end of successive lines.[8]

After exploring the labyrinthine geometry of the cosmos, Dante finally enters the Empyrium and the presence of God. He likens the experience, and his inability to express himself, to a geometer faced with an insoluble problem – the squaring of the circle.

> As the geometer his mind applies
> To square the circle, not for all his wit
> Finds the right formula, howe'er he tries
>
> So strove I with that wonder – how to fit
> The image to the sphere; so sought to see
> How it maintained the point of rest in it.[9]

## A Sage Who Knew His Onions

The motion of the Sun, Moon, planets and stars must have been familiar to the earliest humans. Astronomy is the oldest science; indeed, it was the contemplation of the skies that ultimately led to the birth of science. There are two inter-twined threads that lead from Ancient Greece to the birth of modern astronomy. One thread was spun by philosophers such as Aristotle.[10] The other thread that leads from the ancient past to the astronomy of medieval Europe was woven by the professional astronomers who, over the course of many ages, developed the first precise observational science. Their main occupation was to record the positions of the Sun, Moon and planets and to predict their future positions in order to divine their religious and astrological implications. Understanding the cycles of the Sun and Moon was vital for tracking the passage of time and the functioning of a workable calendar.

There are other, longer cyclical patterns in the heavens. The path of the planet Venus follows an eight-year cycle through our skies,[11] and eclipses of the Sun repeat in eighteen-year cycles known as saros cycles. More precisely, the length of a saros cycle is 18 years 11⅓ days. For instance, there was a total eclipse on 18 March 1988 that was visible in the Philippines and Indonesia. 18 years 11⅓ days later and one-third further round the globe (due to the extra one-third rotation of the Earth), there was another total eclipse that I was lucky enough to see in Turkey on 29 March 2006. In April 2024, the Sun will be eclipsed again. This time, the eclipse will be visible in the United States. These three eclipses form part of a series known to modern astronomers[12] as saros cycle 139. The solar eclipses that occur between these eclipses form parts of other saros cycles.[13]

The Greek astronomers were greatly indebted to their Babylonian predecessors. The Babylonian priests compiled observations of the Sun, Moon and planets that stretched back into the dim and distant past. They were aware of the cycles of the heavens and could use them to predict the future positions of the celestial bodies. The earliest record that we have of an astronomical prediction was made by the mathematician Thales of Miletus, who was regarded as one of the Seven Sages of Greece. According to the Greek historian Herodotus,[14] during a five-year war between the Lydians and the Medes, battle was engaged at a site in modern-day Turkey, when suddenly day was turned to night. Thales had foretold this event and, when the spectacle duly arrived, it was enough to induce the warring sides to make peace.[15]

Since ancient times, this incident has been interpreted as the prediction of an eclipse of the Sun. Modern historians believe that this was the eclipse that took place on 28 May 585 BC.[16] It is assumed that Thales was able to make this prediction because he was aware of eclipse cycles discovered by the Babylonians and had access to their eclipse records.[17]

The Babylonians may have been skilled observers, but they saw the planets as gods and, as far as we know, they did not seek a physical mechanism behind the planetary motions. With records that have been kept for many years, it is possible to discern the periodic patterns of the heavenly bodies without the need to enquire into the causes of these cycles.

The quest for a mechanical or geometrical explanation of the cosmos began with the analytical approach of Greek mathematicians such as Thales. It was a very important first step towards modern science. The earliest geometrical models of the universe that we know of date from a couple of centuries after Thales. These models include a stationary Earth, surrounded by Aristotle's spheres. This meant that the heavens in their entirety must travel around the Earth once every day. Superimposed on the daily rotation of the heavens, the Sun followed its annual course around the Earth, and this produced the yearly cycle of the seasons.

The task of constructing a system which could accurately describe the paths of the planets across the sky was a good deal more challenging. Guided by philosophers such as Aristotle, astronomers adopted the rule that the circle was the perfect geometrical figure, and the only one that was suitable to represent the motions of the planets. This meant that their attention was restricted to systems in which the heavenly bodies follow circular paths. A second rule insisted that the planets must follow these circles at a uniform speed. If the planets really did cross the sky at a uniform speed, then predicting their motion would be simple, but this is not how the planetary system works. Indeed, there are times when a planet seems to reverse its course and loops backwards before travelling onwards again. These retrograde loops make the heavens much more difficult to model than Aristotle's simple scheme would suggest.

Apollonius of Perga, a mathematician of the third century BC, proposed a solution that met the demands of circular motion. His idea was that a planet did not just orbit the Earth on a circular path, but followed a course around a circle whose centre simultaneously moved around the Earth on a circular orbit, as depicted in the diagram below. The name for this figure is an epicycle.

Thus, the basic principle of circular motion was preserved, but the planet itself, as seen from the Earth, would no longer follow a circular orbit. The epicycle would remain a feature of every detailed astronomical model for two thousand years. The most famous book written by Apollonius of Perga is *The Conics*, a geometry textbook which analyses the shapes that are produced by slicing a cone at different angles. These shapes are known as circles, ellipses, parabolas and hyperbolas. It is a remarkable fact that this very book contains the seed

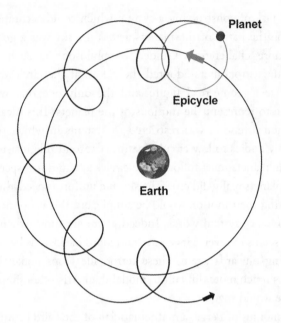

Figure 3 In the epicyclic systems of Hipparchus and Ptolemy each planet moved on a circle, known as an epicycle, around an imaginary point that moved around the Earth on a larger circle, known as the deferent.

that would eventually germinate and blossom in the mind of an astronomer of the distant future, who would overthrow the age-long obsession with epicycles, as we will see in the next chapter.

## *The Antikythera Mechanism*

The greatest astronomer of antiquity lived four hundred years after Thales, from around 190 BC to around 120 BC. His name was Hipparchus, and he came from Nicaea, which is now the city of Iznik, in Turkey. Like Thales, he is thought to have based his astronomy on the observations and techniques of the Babylonians. But, Hipparchus was also a very original researcher. He invented many astronomical instruments, such as the astrolabe, which he used to measure and catalogue the positions of almost 1,000 of the brightest stars. Hipparchus was also a great mathematician and is credited with the invention of trigonometry. He is known to have constructed a detailed system of the heavens, based on epicycles. This gave a comparatively simple geometrical method to predict the positions in the night sky of each of the planets.

In the year 1900, a shipwreck was discovered by sponge divers off the coast of the Greek island of Antikythera. For over two thousand years, the wreck had been holding a mysterious artefact that sheds light on the technology of the age of Hipparchus and the ancient Greek conception of the heavens. The divers found a green, corroded lump of metal containing a collection of toothed wheels. This object is now housed in the National Archaeological Museum in Athens. It has been studied for over a century. Recent X-ray analyses, along with a great deal of painstaking detective work, have finally revealed its secrets. Within the corroded fragment are the remains of 27 gear wheels and, originally, there would have been more. The Antikythera Mechanism, as it is known, is believed to be the remains of a device that could calculate the positions of the Sun, Moon and planets and even predict eclipses by replicating the saros cycle with its gears.[18] From the number of teeth on the wheels, it is possible to deduce which cosmic cycle they replicated. For instance, one of the wheels has 223 teeth, which is the number of lunar months in each saros cycle. This number has been confirmed from fragments of text on the machine that have been read using sophisticated modern photographic enhancement techniques. Plate 2 shows a virtual reconstruction of the Antikythera mechanism.

**Figure 4** Fragment A of the Antikythera Mechanism.

No-one knows who made the Antikythera mechanism, but it gives a unique glimpse of ancient Greek technology. The intermeshed gears of the mechanism are a concrete realisation of the ideas of astronomers such as Hipparchus in metal. The mechanism is so complex and sophisticated that it cannot have been unique; it must have been part of a long tradition of such devices. One day, perhaps, other examples of such machines from the distant past will be discovered.

## *Rewinding the Epicyclic Clock*

The system of epicycles works rather well. The reason for this, from a modern perspective, is that the main circle, or deferent, models the planet's orbit around the Sun, and the epicycle models the Earth's orbit around the Sun. When these two circles are combined, they give a good approximation to the path of the planet as seen from Earth. This works very well, because the orbits of the Earth and planets around the Sun are almost circular. We do not know the details of the early systems, but Hipparchus may have included additional circles to compensate for some of the inaccuracies. The entire planetary system would have kept track of the movement of the planets for many years but, eventually, the synchronisation with the heavens would be lost. At this point, astronomers of a later generation would need to make new measurements of the planets and bring the system back into synchronisation, effectively rewinding the epicyclic clock. One of these later astronomers was Claudius Ptolemy (c. 90 AD – c. 168 AD), who lived three centuries after Hipparchus. Ptolemy would eventually pass the astronomy of the ancient world on to the future.

Ptolemy was a Greek who lived in the leading intellectual centre of his age, the Egyptian city of Alexandria, which was at that time part of the Roman Empire. Ptolemy relied heavily on his predecessor Hipparchus, but he made his own important improvements to the epicyclic system. It was the Ptolemaic version of the universe that was known to later Arabic and European astronomers. Ptolemy's astronomical system was contained in one of four books known to the ancients as the *Tetrabiblos*, the other books being concerned with geography, astrology and philosophy.

Ptolemy's book of astronomy was known to medieval Europe as the *Almagest*, translated into Latin from Arabic intermediaries. His universe was the last in a long tradition of ancient cosmologies which took as their starting point the idea that all motion of the heavenly bodies must be circular. The full epicyclic system was very complicated and included

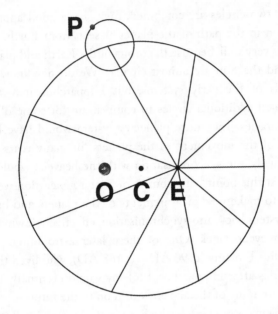

**Figure 5** The diagram shows a deferent and its epicycle. The labels are:
O – the Earth, C – the centre of the deferent, E – the equant point,
P – a planet.
As viewed from the equant point, the vacant point at the centre of the
epicycle moves around the deferent at a constant rate. In the diagram, the
deferent is divided into nine arcs. The point at the centre of the epicycle
would pass through these nine arcs in equal periods of time.

various devices to improve its accuracy. One significant feature of Ptolemy's system was that the centre of each planet's
deferent was located near to, but not actually in, the Earth.
At an equal distance from the centre on the opposite side to
the Earth was the *equant point*. As viewed from this point,
the centre of the planet's epicycle would appear to revolve
around the deferent at a steady rate, as shown in the figure

above. This looks like a strange way to comply with the philosophical demand for regular circular motion but, rather surprisingly, it does represent the motion of the planets to a good approximation.

Although Ptolemy's epicycles offered a computational procedure by which the motion of the planets could be accurately predicted, the overall system was extremely arcane and complicated. It was an exercise in geometry designed to 'save the appearances', which meant that it could predict the positions of the planets, but it did not offer a physical mechanism to describe how or why the planets should move in the way that they did. The system was purely descriptive. Nevertheless, it would not be superseded until the 16th century.

## The Copernican Revolution

Copernicus is the Latinised name of the renowned Polish astronomer and cleric born in 1473. He was educated first at the University of Krakow, and then at the University of Bologna in Italy. As early as his student days in Bologna in the 1490s, he began to question the validity of the traditional and ancient Ptolemaic system of the planets. Copernicus believed that the fundamental flaw in the ancient system was that it was geocentric; it positioned the Earth stationary at the centre of the universe. He thought that placing the Sun at the centre would produce a much better model. In his new model – the heliocentric model – the Earth and all the planets would orbit the Sun, and the Earth would rotate on its axis once every day. Some time around 1514, he wrote an outline of his ideas in a tract that is known as the *Commentariolus* (*Nicolai Copernici de hypothesibus motuum coelestium a se constitutis commentariolus*). This was circulated in manuscript form among Europe's leading intellectuals, but Copernicus was hesitant about publishing a fully developed model to rival Ptolemy's.

The big advantage of the heliocentric system was that the stars would be stationary and their apparent daily rotation would be due to the rotation of the Earth, and not a frantic whirling motion of the entire heavens. As Copernicus well knew, he was not the first to propose this idea; the Greek astronomer Aristarchus had suggested the same model in antiquity. Copernicus felt that this added weight to the idea. However, there is a very good reason why the heliocentric model had failed to catch on. If the Earth orbits the Sun once every year, then there should be a seasonal shift in the positions of the stars. It was the failure to observe such shifts that convinced the ancient astronomers that the Earth must reside at the centre of the universe.

The only explanation that Copernicus could offer was that the stars must be very distant – much more distant than anyone had previously considered possible. This is what made Copernicus's proposal so explosive. It would shatter the cosy medieval worldview. Prior to Copernicus, the Church could represent the universe as a relatively small enclosed space, where everything had its purpose and which had been created for the benefit of Mankind. The problem was not so much that the Earth moved rather than the Sun, but the implication that the universe must be vast. The heliocentric model opened up the possibility that the universe might be essentially infinite in scale. (In a sense, this was the spatial equivalent of Darwin's temporal expansion of the universe three centuries later. Darwin's ideas about evolution by natural selection implied that the Earth must be ancient; it could not have been created recently, as the Church supposed.)[19]

So why did people believe that the Earth was stationary at the centre of the Universe, when it is so obvious to everyone today that the Earth is orbiting the Sun?

## *A Journey to the Stars*

Most ancient astronomers believed that the Earth lay at the centre of the cosmos. The strongest argument for this belief was that the relative positions of the stars were fixed during the course of a year. If the Earth orbits the Sun, then the positions of the stars should shift as the Earth moves from one side of the Sun to the other. This effect is known as parallax.

We can get an immediate experience of parallax if we close one eye, then open it and close the other. Nearby objects seem to shift in relation to more distant objects, as our viewpoint changes by a few centimetres to the left or to the right. Similarly, as the Earth's position changes by the enormous distance from one side of the Sun to the other, we would expect the apparent positions of nearby stars to shift relative to the more distant stars.

Ancient astronomers observed no seasonal change in the shape of the constellations, so they believed that the Earth was stationary at the centre of the universe. They had no idea just how distant the stars were, but assumed that they were probably just beyond the planets because, according to Aristotle, it was the rotation of the sphere of the fixed stars that drove the spheres of the planets. As they didn't know of the outer planets, that would mean the stars were just beyond Saturn. But, of course, they didn't know how distant Saturn was, either.

When Copernicus placed the Sun at the centre and overthrew the ancient Earth-centred cosmology, he offered no new evidence to support this radical rearrangement of the Heavens. Astronomers still had not detected any shift in star positions due to parallax. But if Copernicus's proposal was to be accepted, the only possible explanation was that the distances to the stars must be immense.[20]

**Figure 6** Diagram showing the much exaggerated shift in position of a celestial body due to parallax. When the Earth is on one side of its orbit, the body will appear in a different position against the background stars relative to its position when viewed from the other side of the Earth's orbit.

## *So How Distant are the Stars?*

To work out the distance to a star from a parallax measurement, an astronomer would measure the position of the star at one time in the year – say, 1 January – and then measure the position of the star six months later on 1 July from a viewpoint on the other side of the Earth's orbit. From the angular shift in the position of the star, the distance to the star can then be determined as a multiple of the diameter of the Earth's orbit by a simple piece of geometrical reasoning. If the shift in the position of a celestial object is one degree, then the distance to the object would be about sixty times the diameter of the Earth's orbit.[21]

In the days of Copernicus, the distance to the Sun was unknown. We now know that the diameter of the Earth's orbit is about 300 million kilometres. This means that a star that shifted in position by as much as one degree during the course of the year would be 60 × 300 million kilometres = 18,000 million kilometres distant. This is about four times the distance to Neptune.

The apparent diameter of the Moon in the sky is around half a degree, so a shift in position as large as one degree over the course of a year would be very noticeable. Shifts due to parallax are seen in the positions of the planets, and these shifts are the reason why the outer planets move in retrograde loops when the Earth overtakes them each year.[22] The implication of this is that even the nearest stars must be much more distant than the outer planets.

It turns out that the shifts in the nearest stars are less than a thousandth of a degree. They are measured in seconds of arc. There are 60 minutes of arc in one degree, and 60 seconds in one minute, so the distance to a star that shifts by just one second of arc is 3,600 times the distance of an object with a shift of one degree. $3,600 \times 18,000$ million is approximately 65 trillion (where trillion means one million million), so such a star would be around 65 trillion kilometres distant – a distance of around six and a half light years. (Light travels 300,000 kilometres in a second; in a year, light travels just under ten trillion kilometres, which gives us a much more convenient unit to express the distances to the stars.)

It was not until the 19th century that accurate telescopic observations first enabled an astronomer to measure the tiny shift in the position of a star due to the change in the Earth's position as it orbits the Sun. The astronomer who first achieved this was the German Friedrich Wilhelm Bessel, who announced in 1838 that he had measured the parallactic shift of the nearby star 61 Cygni. Bessel measured the shift to be about two thirds of an arc second,[23] and so calculated that 61 Cygni must be 10.4 light years away.[24] 61 Cygni is in our cosmic backyard; it is one of our nearest stellar neighbours. Its incredible distance explains why the constellations retain their shape throughout the year, and why the shift due to parallax was undetectable in antiquity.

In 1989, the European Space Agency (ESA) launched the satellite Hipparcos, named after the greatest of the Ancient Greek astronomers, who, as we have seen, drew up an early star catalogue. The satellite's name also represents a rather contrived acronym "HIgh Precision PARallax COllecting Satellite". As this acronym suggests, one of the main goals of Hipparcos was to measure the shift in the apparent positions of stars due to parallax. During its four-year period of operation, Hipparcos compiled a high-precision catalogue of 100,000 stars, measuring their positions in the sky to within 0.001 arc seconds. This enabled astronomers to determine the distances to around 20,000 stars with greater than 10% accuracy. [25]

In December 2013, ESA launched a satellite named Gaia that will build on the work of Hipparcos. Gaia is an incredibly ambitious project that will amass data on the positions of around one billion stars. This information will be used to calculate precise distances to a significant proportion of the stars in the Milky Way. These distances will be used to create a three-dimensional picture of our galaxy in order to better understand the history and evolution of the galaxy and the stars within it.

## *An Infinity of Worlds*

Copernicus completed the manuscript describing his helio-centric system in around 1532, but, despite the encouragement of his friends and even some leading members of the Church, he was very hesitant about releasing it to the world. It was not until he was on his deathbed in 1543 that his book *On the Revolutions of the Celestial Spheres* (*De revolutionibus orbium coelestium*) was finally published. The influence of *De Revolutionibus*, as it is usually known, was not due to the details of Copernicus's model and how they compared to the ancient geocentric models. Its success derived from the fact that it contained a simple idea, a 'sound bite', that could be easily disseminated – the Earth moves around the Sun. The power of this statement is clear. Very few people study celestial mechanics, but everyone knows that the Earth orbits the Sun.

Copernicus's caution was not unwarranted. The full implications of his model were spelt out towards the end of the century by the Italian Dominican friar Giordano Bruno, who drew the logical conclusion from Copernicus. He believed that the Sun was simply one star among many, that the other stars had planetary systems similar to our own and that some of them were probably the homes of other civilisations. In 1584, Bruno wrote:

> Thus is the excellence of God magnified and the greatness of his kingdom made manifest; he is glorified not in one, but in countless suns; not in a single earth, a single world, but in a thousand thousand, I say in an infinity of worlds.[26]

On the Infinite Universe and Worlds – Giordano Bruno (1584).

Bruno travelled Europe, expounding these views, and published pamphlets in Venice and England where he forcefully expressed them. On his return to Venice in 1592, he was denounced to the authorities, who arrested him and then passed him on to the Roman Inquisition. He was charged with holding opinions contrary to the Catholic faith, including claiming the existence of a plurality of worlds and their eternity. After a long trial, on 17 February 1600, Bruno was burnt at the stake in a marketplace in central Rome, the Campo de' Fiori.

Copernicus did away with the Earth-centred cosmology of the ancients, but he did not see the great opportunity that this offered for simplifying the planetary system. The epicycle supposedly followed by a planet is actually a projection onto the sky of the Earth's motion around the Sun, so placing the Sun at the centre of the system removes the need for epicycles. But Copernicus retained almost all the features of the ancient systems, including equant points and epicycles. The result was that his model was a rickety and convoluted mish-mash of ideas. It 'saved the appearances', just as the older models had, and the mechanical circles on circles could be used to compute the future positions of the planets to a reasonable accuracy, but this was done in a manner that was incredibly complicated and inelegant. However, the idea of placing the Sun at the centre gave a whole new perspective on the mechanics of the solar system. It would now be possible to seek a more physical description of how the planets move.

This advance in our understanding of the universe would be the life work of Johannes Kepler. The heliocentric model was Kepler's starting point. He would not be content with a model of the solar system that simply gave reasonable predictions of the planetary positions. Kepler aimed to know the mind of God, to discover the fundamental blueprint of the cosmos. And it was not a general plan that Kepler sought, but the precise details of the planetary system.

Chapter Two

# THE SECRET OF THE UNIVERSE

There are more things in heaven and earth, Horatio,
Than are dreamt of in your philosophy.

William Shakespeare, *Hamlet*, I, v

## *What is Your Star Sign?*

Plate 3 is a beautiful early 15th century depiction of the zodiac from a book of hours showing supposed celestial influences on the human anatomy. Just as the roots of chemistry lie in alchemy, there is no denying that the roots of astronomy lie in astrology. The traditional astrology of the Middle Ages was much more geometrical than its bastard descendent, the newspaper horoscope. The medieval astrologer required the precise time and date of his patron's birth. He would then calculate the position of all the planets. The planetary orbits all lie in a plane that cuts through the Sun at its equator; when projected onto the sky, it is called the ecliptic. The paths of the planets across the sky always lie near to this circle.

Long ago, the Ancient Babylonians organised the prominent stars close to this circle into a convenient collection of twelve constellations. This was useful because, during a year, the Sun spends approximately one month in each constellation. However, these constellations are not all the same size, so astrologers have neatly spliced the ecliptic into twelve equal 30-degree chunks and labelled each with the name of the nearest constellation. We know these twelve signpost constellations as the signs of the zodiac. This makes it quite natural to plot an astrological chart on a disc. The astrologer labels the circle surrounding his disc with the twelve signs of the zodiac, and then marks the position of each planet around the circle.

The most important feature of the planetary positions was the angle that was formed between one planet, the soul of the newly-born infant on Earth and a second planet. The astrologers believed that these angles, known as aspects, would determine the fate of the individual. At certain angles, there would be a cosmic resonance that would heighten the effect. For instance, if the two planets were in the same part of the zodiac, so that the angle was zero, they would be in conjunction, which greatly increased their influence. Other important angles were 60 degrees, which was known as sextiles; 90 degrees, known as quadrature; 120 degrees, or trines; and 180 degrees, or opposition – in the case of the Moon, this would be Full Moon.

Even the great astronomer Johannes Kepler (1571–1630) relied on astrology to supplement his income. He described it as the 'handmaiden of astronomy'. Along with most of his contemporaries, Kepler believed that the Sun, the Moon and the planets have a significant astrological influence on life on Earth. It was just not clear exactly what that influence was. His quest would be to reveal the truth. In his words:

> one must separate the precious stones from the dung, one must glorify the honour of God, by taking for one's purpose the contemplation of nature, must lift up others by one's own example and exert oneself to move into the bright daylight from the darkness of the human race.[1]

The geometrical calculations that Kepler would use to transform astronomy into a modern science would be a close cousin of the astrological geometry of aspects.

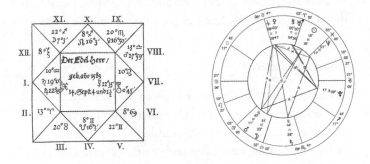

**Figure 7** Left: Horoscope of General Albrecht von Wallenstein drawn up by Kepler in 1608. Right: Circular horoscope depicting the angles between the planets, known as aspects.

Kepler had an unruly upbringing in the small German town of Weil-der-Stadt. His father was a rogue who, although a Lutheran himself, abandoned the family to fight as a mercenary for the Catholic forces in the Low Countries. Kepler's mother was a maker of potions who meddled in other people's affairs and made many enemies. Kepler's childhood was spent with his mother and siblings, living in a tavern owned by his grandparents. His interest in astronomy developed at an early age. He recalled much later that his mother had taken him to view an eclipse of the Moon and, on another occasion, the comet of 1577. Despite his disorderly family life, Kepler gained a good education and his intelligence impressed everyone he met. After school, he went to the University of Tubingen to study theology, with the intention of entering the priesthood. At university, his tutor, Michael Maestlin, introduced him to the Sun-centred system of the planets as devised by Copernicus. Maestlin presented the Copernican system as a useful mathematical tool for making calculations without committing himself to its validity. But Kepler knew at once that it must be correct.

## Cosmic Symmetry

After university, Kepler was employed in a seminary school in the Austrian city of Graz. He was an enthusiastic teacher of mathematics and astronomy, but his ideas came thick and fast, so his lessons were filled with endless digressions as his mind wandered among the stars, while his pupils were left behind in the classroom. Inevitably, the numbers attending his classes soon dwindled.

Kepler spent his time between lessons pondering the rules devised by God to construct the system of the universe. He was certain that there must be a simple relationship that would explain why there were only six planets and why they were arranged in just the way that we observe. During one lesson in July 1595, he had a revelation that would inspire his life's work. Kepler drew a diagram for his pupils illustrating how successive conjunctions between the two outer planets Jupiter and Saturn travel around the zodiac. Roughly speaking, it takes Jupiter twelve years[2] to orbit the Sun and it takes Saturn around 30 years. In 20 years, Saturn will have completed two-thirds of an orbit and Jupiter will have completed one full orbit and two-thirds of a second orbit. This means that 20 years after one conjunction, the two planets will meet again in the night sky, two-thirds of the way around the zodiac. Thus, conjunctions between Jupiter and Saturn occur every 20 years, and three successive conjunctions are located at the corners of a zodiacal triangle, or nearly so.

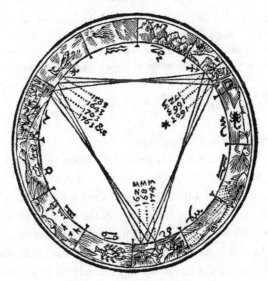

**Figure 8** Kepler's diagram showing the positions of successive conjunctions of Jupiter and Saturn around the zodiac between 1583, when the conjunction occurred in the constellation Pisces, and 1763, by which time the conjunction would have moved a few degrees further round the zodiac into the constellation of Aries.

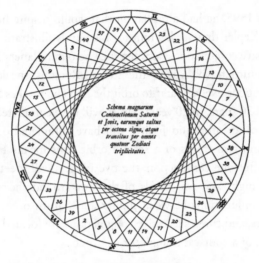

**Figure 9** Kepler's diagram showing a full circuit of 40 successive conjunctions over a period of 800 years. Conjunction number 1 is shown on the boundary between Pisces and Aries, which is the start of the astronomical year (corresponding to the spring equinox), and very close to the actual position of the conjunction in 1583 – the one immediately preceding Kepler's speculations.

After drawing the sequence of conjunctions, Kepler was struck by the circle at the centre of the diagram formed by the edges of the lines between successive conjunctions. It looked like the orbit of Jupiter was inscribed within the orbit of Saturn such that, if the outer edge of the diagram represented Saturn's orbit, then the inner circle might represent Jupiter's orbit. In a flash, he had an idea that seemed to explain the sizes of the planetary orbits in terms of geometry. If he was right, he had discovered a part of God's master plan for the universe.

The idea was this: starting with a circle to represent Saturn's orbit, he could draw an equilateral triangle within the circle – just like in the diagram – and then, within this triangle, he could draw a circle, such that the circle would touch the midpoint of each edge of the triangle. This second circle would then represent the orbit of Jupiter, and its size would be completely determined by the geometrical construction. Kepler's next step was to draw a square within Jupiter's orbit and then, within the square, draw a circle that would represent the orbit of Mars. The sequence of polygons and circles could then be continued to determine the orbits of the other planets. Within the orbit of Mars would be a regular pentagon, and the circle within the pentagon would represent the orbit of the Earth. Next would be a hexagon whose incircle would be the orbit of Venus. Within this orbit would be a heptagon and finally, within the heptagon, would be the orbit of Mercury.[3]

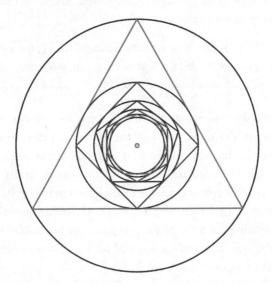

**Figure 10** Kepler's Polygonal Model. The outer circle represents the orbit of Saturn. Moving inwards, the other circles represent the orbits of Jupiter, Mars, Earth, Venus and Mercury, with the Sun at the centre.

In the middle of his lesson, Kepler was lost in this reverie on the structure of the cosmos. He does not record the reaction of his pupils to his flight of fancy. No doubt, by this point, they had lost all interest in the ramblings of their eccentric teacher.

---

**Puzzle 1**

A collection of polygons that covers a plane without leaving any gaps is known as a tessellation. The tessellation is regular if the polygons are all regular and of the same type. For instance, there is a regular tessellation formed from equilateral triangles, with six of the triangles meeting at each vertex. There is also a tessellation of squares, where four squares meet at each vertex, and a tessellation of regular hexagons, where three hexagons meet at each vertex. Why is it only possible to construct these three regular tessellations?

HINT: The angles of an equilateral triangle are 60°, the angles of a square are 90° and the angles of a regular hexagon are 120°.

---

Over the following months, Kepler sought out information on the dimensions of the planetary orbits in order to compare his idea to the best astronomical observations. Although the absolute sizes of the planetary orbits were unknown in Kepler's time, the relative sizes of the orbits were well known. Unfortunately, Kepler's model didn't fit at all. He tried altering the order of the polygons, but he couldn't find a solution that accurately accounted for the distances between the planetary orbits.

That might have been the end of the matter and no-one would ever have known about this curious idea. A few months later, however, Kepler had a new idea. Instead of fitting regular polygons between the circular orbits of the planets, he would inscribe regular polyhedra between the spherical orbs of the planets. Since antiquity it had been known that there are just five regular polyhedra, also known as the Platonic solids. Kepler believed that by fitting these five polyhedra between the six spheres carrying the planets, he could simultaneously explain the size of each planetary orbit and why there were just six planets.

---

### Answer to Puzzle 1

The angles of the polygons that meet at each vertex of a tessellation must sum to 360°, or a complete rotation. At least three polygons must meet at a vertex. The only way to do this with regular polygons is with six equilateral triangles, as $6 \times 60° = 360°$; four squares, as $4 \times 90° = 360°$ or three hexagons, as $3 \times 120° = 360°$ (three pentagons would give: $3 \times 108° = 324°$, for instance).

---

After some experimentation, Kepler settled on the following scheme: between the orbits of Saturn and Jupiter was a cube, between Jupiter and Mars was a tetrahedron, between Mars and the Earth was a dodecahedron, between Earth and Venus was an icosahedron and between Venus and Mercury was an octahedron. With a bit of flexibility with regards to its precise construction, Kepler was able to show that it fitted the dimensions of the solar system reasonably well, so well that he was convinced that he had discovered one of the most fundamental secrets of the universe. He would reveal this great discovery to the world in his first book *Mysterium Cosmographicum (The Secret of the Universe)*, published in 1596. The 24 year old

---

**Puzzle 2**

A collection of polygons joined at their edges to enclose a volume of space without leaving any gaps is known as a polyhedron. The polyhedron is regular if the polygons are regular and all of the same type, with the same number meeting at each vertex. Why are there only five regular polyhedra?

HINT: In the square tessellation, four squares meet at each vertex, whereas in the cube only three squares meet at each vertex. In the equilateral triangle tessellation, six triangles meet at each vertex, whereas in a tetrahedron only three triangles meet at each vertex.

---

Kepler would send copies of the book to many of the leading astronomers in Europe, including Galileo and Tycho Brahe.

This book, Kepler's earliest publication, is suffused with a strange mystical geometry and an enthusiasm to honour God by finding the blueprint of the universe. It is all quite mad from a modern perspective, but Kepler was now convinced that he must dedicate his life to astronomy and the quest for the true laws of nature.[4] Kepler's later writings would also be enveloped in strange mystical ideas and heavenly harmonies, but somehow in the midst of the wild fantasies would be some of the most profound ideas ever dreamt up. This was the start of an obsessive yearning to understand the structure of the universe that would ultimately lead to the dawn of the modern scientific era.

**Answer to Puzzle 2**

The angles of the polygons that meet at each vertex of a polyhedron must sum to *less* than 360°, and at least three polygons must meet at a vertex. The only way to do this with regular polygons is with three, four or five equilateral triangles meeting at each vertex (which corresponds to the tetrahedron, octahedron and icosahedron, respectively), three squares meeting at each vertex (which corresponds to the cube) or three pentagons meeting at each vertex (which corresponds to the dodecahedron).

Kepler tried to persuade Frederick, Duke of Wuerttemberg, to commission a cup designed in accordance with his model of the universe. In the words of Kepler's biographer Arthur Koestler:

> Kepler went on to suggest that the various parts of the cup should be made by different silversmiths, and then fitted together, to make sure that the cosmic secret would not leak out. The signs of the planets could be cut in precious stones – Saturn in diamond, Jupiter in jacinth, the Moon a pearl, and so on. The cup would serve seven different kinds of beverage, conducted by concealed pipes from each planetary sphere to seven taps on its rim. The Sun will provide a delicious aqua vita, Mercury brandy, Venus mead, the Moon water, Mars a strong Vermouth, Jupiter 'a delicious new white wine', and Saturn 'a bad old wine or beer', 'whereby those ignorant in astronomical matters could be exposed to shame and ridicule'.[5]

Duke Frederick suggested that Kepler should first construct a model in copper. The cash-strapped Kepler spent a week

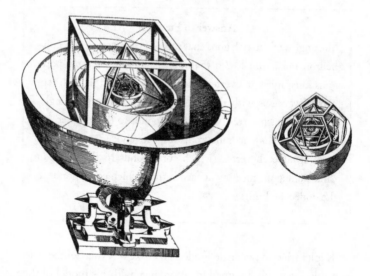

**Figure 11** Kepler's polyhedral model of the solar system.

manufacturing his design in coloured paper. He sent it off to the Duke, apologising for its size. Ultimately, his plans for the grand silver goblet would come to nothing – but the spiritual quest to understand the mind of God and discover the architecture of the universe had only just begun. What Kepler craved were the reasons for the number, size and pathways of the planets. The task he set himself was to discover the celestial harmonies that he felt must govern the planetary motions. The only way in which he could fruitfully spend his time was in gathering proof of the heliocentric view of the universe. And there was just one man in Europe who had observed the planets with sufficient accuracy to settle Kepler's questions. This was the eccentric Danish nobleman Tycho Brahe.

## *A Giant of Astronomy*

Tycho Brahe (1546–1601) is one of the most incredible characters in the history of science. His life was dedicated to making the most precise measurements of the planetary positions that had ever been taken, and he designed instruments of gargantuan proportions to achieve the accuracy that he demanded.

Tycho was born into one of the leading aristocratic families in 16th century Denmark which, at the time, was a major north European power holding what is now the southern tip of Sweden and, thereby, controlling the entrance to the Baltic Sea between Helsingborg and Elsinor Castle. The Danish crown was able to exact duties on all the merchant vessels that pursued their lucrative trade through these waters. Tycho's father Otto Brahe, and other close relatives, were members of the Danish Council of State that formed the tier of government beneath the Danish king. Tycho was the first-born child and, when a second child arrived about a year later, Tycho was kidnapped by his uncle Jorgen, who was a great sea captain. Jorgen had distinguished himself in Denmark's naval encounters and later became the vice-admiral of the Danish navy. He appears to have had an understanding with Tycho's father that he would adopt Tycho as soon as a second child was born. Tycho's parents eventually reconciled themselves to their child being raised by Jorgen and his wife, and Tycho seems to have benefited from the attention of two sets of parents.

In 1565, Jorgen was accompanying King Frederick II over a bridge outside Copenhagen after a heavy drinking session. The king was thrown from his horse into the water. Jorgen jumped in and rescued the king, but later died of pneumonia. The king remained grateful for Jorgen's sacrifice, and this might explain the enormous generosity that he later showed to Tycho.

As a young student, Tycho saw a partial eclipse of the Sun in Copenhagen on 21 August 1560. He was so impressed that it was possible to predict such events that he began a lifelong interest in astronomy. He bought an astrolabe and began to make his own observations. A few years later, in 1563, still aged just 16, he observed the conjunction of Jupiter and Saturn and compared his own observations to the tables in the almanacs. All the published almanacs were woefully inaccurate in their predictions of the date of closest approach of the two planets. Indeed, the Alfonsine tables, which dated back to the 13th century and were based on the Ptolemaic system, were out by a whole month, and even the Prutenic tables, published just over a decade earlier in 1551 and based on the Copernican system, were out by several days. It was clear to Tycho that astronomy was in need of an overhaul, and that accurate and systematic measurements taken over a long period of time would be required to achieve this. With Jorgen's death, in 1565, Tycho inherited a substantial amount of money, providing him with the funds to undertake this immense task.

Duelling was endemic amongst the Danish aristocracy, as was heavy drinking. During the drunken Christmas celebrations of the following year, Tycho fell into a dispute with a distant cousin, Manderup Parsberg, and they retired outside to duel with rapiers. Tycho was slashed across the face with the rapier and his nose was severed. Remarkably, following this disfiguring and almost fatal clash, Tycho and Parsberg became lifelong friends. For the rest of his life, Tycho would wear a prosthetic copper nose and, on special occasions, a nose forged from an alloy of silver and gold.[6]

## *Shattering the Crystal Spheres*

In 1572, Tycho was amazed to see a new star appear in the constellation of Cassiopeia.

> On the 11th day of November in the evening after sunset, I was contemplating the stars in a clear sky. I noticed that a new and unusual star, surpassing the other stars in brilliancy, was shining almost directly above my head; and since I had, from boyhood, known all the stars of the heavens perfectly, it was quite evident to me that there had never been any star in that place of the sky, even the smallest, to say nothing of a star so conspicuous and bright as this. I was so astonished at this sight that I was not ashamed to doubt the trustworthiness of my own eyes. But when I observed that others, on having the place pointed out to them, could see that there really was a star there, I had no further doubts – a miracle indeed, one that has never previously been seen before our time, in any age since the beginning of the world.

When it first appeared, Tycho estimated the new star to be as luminous as the planet Jupiter, but soon it brightened significantly until it even outshone Venus – the brightest of the planets. For about two weeks, it could be seen in daylight. It then gradually faded and, as it did so, it changed in colour from white to yellow to orange to pale red. After about sixteen months, it became too faint to see. Tycho measured the position of the new star against the background stars and attempted to determine its parallax by recording its position during the course of the year, but found no shift. This proved that the star must be more distant than any of the planets. Tycho published his observations in 1573 in *De Stella Nova* (*The New Star*).

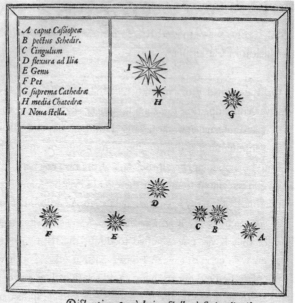

A caput Caſſiopeæ
B pectus Schedir.
C Cingulum
D flexura ad Ilia
E Genu
F Pes
G ſuprema Cathedræ
H media Chatedræ
I Noua ſtella.

Diſtantiam verò huius ſtellæ à fixis aliquibus
in hac Caſſiopeiæ conſtellatione, exquiſito inſtrumento,
& omnium minutorum capacj, aliquoties obſeruaui. In-
ueni autem eam diſtare ab ea, quæ eſt in pectore, Schedir
appellata B, 7. partibus & 55. minutis: à ſuperiori
verò

**Figure 12** Illustration from *Stella Nova*. Stars F, E, D, B, G form the familiar W-shaped outline of the constellation Cassiopeia. Star I is the new star.

As Tycho was keen to point out, his observations demolished Aristotle's claims that although the sub-lunar sphere was subject to decay, beyond the sphere of the Moon the heavens were eternal and unchanging. We now know that the 'new star' was the result of a supernova explosion, in which a star blew itself apart in its almighty terminal blast.[7] Tycho's booklet *Stella Nova* was circulated throughout European learned circles and made Tycho's work famous.

A few years later, in 1577, Tycho dealt Aristotle's cosmos another crushing blow. In that year there was a bright comet. Tycho tracked the course of the comet,[8] which had a blue-white head and a reddish tail, from 17 November until January, and demonstrated conclusively that the comet must be further away than the Moon. Since Aristotle, the heavens were assumed to be composed of a nested sequence of crystal spheres, whose function was to guide the planets in their paths around the Sun. Tycho's analysis of the comet's motion showed that the crystal spheres could not have any real physical existence. The comet had crossed the orbits of the planets and would have shattered them.

King Frederick was duly impressed and rewarded Tycho on a magnificent scale. This would be one of the most important investments in the history of science. His distinguished astronomer was given the use of the island of Hven and grants of a number of fiefdoms and benefices that would provide an income to build and run an observatory there. Tycho would transform it into an enchanted island rising out of the misty waters of the Øresund.

## *An Enchanted Isle*

> Be not afeard; the isle is full of noises,
> Sounds, and sweet airs, that give delight and hurt not.
> Sometimes a thousand twangling instruments
> Will hum about mine ears; and sometime voices
> That, if I then had waked after long sleep,
> Will make me sleep again; and then in dreaming,
> The clouds methought would open, and show riches
> Ready to drop upon me, that when I waked
> I cried to dream again.

William Shakespeare, *The Tempest*, III, ii

Hven is a small island, around five kilometres long by two kilometres wide, within sight of Helsingborg in the straits between present-day Denmark and Sweden. On its highest point, Tycho built his observatory home Uraniborg (Urania's Castle, Urania being the muse of astronomy). Uraniborg was surrounded by a geometrically laid out botanical garden aligned with the cardinal directions, where medicinal herbs were grown. At the centre of the garden, Uraniborg was designed in an Italianate style reminiscent of the Doge's Palace in Venice. There was an elaborate clock tower. Two further towers were designed to hold Tycho's huge instruments, and each was fitted with a conical wooden roof whose triangular sections could be removed to reveal the sparkling jewels of the night sky.

**Figure 13** The main building of Tycho's Uraniborg on the Island of Hven.

Plate 4 shows Tycho's giant quadrant and a mural that offers us a glimpse into the rooms within Uraniborg. In the cellars are Tycho's alchemical laboratories, filled with furnaces and all the paraphernalia of the hermetic arts. Above the laboratory is a circular library, in the centre of which is a great brass globe that was the focus of Tycho's painstaking research. During the course of his observations, Tycho systematically measured the positions of 777 of the most prominent stars in the sky, and steadily plotted each on this globe. He even built a paper mill and a printing press to publish his results. It has been estimated that his lavish expenditure accounted for as much as one percent of the total income of the Danish Crown.[9] Tycho is also reputed to have devised a communication system by which he could ring a bell in any room in the observatory to summon his assistants, almost as though he were summoning spirits to do his bidding.

The magical island attracted noble visitors from throughout Europe. In 1589, James VI of Scotland married Anne of Denmark, daughter of the Danish king Frederick II, who had died the previous year. After visiting Denmark, James and his new wife were caught in a storm and took shelter on Tycho's island on 20 January 1590.[10] In 1601, James would succeed to the throne of England. It has been suggested that Shakespeare's play *The Tempest*, performed for James in 1611, recalls the visit of the monarch to Tycho's wondrous domain.

Tycho built a second observatory on the island called Stjerneborg, or Star Castle. This observatory was constructed underground to increase the accuracy of the measurements, as it would be out of the wind and built on secure foundations that would not be subject to even the slightest disturbance. Tycho examined the origins of all possible inaccuracies in his observations and went to great lengths to eliminate them where possible. He was the first to systematically take account of these various sources of error and to estimate their size. For instance, he measured the effects of refraction due to the atmosphere on the position of stars near the horizon, so that he could correct for this displacement. He also took account of the distortions in the shape of his huge instruments as they bent slightly under gravity. This type of analysis is standard in modern science, but it all began in Tycho's feudal barony on the island of Hven.

After accounting for all possible errors, Tycho was confident that his observations were accurate to between one and two minutes of arc (to put this in context, the diameter of the Moon is about 30 minutes of arc).[11] This was about ten times the accuracy achieved by any previous astronomical observer. For several decades, Tycho used his giant-sized apparatus to determine the positions of the stars and the planets with unrivalled precision.

He believed that the true system of the universe was a half-way house between the systems of Ptolemy and Copernicus. In the Tychonic system, the Earth was stationary at the centre of the universe, orbited by the Moon, but all the planets orbited the Sun, and the Sun in turn orbited the Earth. This enabled Tycho to account for the fact that he was unable to observe any movement of the stars due to parallax. However, the resulting system was an inelegant compromise.

Following the death of King Frederick, Christian IV succeeded to the Danish throne and Tycho's world was turned upside down. The new king was hostile to Tycho and, as the years passed, relations between them deteriorated dramatically. Finally, in 1597, Tycho left his homeland, taking his entourage with him. After Tycho's departure, King Christian ordered his observatories to be demolished.

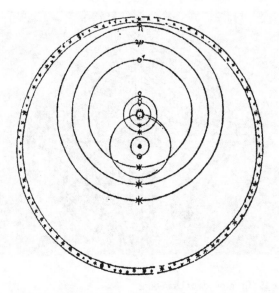

**Figure 14** The Tychonic system. The Earth is at the centre. The Moon orbits the Earth. The Sun also orbits the Earth and all the planets orbit the Sun. Note that the fixed stars form a thin shell that encloses the universe.[12]

Tycho's immense reputation secured him the position of Imperial Mathematician to the Holy Roman Emperor in Prague. His task would be to prove his Tychonic system of the heavens and to compile a new up-to-date set of astronomical tables that would be superior to all previous tables, dedicated to his new patron Rudolf II. Tycho was soon joined by the ideal assistant in Johannes Kepler. Tycho had been impressed by the originality and the mathematical ability shown by Kepler. From Kepler's point of view, the situation was perfect; he would be working for the only man in Europe whose observational data was accurate enough to answer his urgent questions about the structure of the universe.

**Figure 15** The grounds of Uraniborg.

**Figure 16** The remains of Uraniborg on Hven. (© 2005 Google, © 2006 Europa Technologies, Image © 2006 DigitalGlobe)

## *The Battle with Mars*

Kepler began work with Tycho in February, 1600. Tycho was now 53 years old and Kepler was still just 28. Longomontanus, who was Tycho's chief assistant, had been assigned the task of determining the orbit of Mars, but he had made little progress. Kepler was so keen to demonstrate his abilities that he boasted he could complete the job within eight days, and so the task fell to him. Tycho kept a tight grip on his valuable observations, and doled them out to his assistants on a need-to-know basis. This created much antagonism with his ambitious new mathematician, but at least Kepler now had some access to up-to-date and accurate measurements of the planetary positions. As Kepler began the painstaking analysis of the observations that Tycho had compiled, the scale of the challenge became clear.

Then suddenly, everything changed. The larger-than-life figure of Tycho was struck down in a most surprising way. At a banquet held by Baron Rosenberg in Prague, Tycho consumed large quantities of food and drink but, according to Kepler's account, for the sake of etiquette he would not leave the banqueting table to go to the toilet. In Kepler's words: 'he put politeness before his health', with the consequence that he strained his urinary system. By the time he had returned home, he found that he could not urinate at all. Kepler's account seems all the more remarkable, as the mighty Tycho was very familiar with courtly habits, and especially with eating and drinking on a grand scale. The feverish Tycho took to his bed, sleeping fitfully – if at all – and lapsing into delirium. He remained unable to urinate without experiencing excruciating pain. Eleven days after the banquet, he died. On his deathbed, Tycho pointed towards Kepler and then towards the heavens mumbling: 'Let me not seem to have lived in vain'.

**Figure 17** Tycho's tomb in the Church of Our Lady Before Týn in Prague.

In 1901, exactly three hundred years after Tycho's death, his tomb in Prague was opened and his bones were examined. The skull showed the wound from the duelling sword and close inspection revealed the greenish tinge produced by traces of Tycho's copper nose. Tycho's casket still contained strands of his ruddy beard, some of which were removed as souvenirs of the occasion. In the 1990s, samples of the beard hair were analysed and the results revealed a darker side to the story of Tycho's strange death. The hair sample contained high concentrations of the toxic metal mercury, indicating that Tycho had consumed a large quantity of mercury in two doses, one about ten days before his death, which would coincide with the time of the banquet when he initially fell ill, and a second dose just a few hours before death. Furthermore, Tycho's symptoms are consistent with the effects of kidney failure due to mercury poisoning. So, who was responsible? [13]

## Something Rotten in the State of Denmark?

> HAMLET: Murder?
>
> GHOST:   Murder most foul, as in the best it is;
>          But this most foul, strange and unnatural.[14]

The finger of suspicion has been pointed towards Kepler.[15] It is certainly true that he was the main beneficiary of Tycho's demise. Within days, an emissary arrived from the emperor to inform Kepler that he had been appointed the new Imperial Mathematician.

But there is a more credible suspect. A few days before Tycho was taken ill, a dissolute and impoverished distant relative, Erik Brahe, from the Swedish branch of the family, arrived in Prague. The historian Peter Andersen claims that the recently discovered diary of Erik Brahe implicates him in Tycho's downfall.[16] According to Andersen, Erik was an agent sent by King Christian IV of Denmark to take Tycho's life. Furthermore, as a guest at Rosenberg's banquet, he had the opportunity to add a mercury compound to Tycho's goblet and another chance to administer the fatal dose on the evening before his death. Anderson has speculated that the reason for King Christian's hatred of Tycho was that rumours were circulating in Denmark about an old love affair between the king's mother and Tycho, casting doubts on Christian's legitimacy and, therefore, his right to the Danish throne. In November 2010, Tycho's body was exhumed again for a more detailed and modern analysis. We may soon know the truth about his untimely death.

Wrangling over the inheritance began at once, with Tycho's heirs and entourage jockeying for position. Kepler realised that he must secure Tycho's four decades of planetary observations or his celestial journeys might end before they had barely begun. Kepler took possession of the grand chest containing the valuable data, and refused to hand them over to Tycho's relatives. This was extremely fortuitous for the future of humanity. Tycho's observations were in the hands of the one man who would be able to make use of them and raise the phoenix of modern science out of the ashes of medieval mysticism.

## Complex Gyrations

It is easy to take for granted the reckoning of time. The complex gyrations of the Sun, the Moon and the planets barely elicit a passing thought. If we want to know the position of Mars, Jupiter or Saturn in the night sky, we can consult a computer program that will give us their precise location.[17] But this knowledge was hard won. Kepler's official duty would now be to determine the true system of the universe and to compile the tables that would serve future generations of astronomers. They would be named the Rudolfine Tables, in honour of Kepler's patron, the Emperor.

With unhindered access to Tycho's data, Kepler could concentrate all his efforts on revealing the secrets of the heavens. Copernicus had adopted the epicycles and other machinery of Ptolemy's system to produce a model that was no less convoluted than the systems of the ancients. Kepler believed that the universe was constructed on simple geometrical principles, so he recoiled in horror from the details of the Copernican system. Although he was a great admirer of Copernicus, he felt that his illustrious predecessor never knew the treasure that was within his grasp. Kepler realised that placing the Sun at the centre of the system made much of the machinery redundant. He now had the data to construct a far superior system.

Kepler had a vision of a completely different universe – one in which the planets were controlled by forces. In his early writing, he refers to the planets being guided by spirits or minds. Later he was strongly influenced by William Gilbert, who published *De Magnete* in 1600.[18] Gilbert described magnetism in terms of forces acting at a distance, and this was the view that Kepler adopted. For Copernicus, the role of the Sun was to provide light and heat from the centre of the universe. Kepler believed that the Sun was the heart of the mechanical system of the universe, and that its influence emanated outwards and controlled the motion of the planets. No-one had ever viewed the solar system in this way before. Kepler would never fully realise this vision, but it would guide him towards a clearer picture of the planetary motions than had ever been achieved before, paving the way for the modern understanding of the universe.

Kepler's task was a monumental one. It would consume six years of his life, but they would represent the pinnacle of his creativity. During the course of these investigations, he would systematically dismantle all the ancient machinery of epicycles, deferents and equants that had been used during the two millennia between Hipparchus and Copernicus, and reconstruct the planetary system using a totally new and elegant machinery of his own devising. At the start of the project astronomy was an arcane medieval art. With the publication of Kepler's results, astronomy would become the first recognisably modern science. Kepler's achievement must be ranked as one of the greatest in the history of human thought. We are extremely fortunate that he has left us an unembellished account of each step along the road to the correct solution, including all the dead ends and wrong turns.

Kepler had access to the most accurate and complete set of astronomical observations in existence. The observations recorded the position in the sky of each planet over the course of several decades, but disentangling the meaning of all this information in order to construct the geometry of the solar system would be far from easy. Just converting Tycho's raw data into a usable form was a major undertaking. The mathematical techniques that are taught in schools today were not available. Algebra was in its infancy, coordinate geometry was unknown, and calculus did not exist. Consequently, the calculations that Kepler had to undertake were extremely lengthy and tedious. The only mathematical tools available to him were basic arithmetic, a little trigonometry and the classical geometry contained in the works of the great Ancient Greek mathematicians Euclid, Archimedes and Apollonius. Beyond this, Kepler would have to devise his own methods.

## *Of Darkness and Light*

We mark out the days in periods of darkness and light, so it is natural that we should measure the length of a day by reference to the position of the Sun. However, the rate at which the Earth travels round the Sun varies. The Earth moves fastest when it is closest to the Sun, which is around 3rd January. So the motion of the Sun across the sky is not exactly constant,[19] as was well known even in antiquity. The Earth's rotation, on the other hand, is extremely regular, so it is convenient to divide up the year into days of equal length.[20]

This led to the notion of the mean Sun, which is the position that the Sun would occupy if it crossed the sky at the same rate throughout the year, and this is why Greenwich Mean Time is so called.

When Copernicus constructed his heliocentric system, rather surprisingly, it was the mean Sun that he placed at the centre of the system and not the true Sun. This seems not to have mattered much to Copernicus, as his aim was to produce a geometrical system that 'saved the appearances'. Kepler found this idea absurd, and it reflects his profoundly different view of the cosmos. Kepler felt that the Sun must somehow control the motion of the planets. This was a physical and causal relationship. It therefore made absolutely no sense to relate the motion of the planets to a fictitious body such as the mean Sun. The first act of his revolution was to depose the mean Sun and set the true Sun at the heart of his system as the ruler of the planets.

There was an immediate pay-off to the promotion of the true Sun to its rightful place. The planetary orbits are almost in the same plane, like a collection of concentric circles, which is why the planets are confined within the band of zodiacal constellations. However, the alignment is not perfect; each orbit is inclined at a small angle to the others. For example, as Kepler deduced from Tycho's data, the orbit of Mars is inclined by just under two degrees relative to the orbit of Earth.[21] In the rickety Copernican system, the orbit of each planet was completely independent, but Kepler could now see that the plane of each orbit intersected at the Sun, which reinforced his belief that the Sun was ruling the system of planets. This result is sometimes referred to as Kepler's Zeroth Law of Planetary Motion.[22] It was a first step towards a new system of the planets.

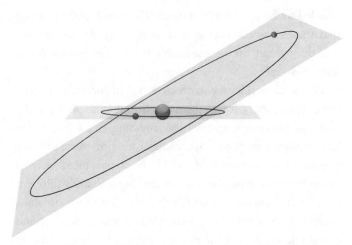

**Figure 18** Kepler used Tycho's data to show that the plane of a planet's orbit is fixed in space and the Sun lies in the plane of each planet's orbit. This is sometimes known as Kepler's Zeroth Law (in contrast to the diagram, the orbits of the planets in the solar system are almost concentric).

## *Eight Minutes that Shook the World*

Kepler was keen to stress that Ptolemy and the other ancients who claimed to be preserving uniform circular motion in their theories had really been doing nothing of the sort. Kepler drew a diagram of the true path of Mars in the Ptolemaic system. He likened the looping epicyclic course of Mars to a pretzel, as illustrated in his diagram below. As Kepler pointed out, the path was not circular and the motion was not uniform. These ancient prejudices had forced astronomers into contortions, just like their planets.

Kepler dismissed the idea of epicycles as intellectually unsound. He believed that the correct solution must be much more elegant. He set off in pursuit of Mars by assuming that its orbit was a perfect circle around the Sun. This would not

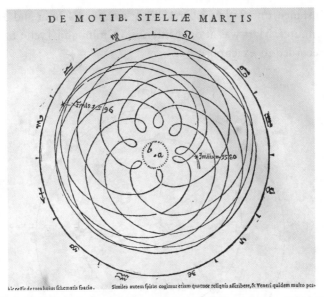

**Figure 19** Mars's 'pretzel' pathways, illustrating the pretzel logic of Kepler's predecessors.

work if the Sun were located at the centre of the circle, so he shifted the centre relative to the Sun. Initially, Kepler retained Ptolemy's notion of the equant point, a point close to the centre of the circle from which the motion of Mars would look uniform.

To trace out the path taken by Mars, Kepler searched through Tycho's data for the exact times and positions of Mars at opposition. This is when Mars is diametrically opposite to the Sun in the sky, so Mars rises as the Sun sets and sets as the Sun rises. At these times, the Sun, Earth and Mars are in a straight line, which greatly simplifies the calculations. Such oppositions occur every two years and seven weeks or so, and there were ten oppositions in Tycho's data, plus two that had been taken since Tycho had died. For instance, on 18 November 1580, at a time of 1 hour and 31 minutes, Mars was at opposition in Gemini and Tycho had recorded its exact position.

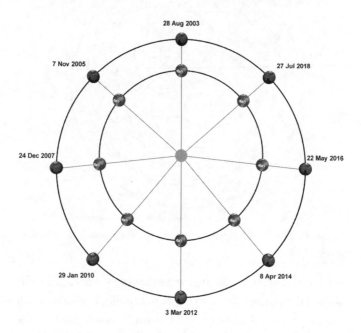

**Figure 20** The figure shows the position of Mars when it reaches opposition on eight consecutive occasions. Kepler used Tycho's observations of the position of Mars at opposition to map out Mars's orbit.

By taking four of these observations, Kepler could find a circular orbit and locate the equant point, thus producing a possible orbit for Mars. The next step would be to check whether this solution matched the other eight oppositions. If not, Kepler would have to make a slight adjustment to bring the orbit in line with these other observations. By trial and error, grinding through almost endless computations, Kepler gradually moved towards a solution that would fit Tycho's data. He would write in his *New Astronomy*:

> If this wearisome method has filled you with loathing, it should more properly fill you with compassion for me as I have gone through it at least seventy times at the expense of a great deal of time. [23]

Finally, after these lengthy and tedious calculations, he obtained a circular orbit that fitted all twelve observations of the oppositions of Mars to within two minutes of arc. At this point, all Kepler's predecessors would almost certainly have jumped for joy and considered that they had successfully completed their task – but not Kepler. He was determined to find the true description of the heavens. The orbit of Mars had to agree with all of Tycho's observations, not just those at opposition.

Kepler searched for any possible discrepancies. He systematically calculated the course of Mars across the night sky according to his model. He then compared these predictions to the actual positions of Mars, as recorded in Tycho's observations. The calculations were checked for the entire orbit of Mars, including observations far from the oppositions which had been used to derive the orbit. Kepler's model was certainly close, but he could find observations that were as much as eight minutes of arc from the predicted position. This is the equivalent of about a quarter of the diameter of the Moon. No astronomer before Tycho had taken observations that were this accurate, but Kepler knew that Tycho had gone to great lengths to ensure that his observations were as accurate as they possibly could be. Kepler was certain that Tycho's observations were accurate to within two minutes of arc. He knew that if his model did not agree with Tycho, then there could only be one conclusion – it was wrong – and he would have to start again. In the words of Kepler: '*These eight minutes showed the way to a renovation of the whole of astronomy.*' [24]

> After the divine goodness had given us in Tycho Brahe, so careful an observer, that from his observations the error of calculation amounting to eight minutes betrayed itself, it is seemly that we recognise and utilise in thankful manner this good deed of God's, that is we should take the pains to search out at last the true form of the heavenly motions. [25]

Kepler was now convinced that he should discard all the rest of the ancient astronomical machinery and start again with a blank slate.

## *Kepler Lays An Egg*

Kepler's task would have been impossible without his deep-seated conviction that the universe was constructed from simple geometrical principles. In the Sun-centred model, the Earth orbits the Sun. This exacerbates the problem of finding the paths of the planets, because it means that observations are taken from a moving platform. Kepler decided that he could only make progress with a better understanding of the Earth's motion around the Sun, so he now set out to accurately determine the characteristics of the Earth's orbit.

Kepler's idea for how this could be done was typically brilliant. He imagined viewing the Earth from Mars. He would choose a particular date in the Martian calendar and work out the position of the Earth on this date for successive Martian years.

Mars would be at exactly the same position in its orbit for each observation, so any irregularities in the Martian orbit would be irrelevant. If the direction to Earth from Mars on that date was plotted for successive Martian years, this would map out the shape of the Earth's orbit. It takes Mars 687 Earth days to orbit the Sun. By finding a sequence of measurements of the position of both Mars and the Sun made at intervals of exactly 687 days, Kepler could begin his task. On these dates, the Sun and Mars would be in the same positions. Only the Earth would have moved between the observations. By calculating the angle between the Sun and Mars from each observation, it would be possible to plot out the path of the moving Earth. The calculations would be just like working out the aspects for an astrological chart.

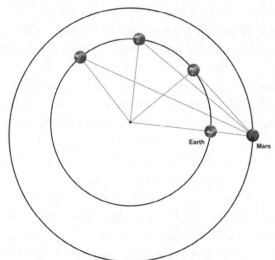

**Figure 21** Kepler plotted out the orbit of the Earth by imagining that he was viewing it from Mars on the same Martian date in successive years. As shown in the figure, the position of Mars is the same for each observation, but the Earth has moved around its orbit.

Kepler succeeded in finding the precise course of the Earth's orbit around the Sun and could return his attention to Mars.[26] Now, when he plotted out the path of the red planet, he thought he had the answer. It was shaped like an egg! It seemed as though the orbit was rounded when Mars was furthest from the Sun, and narrower when close to the Sun.

## Heavenly Movement

Kepler struggled on with his egg-shaped orbit for several years without ever being convinced that he had solved the problem. Finally, it all fell into place. Kepler realised that he had been holding the orbit in his hands all the time. One of the most famous books of mathematics to survive from antiquity was the *Conics* by Apollonius of Perga. Kepler was very familiar with the book and had used it in his work on optics.[27] Apollonius examined the properties of the geometrical figures that are produced by slicing through a cone. For instance, if a cone is cut by a horizontal slice, the cross-section is a circle. However, if the cone is sliced at an angle, the shape of the cross-section is an ellipse. Increasing the angle of the slice increases the eccentricity of the ellipse. If the slice is parallel to the edge of the cone, then the figure will be open-ended. This shape is known as a parabola.

There are other ways to construct these figures, as Apollonius showed. It is easy to define a circle. The circle consists of all the points whose distance from the centre are equal to the radius of the circle. An ellipse can be defined in a similar way but, this time, two points are required. Each is known as a focus of the ellipse. Take a string and attach one end to each focus. The ellipse consists of all the points that can just be reached when this string is stretched taut, as

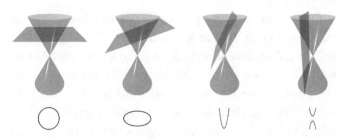

**Figure 22** Conic sections. From left to right: circle, ellipse, parabola, hyperbola.

illustrated in the diagram below. If the two foci are moved further apart, the eccentricity of the ellipse increases. If they are moved together, the eccentricity of the ellipse decreases until it becomes a circle, when the two foci merge together at the same point – the centre of the circle.

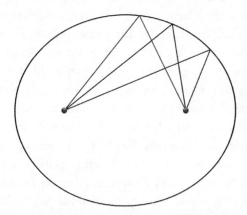

**Figure 23** An ellipse can be constructed by specifying two interior points, each known as a focus of the ellipse – then, with a piece of string fastened to each focus, every point that can just be reached by making the string taut is on the ellipse. In other words, take any point on an ellipse and draw straight lines to the two foci; the sum of the lengths of these two lines is the same for all points on the ellipse. Three examples of such pairs of lines are shown in the illustration.

One of the interesting properties of an ellipse is that if there were a light bulb at one focus, then all the light that it emits would reflect off the ellipse and converge at the other focus. This is why Kepler originally used the name *focus* for these points. Furthermore, if one focus is removed all the way to infinity, then the ellipse becomes a parabola. To a very good approximation, any light entering the parabola from a distant light source will appear to arrive from the focus at infinity. It will therefore reflect off the parabola and converge at the other focus. This is the basis for the design of the reflecting telescope. The 'parabolic' mirror in such telescopes is shaped like the end of a parabola rotated around its axis.

Kepler finally realised that the orbit of Mars must be an ellipse, with the Sun positioned at a focus of the ellipse. This was a remarkable result. It is known as Kepler's First Law of Planetary Motion. The ellipse might not be quite as symmetrical as a circle, but it was a wonderful second best. It was certainly vastly better than an ill-defined egg shape. Much more importantly, it accurately fitted the facts.[28] Kepler went on to show that all the other planets also follow elliptical orbits around the Sun. As it turns out, it was quite fortuitous that Kepler had undertaken his epic struggle with Mars. None of the other planets could have provided the data for this discovery. Mercury's orbit is very eccentric, but it is so close to the Sun that it is only visible in the twilight, and this means that it is very difficult to make accurate observations. The orbit of Venus has a very low eccentricity, so it would have been extremely difficult to distinguish it from a circle. It takes so long for Jupiter and Saturn to orbit the Sun that several lifetimes would be needed to collect sufficient data.

## *The New Astronomy*

The shape of the planetary orbits went only part way to answering Kepler's questions. He also demanded the rules that determine the speed of each planet. Kepler knew that a planet would move more quickly when it was close to the Sun.

**Figure 24** Johannes Kepler, painted in 1610 by an unknown artist.

This seemed reasonable, because he believed that the Sun as the centre of the heliocentric system must somehow be propelling the planets around. Tycho's observations appeared to confirm this idea, but Kepler believed that it should be mathematical and quantifiable. What he wanted was a precise geometrical or arithmetical expression for the way in which a planet's speed changes as it approaches and recedes from the Sun, and he was determined to find one. He found the answer even before he knew the correct shape of the orbits.

After rejecting the equant point, Kepler discovered what he thought was a useful, but approximate, way to determine the motion of a planet.[29] He later realised that his rule held exactly. It goes as follows: a planet sweeps out sectors of its orbit of equal area in equal periods of time. Kepler's laws are numbered in logical order and not in the order in which he found them, so this law is known as Kepler's Second Law of Planetary Motion.

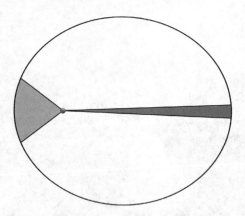

**Figure 25** Kepler's Second Law states that a planet sweeps out sectors of its orbit of equal area in equal periods of time. The illustration shows two such sectors.

Kepler's revolutionary system of the universe was revealed to the world in 1609 in his book *Astronomia Nova* (*The New Astronomy*). This was Kepler's masterpiece, the product of many years of intensive work. It was the first book ever written that would explain natural processes by comparing accurate measurements to a mathematical and deterministic theory. It has become the model for how theoretical physics works, and its importance for the future of science is unparalleled.

## *The Harmony of the World*

In 1614 a Scottish mathematician, John Napier, published *Mirifici Logarithmorum Canonis Descriptio*. This was the first book of logarithms ever published. Part of the book was an explanation of the theory behind logarithms, and the rest consisted of 90 pages of tables. The key feature of logarithms was that they enabled mathematicians to dramatically simplify their calculations by converting multiplication and division sums into addition and subtraction sums. To multiply two numbers together, an astronomer would look up each number in the tables of Napier's book and read off the value of the logarithm in each case. These two logarithms would then be added together. The astronomer would then look in another table to find the number whose logarithm was equal to this result, and this number would be the answer to the multiplication sum.

For an astronomer such as Kepler, this offered an enormous saving in labour. Kepler obtained a copy of Napier's book within two years of its publication. He was so grateful for Napier's method that he dedicated his *Ephemeris* to the Scot. Throughout his life, Kepler searched for the harmonic laws of the heavens – rules that would explain the motion of the planets inspired by the Pythagorean notion of the music of the spheres. In 1618, he had a sudden revelation in which he saw a relationship between the planet's orbital period and the planet's distance from the Sun. Napier's logarithms almost certainly played a key role in this discovery. What Kepler discovered was his Harmonic Law, which states that the square of the orbital period is proportional to the cube of the orbital radius.

The following example illustrates how the relationship works. Take the radius of the Earth's orbit to be one astronomical unit, then the radius of Saturn's orbit is about nine astronomical units. The period of the Earth's orbit is one year. Kepler's Harmonic Law says that if we cube the radius of Saturn's orbit and then take the square root, we will find the period of Saturn's orbit in years. Nine cubed is 729. The square root of 729 is 27. By this reckoning, Saturn should orbit the Sun once in 27 years. In fact, we have rounded the figures to make the calculations simpler for the purposes of this illustration. (The radius of Saturn's orbit is 9.537 astronomical units and its period is 29.45 years. It is worth putting these more precise numbers into a calculator to see just how accurate the relationship is.)[30]

---

**Puzzle 3**

A hypothetical asteroid orbits the Sun at four times the distance of the Earth. How long does it take the asteroid to orbit the Sun?

---

Stumbling across such a relationship amidst a mass of figures would have been quite unlikely. However, with the assistance of logarithms, the task becomes much simpler.

After taking logarithms of the orbital periods and orbital radii of the planets, the relationship would be that twice the logarithm of the orbital period would be proportional to three times the logarithm of the orbital radius. A graph of this data for each planet would be a straight line. Although Kepler would not have drawn such a graph, the numbers were so familiar to him from his endless calculations that the relationship between these quantities would eventually leap out at him. The Harmonic Law is also known as Kepler's Third Law of Planetary Motion.

---

**Answer to Puzzle 3**

Kepler's Third Law is the key to answering this puzzle – the cube of the radius of the orbit is proportional to the square of the orbital period. The cube of the size of the asteroid's orbit is 64 times the size of the Earth's orbit cubed. To find the period of the orbit, we must take the square root to give eight times the period of the Earth's orbit, or eight years.

---

## Measuring the Shadows of the Earth

Kepler published the long awaited Rudolfine Tables in 1627, setting a new standard for the accuracy of astronomical tables. Far more important, though, was the conceptual revolution that Kepler initiated by showing that the planetary orbits are ellipses. Kepler's research can be succinctly distilled into his laws of planetary motion. These are:

0. *The plane of a planet's orbit is fixed in space and the Sun is situated in this plane.*

1. *Each planet orbits the Sun in an ellipse, with the Sun located at a focus of the ellipse.*

2. *Each planet sweeps out sectors of its orbit with equal area in equal intervals of time.*

3. *The cube of the length of the major axis of a planet's elliptical orbit is proportional to the square of its orbital period.*

Kepler believed that the universe is controlled by the operation of forces and, more specifically, that the Sun produces the driving force that maintains the planets in their orbits. His speculations about how this might work were unsuccessful. His best guess was that the rotation of the Sun produced an influence that would sweep the planets round. He also toyed with the idea that the force might be some kind of magnetic influence. This is, of course, completely wrong. It might seem obvious to us today that the force that holds the planets in orbit is another manifestation of the force that holds us to the ground, but this was far from obvious, even to a researcher with the imagination and tenacity of Kepler. However, the laws of planetary motion that Kepler discovered would play a decisive role in enabling Sir Isaac Newton to discover his laws of motion and his Universal Law of Gravitation, as we will soon see.

Kepler died on 15 November 1630, and was buried in the Bavarian city of Regensburg. The cemetery was destroyed by a Swedish army just two years later, during the Thirty Years War, so Kepler's tombstone has been lost. But, the epitaph that Kepler wrote for himself has survived:[31]

I measured the Heavens, now I measure the shadows of the Earth. The mind belonged to Heaven, the body's shadow lies here.

Chapter Three

## THE MAGIC SPYGLASS

He scarce had ceas't when the superiour Fiend
Was moving toward the shore; his ponderous shield
Ethereal temper, massy, large and round,
Behind him cast; the broad circumference
Hung on his shoulders like the Moon, whose Orb
Through Optic Glass the Tuscan Artist views
At Ev'ning from the top of Fesole,
Or in Valdarno, to descry new Lands,
Rivers or Mountains in her spotty Globe.

John Milton, *Paradise Lost*, Book I, Lines 283–291, (1667).

### *The Starry Messenger*

The year 1609 is not remembered as a particularly significant year. It is not engraved into our consciousness in the way that 1066, 1492, 1815 or 1945 might be. But if any year could be singled out as the beginning of the modern world, then this year probably has the best claim to that status. As we have seen, 1609 was the year in which Kepler published his *New Astronomy*, the book that overthrew two thousand years of astronomy and replaced it with a modern understanding of the planetary motions. This revolution in theoretical astronomy coincided with an equally momentous transformation of observational astronomy. In 1609, the Italian scientist Galileo Galilei heard news that a remarkable optical instrument had been invented in the Netherlands. Galileo began to experiment with lenses and soon constructed his own instrument – a spyglass or telescope. With further experimentation, he was able to increase the magnification of the telescope, and he then began to use it to observe the night sky as it had never been seen before. What he saw was astonishing.

Within a few months, in March the following year, Galileo published a short booklet describing his discoveries. It came like a bolt out of the blue. *The Starry Messenger*, as it was called, began with a triumphant fanfare:

THE STARRY MESSENGER revealing great, unusual, and remarkable spectacles, opening these to the consideration of every man, and especially of philosophers and astron-omers; AS OBSERVED BY GALILEO GALILEI Gentleman of Florence Professor of Mathematics in the University of Padua, WITH THE AID OF A SPYGLASS lately invented by him, in the surface of the Moon, in innumerable Fixed Stars, in Nebulae, and above all in FOUR PLANETS swiftly revolving about Jupiter at differing distances and periods, and known to no one before the Author recently perceived them and decided that they should be named THE MEDICEAN STARS[1]

Galileo made sensational discoveries everywhere he looked in the night sky. He found that, contrary to accepted wisdom and the claims of the followers of Aristotle, the Moon is not a perfectly spherical globe, but, like the Earth, it is covered with mountains and crevasses. Throughout the heavens, he saw multitudes of stars that were too faint to see with the naked eye. The Milky Way was resolved into vast swarms of faint stars for the first time.

But Galileo's greatest discovery, as he presaged in his frontispiece, was the existence of four satellites of Jupiter. His name 'The Medicean Stars', however, did not catch on, and these satellites are known today as the Galilean moons of Jupiter: Io, Europa, Ganymede and Callisto. Galileo first saw three of the moons on 7 January 1610. On this first night, he assumed that they were background stars, although he noted that they were all in a line right on the ecliptic. After another couple of nights, it was clear that they were actually satellites dancing around the globe of Jupiter. Galileo drew the position of the satellites night by night over the course of the next two months running up to the publication of *The Starry Messenger*.

As Galileo pointed out, the new moons were another blow to the traditional view of the heavens. There was clearly much in the universe that was unknown to the ancients and moderns alike. It is very easy to see the Galilean moons of Jupiter with modern equipment. They are revealed by a casual view of Jupiter with even the smallest telescope or a pair of binoculars.

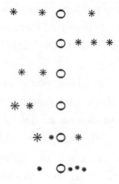

**Figure 26** Galileo's drawings of the moons of Jupiter from *The Starry Messenger*. From top to bottom, as observed with his spyglass on 7, 8, 10, 11, 12 and 13 January, 1610.

Galileo was born in Pisa in 1564. He was the son of Vincenzo Galilei, who was a famous musician and music theorist with a healthy scepticism about established authority. Galileo became an accomplished lutenist, and his sense of rhythm and timing may have played a part in some of his most famous discoveries. In 1581, Galileo enrolled at the University of Pisa to study medicine. Galileo's biographer, Vincenzo Viviani, tells the story that while Galileo was in the cathedral in Pisa, he noticed that the great chandelier was swinging back and forth. Using his pulse to time the chandelier, he realised that the time taken to complete a full swing was the same, whatever the size of the swing [2] (as Galileo later demonstrated in his experiments with pendulums, this is only strictly true for small oscillations). [3]

Galileo realised that his discovery might have a very important application. The swing of the pendulum could be used to measure time. Many years later, Galileo designed a pendulum clock. His son Vincenzo was charged with its construction, but it was never completed. Galileo's idea would eventually come to fruition when the Dutch physicist Christiaan Huygens constructed the first pendulum clock in 1656. This was a great technological breakthrough. Pendulum clocks remained the most accurate timekeepers until the invention of the atomic clock in the 1930s.

## Escaping the Dark Labyrinth

> Philosophy is written in this immense book that stands ever open before our eyes (I speak of the universe), but it cannot be read unless we first learn the language and recognise the characters in which it is written. It is written in mathematical language, and the characters are triangles, circles and other geometrical figures, without the means of which it is humanly impossible to understand a word; without these philosophy is a confused wandering in a dark labyrinth.[4]

> Galileo, *The Assayer* (1623).

In 1602, while Kepler was looking up to the heavens and wrestling with the orbit of Mars, Galileo began a systematic investigation of motion closer to home. Galileo rejected the traditional explanations of the world dating back to Aristotle. He believed that the universe operated along mathematical principles that could be revealed through measurement and experiment. It sounds so obvious from our vantage point but, prior to Galileo, the world was the subject of philosophical and theological arguments that were very difficult to pin down, made by scholars who rarely felt the need to check the assertions that they made.

Galileo is said to have dropped a wooden ball and a cannon-ball from the Leaning Tower of Pisa in order to demonstrate that they hit the ground together. Galileo may or may not have impressed his patrons with a theatrical demonstration such as this. What he definitely did do was construct ramps, down which he could roll balls made of various materials. This slowed the motion of the balls, making it much easier to analyse.

One of the most difficult problems that Galileo needed to overcome was how to accurately measure short periods of time. He designed a water clock that allowed a steady trickle of water to flow. He would then collect and weigh the water in order to quantify the amount of time that had elapsed. Using this simple equipment, Galileo showed that it did not matter what material the balls were composed of – they all rolled down his slopes in the same period of time.

Varying the angle of the slope also led Galileo to the conclusion that the balls would only come to a halt due to the small amount of friction that they were subject to. He believed that if a ball was set in motion on an ideal horizontal track where friction had been completely removed, the ball would continue onwards at the same speed indefinitely.[5] Newton would call this property of matter 'inertia', borrowing the term from Kepler, who believed that matter displayed an inherent laziness. It would be key to Galileo's arguments for why we do not feel the rotation of the Earth.

> Shut yourself up with some friend in the main cabin below decks on some large ship, and have with you there some flies, butterflies, and other small flying animals. Have a large bowl of water with some fish in it; hang up a bottle that empties drop by drop into a wide vessel beneath it. With the ship

standing still, observe carefully how the little animals fly with equal speed to all sides of the cabin. The fish swim indifferently in all directions; the drops fall into the vessel beneath; and, in throwing something to your friend, you need throw it no more strongly in one direction than another, the distances being equal; jumping with your feet together, you pass equal spaces in every direction. When you have observed all these things carefully (though doubtless when the ship is standing still, everything must happen in this way), have the ship proceed with any speed you like, so long as the motion is uniform and not fluctuating this way and that. You will discover not the least change in all the effects named, nor could you tell from any of them whether the ship was moving or standing still. [6]

---

**Puzzle 4**

What is the sum of the first twenty odd numbers?

HINT: The first three odd numbers can be represented as shown above.

---

### *What Are the Odds on That?*

Galileo's next task was to examine the rate at which the balls ran down the slope. What he found was that the speed of the ball would increase as it moved down the slope, but it would do so in a quite regular way. If the distance travelled by a ball in one second was taken as the unit of distance, then in the next second, the ball would travel three units, in the third second it would travel five units, then seven units, and so on. This was a remarkably simple rule and the key to understanding motion close to the Earth. Galileo believed that he had found one of the arithmetical secrets of the cosmos. He called this his Law of Odd Numbers.[7] In modern terms, what Galileo had discovered was that the rate at which the balls were moving

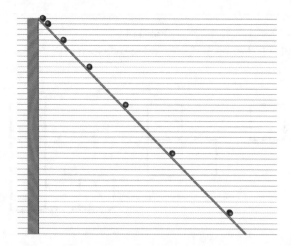

**Figure 27** The diagram shows a ball rolling down a slope under the influence of gravity. The position of the ball is shown at equal intervals of time. The ball obeys Galileo's Law of Odd Numbers. (The slope is much steeper than it would have been in Galileo's experiments.)

**Answer to Puzzle 4**

Odd numbers can be represented as 'L' shaped collections of squares, as shown in the hint. The 'L' shapes fit together to form a larger square. This is shown in the following diagram:

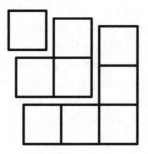

From the diagram it is clear that the first three odds numbers add up to $3^2 = 9$ and, in general, the sum of the first $n$ odd numbers will be equal to $n^2$. The sum of the first twenty odd numbers is therefore $20^2 = 400$.

was increasing steadily; in other words, they were undergoing a constant acceleration due to the force of gravity.

This puzzle illustrates a result that Galileo would later derive from his Law of Odd Numbers. The distance travelled by a ball in one second is one unit. After two seconds, the total distance is four units. After three seconds it is nine units, and so on. In general, the total distance travelled by a ball grows as the square of the time that it is travelling down the slope.[8]

The next step was to consider two motions at once. Galileo arranged for the balls to roll down slopes and then shoot off his table, in order to analyse their trajectory before they hit the floor. He found that the horizontal and vertical motions of the balls were completely independent. The path followed by a ball was produced by combining these two separate motions. In the horizontal direction, the ball continues in a straight line at a constant speed, covering equal distances in equal periods of time, as Galileo had already deduced. Vertically, the motion would obey the odd numbers rule corresponding to a constant acceleration. As we have seen, this means that the distance covered in the vertical direction increases with the square of the time. The path followed by the ball is shown in the illustration below. The shape of the path is known as a parabola. Galileo had now found a geometrical law of nature.

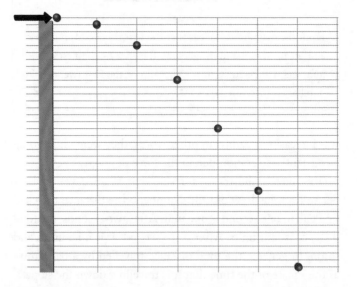

**Figure 28** The diagram shows the trajectory of a ball that is pushed horizontally from the top of a platform. The path followed by the ball is a parabola.

A parabola can be regarded as an extremely eccentric ellipse. The greater the distance between the two foci of an ellipse, the greater its eccentricity. In the limiting case where one focus is taken all the way to infinity, the resulting figure is a parabola. There is a clear connection between Kepler's discovery that the planets move in elliptical orbits around the Sun and Galileo's discovery that projectiles travel in parabolic arcs.[9] However, this connection was not made for many years. Galileo's results were published after Kepler's death, and Galileo does not seem to have paid any attention to Kepler's books.

Galileo recorded the results of these experiments in his book *Two New Sciences*, published in 1638.[10] Galileo wrote in Italian, which was very unusual in the 17th century, when almost all learned discourse was carried on in Latin. He is famous for his eloquent and persuasive prose. His literary style certainly helped his ideas and discoveries to achieve a wide circulation.

Unfortunately, scientific enquiry in his homeland would be brought to a juddering halt, and the centre of gravity of science would move northwards away from the Mediterranean and towards countries where scientific speculation could be pursued without hindrance. In 1633, Galileo was tried and found guilty by the Inquisition for arguing for the Sun-centred cosmology of Copernicus. He was suspected of heresy and required to 'abjure, curse and detest' the views that he had expressed. He was sentenced to imprisonment, but the sentence was later commuted to house arrest in his villa in Arcetri, just south of Florence, which he endured for the rest of his life. Within a few years, he was blind due to a combination of cataracts and glaucoma, but he continued to work. Plate 5 is a painting showing Galileo in his later years.

In 1638, the 74 year old Galileo was visited by a young poet who was travelling around Italy. His name was John Milton, and he would become the greatest English epic poet. In his masterpiece *Paradise Lost*, Milton makes several references to Galileo and his astronomical discoveries, including the extract that opens this chapter. Galileo is the only contemporary figure that Milton mentions in his great work. Galileo died in 1642, four years after his meeting with Milton.

Milton became an ardent champion of the freedom of the press. During the English Civil War, he would find some of his own writings condemned and censored. In 1644, Milton attacked such censorship in the *Areopagitica*, a passionate defence of the rights of an author to publish his work uninhibited by the threat of persecution. He made this reference to his visit to Italy in support of his case:

> There it was that I found and visited the famous Galileo, grown old a prisoner to the Inquisition, for thinking in astronomy otherwise than the Franciscan and Dominican licensers thought.[11]

Although virtually unknown today, Milton's short treatise played an important role in the development of modern views on freedom of expression and had a significant influence on the constitution of the United States when it was drawn up in the following century.

### Venus in the Face of the Sun

On 8 June 2004 and 6 June 2012, the planet Venus passed across the face of the Sun.[12] These were only the sixth and seventh occasions on which this rare spectacle had ever been observed. The first person to witness such an event was a young astronomer called Jeremiah Horrocks, living in an obscure

Lancashire hamlet, who correctly forecast that it would occur on 24 November 1639.[13] This was just a year after Milton's visit to Galileo, and three years before Galileo's death.

Planetary positions can now be predicted many years in advance, and this information is readily available on websites such as www.heavens-above.com. So, we know that the next transit of Venus will not occur until 11 December 2117.[14]

Although Horrocks is not very famous today, he was a brilliant mathematician and astronomer, and his observation of the transit of Venus was not simply a fluke. Indeed, he was probably the first person to realise that the path of a ball thrown through the air might be controlled by the same agency as the orbits of the planets around the Sun. The Newtonian Revolution was partially built on his astronomical research, so his legacy has proved to be very valuable indeed.

But who was Jeremiah Horrocks?

## *Jeremiah Horrocks*

Jeremiah Horrocks was born in 1618 into a family of watchmakers in Toxteth Park in Liverpool. Little is known about his earliest years, but no doubt he was influenced by his family's interest in the measurement of time and its connection to the whirling cycles of the heavens. In 1632, at the age of just fourteen, he was sent off to Emmanuel College in Cambridge, which was a leading centre for the study of mathematics and astronomy. At the college, he befriended John Wallis, who was a couple of years older, but who entered the college in the same year. Wallis would become one the great mathematicians of the age, and one of the founders of the Royal Society. The college gave Horrocks access to books on astronomy and contact with some of England's leading astronomers. It is probable that Horrocks learnt his observational skills from Samuel Foster, the author of treatises on quadrants and sundials. Foster had already been at Emmanuel for sixteen years when Horrocks arrived, and would go on to become Gresham Professor of Astronomy.

In 1635, Horrocks, still only seventeen years old, left Cambridge to return to his native Lancashire. It was just a quarter of a century since Galileo had rocked the learned world with his booklet *The Starry Messenger* and, since then, Galileo's spyglass had revealed numerous features of the universe that had never been seen before. The only way that someone of modest means could acquire a telescope to see these wonders at first hand was to make their own, and this is exactly what Horrocks did. Horrocks confirmed for himself all the discoveries of Galileo. But he was no ordinary observer. What made him special was that he was also an excellent mathematician. Crucially, he had the ability to understand the various astronomical tables that were in existence, and to perform the calculations that would predict the positions of the planets.

Initially, Horrocks used the recent astronomical tables compiled by the Dutch astronomer Philippe van Lansberge and published in 1632. However, these tables were based on Copernicus's model of the solar system, and they completely ignored the huge progress made by Kepler. Horrocks soon realised that Lansberge's tables were hopelessly inaccurate, despite the extravagant claims of their author. Horrocks secured a copy of Kepler's Rudolphine Tables and immediately recognised their clear superiority.

But Horrocks was not simply a meticulous and accurate observer – he was also an accomplished theorist, who understood Kepler's ideas better than any of his contemporaries. Kepler had died in 1630, and Horrocks feared that his great advances might be lost, with astronomers reverting to the complicated epicyclic systems of the past. This made him all the more keen to demonstrate the advantages of Kepler's system. Horrocks confirmed through his own observations that Kepler's ideas worked to a very good approximation, but it was not long before he went even further.

Kepler's universe was built on a divine harmony in which the imperial Sun controlled its family of planets. According to Kepler, the Sun emanated a force that generated the motion of each of the planets. He thought that it must operate like a broom, sweeping the planets around. But ultimately, he failed in all his attempts to find a mechanical explanation of how this solar force might work.

Horrocks recognised that, somehow, the Sun was controlling the movement of the planets – but he could also see that the motion of the planets could not be explained by the action of the Sun alone. His investigations suggested that there must be a force acting between all celestial bodies. This was not merely philosophical speculation; it was based on detailed analysis of the historical records and his own observations.

For instance, when Horrocks analysed the motion of Jupiter and Saturn, the two largest planets in the solar system, it was clear that the two planets affected each other's motion. There seemed to be some sort of mutual attraction. Jupiter orbits the Sun on the inside of Saturn. Every twenty years, it overtakes Saturn. Horrocks showed that as Jupiter closes in on Saturn, it speeds up but, when it has passed Saturn, it slows down. There was a similar effect on Saturn. As Jupiter was catching up, Saturn appeared to slow down then, once Jupiter had passed by, Saturn appeared to speed up again. It was as though the two planets were pulling on each other. This small effect was the key to an understanding of celestial mechanics that was quite different from Kepler's. Indeed, Horrocks was well on the way towards a much more sophisticated view of the force of gravity. Newton would demonstrate definitively that all massive bodies exert a gravitational attraction on all other massive bodies, and this would transform our understanding of the universe.

Horrocks also applied Kepler's ideas to the Moon and was the first to show that the Moon follows an elliptical orbit around the Earth. The Moon's motion proved to be very difficult to model accurately. One of the effects that Horrocks pinned down is that the Moon's orbit precesses. This means that, if a line is drawn joining the point at which the Moon is closest to the Earth to the point at which the Moon is furthest from the Earth, this line does not remain fixed in space, as Kepler's laws would suggest, but it gradually changes direction. In just under nine years,[15] the axis of the Moon's orbit completes a full circuit around the Earth.[16] Horrocks also discovered other periodic variations in the Moon's motion and determined their rate of change. Horrocks was the first to realise that the reason why the Moon's course is so difficult to predict is that it is simultaneously affected by an attraction to both the Earth and the Sun. This was an idea that was half a century ahead of its time.

Horrocks also believed that there might be a connection between the motion of the planets and the gravitational force that we feel on Earth. This was potentially a huge advance on Kepler, and would become a key ingredient in the Newtonian synthesis. Horrocks even suggested that a stone thrown into the air would follow an elliptical path, just like the Moon or a planet, if it was not brought to a premature halt by hitting the ground. In search of further insight into this problem, Horrocks experimented with pendulums.

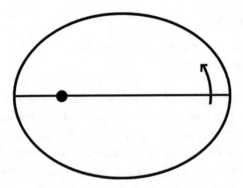

**Figure 29** The Moon's orbit around the Earth is an ellipse to a very good approximation but, as Horrocks discovered, the direction of the axis of the ellipse gradually changes. This is known as precession. A full circuit is completed in about nine years (the eccentricity of the orbit is greatly exaggerated in the illustration).

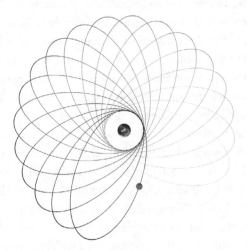

**Figure 30** Diagram showing the precession of the axis of the Moon's orbit around the Earth (the eccentricity of the orbit and the rate of precession are exaggerated).

## *The Pendulum*

England swings like a pendulum do.
Roger Miller (1965).

Kepler had discovered the shape of the planetary orbits and how the speed of a planet changes as it moves around its orbit – speeding up as it approaches the Sun, and slowing down as it recedes from the Sun. He had demolished the astronomical systems of the ancients and replaced them with a much simpler and more accurate system. This was one of the great achievements in the history of science but, as Kepler well knew, it was only a halfway step to a new physics. Kepler's system explained how the planets move, but it did not explain why the planets move in the way that they do.

It was clear that Aristotle's age-old explanations would not work, but what could they be replaced with? Kepler's best guess was that magnetism was somehow involved. He imagined that the rotation of the Sun produced a kind of magnetic whirlpool in space that emanated outwards, and that this swept the planets around the Sun. Of course, these speculations were completely wrong, and the correct explanation would be provided by Isaac Newton, as we will see in the next chapter. But there was another great clue that Kepler discovered that would be critical for later scientists such as Newton. To get an idea about the significance of this discovery, we will take a look at the pendulum, as Horrocks and other 17th century scientists did, to see what insight it offers for the motion of the planets.

Galileo discussed the motion of a pendulum swinging in a single plane, like the pendulum in a grandfather clock, and this is the image that is usually conjured up by the idea of a pendulum. However, a bob suspended from a string can simultaneously swing in two perpendicular directions that we can call 'left-to-right' and 'back-and-forth'. When a pendulum swings in two directions at once, it is known as a conical pendulum. The swinging motion in the two directions combine and a circuit is traced out by the bob.

What is the shape of this circuit? Well, because the period of the swing is independent of its size, the left-to-right motion must take the same period of time as the back-and-forth motion. In other words, the swings in the two perpendicular planes will remain in step. The motion will therefore be periodic, and the shape traced out by the bob will close on itself and repeat indefinitely. If the swings in the two perpendicular directions are equal in size, the shape is a circle. If one swing is bigger than the other, as will generally be the case, then the shape is a squashed circle or, in other words, an ellipse.

This looks like a promising start for a model of a planetary orbit. It certainly offers something to work with that is readily to hand and easier to play with than a planetary system. For these reasons, Jeremiah Horrocks made conical pendulums and explored their properties.

There is one immediate difference between the pendulum and the planet, which is that the force acting on the pendulum

---

**Puzzle 5**

Imagine that the force of gravity operates like a conical pendulum. When the radius of the orbit of our pendulum is 10 centimetres, it takes four seconds to complete one orbit. If the radius of the orbit is increased to 40 centimetres, how long does it take to complete one orbit? HINT: Consider Galileo's discovery about pendulums.

bob is towards the centre of each of the two perpendicular swings. Thus, while in the planetary case the force is towards the Sun, which is located at a focus of the ellipse that forms the planet's orbit, the force on the pendulum bob is towards the centre of the ellipse.

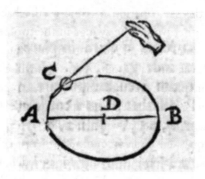

**Figure 31** A diagram from the posthumous papers of Jeremiah Horrocks, in which he illustrates the use of a conical pendulum to mimic gravity.

The second key difference between a conical pendulum and the orbit of a planet shows why Kepler's Third Law was so important for later researchers. Galileo's observation in the cathedral tells us something important about the rate at which the bob completes a circuit. Because the period of a swing is independent of the amplitude of the swing, the time taken for the bob to complete its elliptical orbit must be independent of the size of the orbit. This means that if the planets were held in the solar system by a similar force, each one would take the same period of time to orbit the Sun. We would see Mercury, Venus, Mars, Jupiter and Saturn all cross our skies at the same rate. Indeed, they would all complete their orbit in one year, just as the Earth does. This is not what we see at all – it takes Saturn almost 30 years to orbit the Sun.

---

**Answer to Puzzle 5**

The orbital period of the pendulum bob is independent of the radius of the orbit, so the bob will still take four seconds to complete one orbit, even though the orbit is four times as large. For a pendulum, the equivalent of Kepler's Third Law is that the period of the orbit is independent of the size of the orbit. However, this is not how the planets orbit the Sun. It proves that the force of gravity does not operate like the force that controls the motion of a pendulum bob. Kepler's Third Law would be the key to finding the correct force law obeyed by gravity.

---

From the way in which the period changes with the size of the orbit, it is possible to determine how the force changes with distance. In the case of the pendulum, the periods of the orbits are independent of the size of the orbits. Which implies that the force acting on the bob is proportional to the distance from the centre. At twice the distance, the force is twice as large, at three times the distance it is three times as large, and so on. This makes sense, because it means that the further the pendulum bob is from the centre, the stronger the force pulling it back to the centre and therefore the faster the bob moves in order to complete its bigger orbit in the same time.

This is very different from the way that the solar system works. In the solar system, the further a planet is from the Sun, the slower it travels. It is clear that the relationship between the period of an orbit and the size of the orbit is a good clue to the force that is acting, and this is just the sort of relationship that Kepler spent his whole life searching for. As we saw in the previous chapter, Kepler found just such a relationship in the heavens. What Kepler discovered was that the square of the period of a planet's orbit is proportional to the cube of the radius of the planet's orbit. This relationship is the key to the force that is acting on the planet. Turning the key would unlock the whole of physics and bring about the most sensational revolution in the history of science. The person who turned the key is the hero of our next chapter.

### The Goddess of Love

Kepler had predicted, in the Rudolphine Tables, that Venus would cross the face of the Sun in 1631. Such an event had never been seen. A number of Europe's astronomers watched out for the transit, but with no success (we now know that it was not visible in Europe, as the Sun had set before the transit began; it was only visible from the opposite hemisphere of the Earth, where no-one was watching).

By 1639, Horrocks was living in Much Hoole, a tiny village midway between the Lancashire coastal town of Southport and the market town of Preston. Horrocks knew that, according to the Rudolphine Tables, in November of that year there would be a near miss and Venus would pass just below the Sun's disc. Throughout October, Horrocks tracked the position of Venus from evening to evening. Then, with just over a month to go, he suddenly realised that Kepler was mistaken – Venus was on course to pass directly across the face of the Sun. This was remarkable, as transits of Venus are very rare events; we know

now that every 120 years or so, a pair of transits will occur, separated by an interval of eight years. These two transits are visible from opposite hemispheres of the Earth. All earlier transits visible from Europe would have occurred before the invention of the telescope, so the young Horrocks, isolated in an obscure village in a remote area of Lancashire, had the opportunity to see an astronomical apparition that had never been seen before. On 26 October 1639, he excitedly penned a letter to his friend William Crabtree, a draper who lived in Broughton, just outside Manchester:

> My reason for now writing is to advise you of a remarkable conjunction of the Sun and Venus on the 24th November when there will be a transit. As such a thing has not happened for many years past, and will not occur again in this century, I earnestly entreat you to watch attentively with your telescope, in order to observe it as well as you can. [17]

In preparation for the great event, Horrocks took a sheet of card and drew a six-inch circle, on which he intended to plot the course of Venus across the face of the Sun. He marked the circumference with 360 degree marks, and drew a diameter, which he divided into 120 parts.

His calculations suggested that the transit would begin at 3 pm on 24 November. To ensure that he would not miss this once-in-a-lifetime event due to a misplaced confidence in his own observations, Horrocks set up his telescope a day early and projected the image of the Sun onto the back wall of his room, such that the Sun exactly filled the six-inch circle that he had drawn. He could see one small sunspot, but nothing unusual. The following day, he continued with his vigil. Periodically returning from his duties, he kept watch on the projected image

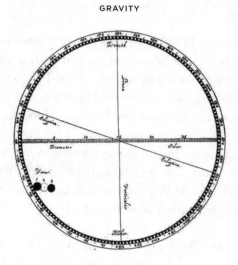

**Figure 32** The diagram on which Horrocks marked the passage of Venus across the Sun, as published by Hevelius.

of the Sun as it appeared and disappeared behind the clouds. Still there was nothing. Time ran on towards mid-afternoon and the hour when he expected the transit to start. Then, he was suddenly *'called away by business of the highest importance, which with propriety could not be neglected'*.[18]

When he returned at a quarter past three, the clouds had dispersed and he saw, in his words: *'a most agreeable spectacle'* – the shadow of a perfectly spherical body that had already fully entered onto the face of the Sun. He watched eagerly for the next half an hour until sunset, regularly recording the position of Venus as the transit progressed.

Meanwhile, in Broughton, William Crabtree had made his own preparations for viewing the transit. Over Manchester, the skies were covered with thick cloud, and the disconsolate Crabtree thought that his opportunity to see this rarest of events would be lost to the Manchester weather. Then, suddenly, at just after half past three, the skies cleared and a

**Figure 33** The 2004 transit of Venus.

stunned Crabtree could see Venus on the face of the Sun for the quarter of an hour until sunset.

It is important to note that it is very dangerous to look directly at the Sun, with or without an optical instrument. Doing so can lead to permanently damaged eyesight.

## *Expanding the Universe*

Horrocks recorded his account of the transit in a remarkable document: *Venus in Sole Visa* (*Venus in the face of the Sun*). Horrocks gives a detailed scientific analysis of his observations and argues convincingly that there could be no doubt that he had indeed seen Venus crossing the Sun's disc, and not some other astronomical phenomenon, such as a sunspot. Horrocks and Crabtree both estimated the size of the disc of Venus and they agreed that it was much smaller than had been anticipated by earlier astronomers. Horrocks concluded that Venus must be much further away than had previously been assumed and, if Venus was further away, this implied that the entire planetary system must be much larger than anyone had suspected.

In later centuries, transits of Venus were recognised as ideal opportunities to precisely determine the size of the solar system. By recording the time at which a transit begins at two well-separated locations, the parallax and, hence, the distance to Venus could be determined and, from this distance, the size of all the planetary orbits could be calculated. This was one of the most important objectives of Captain Cook's expedition to the Pacific. Cook recorded his observations of the transit of Venus from Tahiti on 3 June 1769.

In his writing, Horrocks implored astronomers to make their own telescopic observations and thereby acquaint themselves with the obvious inaccuracies in the existing astronomical tables. They could then confirm, to their own satisfaction, all his claims and conclusions. Horrocks had a rigorous and logical writing style. His account of the transit of Venus reads like a modern scientific paper in every respect but one. Horrocks was so moved by his discoveries that he interspersed poetry amidst his scientific arguments.

> Divine the hand which to Urania's power
> Triumphant raised the trophy, which on man
> Hath first bestowed the wondrous tube by art
> Invented, and in noble bearing taught
> His mortal eyes to scan the furthest heavens.[19]

## *An Incalculable Loss!*

One year after observing the transit, Horrocks arranged to visit his friend William Crabtree in Manchester. On January 4,

1641, Crabtree awaited his friend, but Horrocks did not arrive. He was dead. No explanation of his sudden death has come to light. Crabtree, who recognised the enormous potential shown by Horrocks, was quite naturally distraught. He wrote:

> Thus God sets an end to all earthly things. Ah departed friends (alas, the sadness of it all). O Horrocks most dear to me! Ah the bitter tears this has caused! What an incalculable loss![20]

He treasured Horrocks's papers and the memory of the young astronomer who had taken the study of the heavens beyond all his predecessors. Horrocks's work was known to a small group of Northern tradesmen and amateur astronomers but, over the next two decades, England was in turmoil and the writings of Horrocks remained unpublished. The Civil Wars were followed by the disruption of Cromwell and the Commonwealth. It was not until 1662 that Horrocks's account of the transit of Venus was finally published in Danzig. When the publication of this remarkable document was brought to the attention of the newly founded Royal Society, its members were severely embarrassed that such an important English work had not been recognised in England. The Royal Society gave the task of collecting and publishing all Horrocks's surviving papers to his friend from student days – John Wallis, by now the Savilian Professor of Geometry at Oxford University.

Horrocks was a mere 22 years old when he died, and the scale of his accomplishments in just a few years of isolated study is breathtaking. There is no way of knowing what he might have achieved had he lived. What is certain is that he was an extremely important stepping-stone between Kepler and Newton, which means that his influence played some part in the creation of Newton's magnificent *Principia*, possibly the most important book ever written. Newton, who was not always generous with his praise for others, acknowledged the significance of Horrocks's theory of the Moon. Newton famously recalled that if he had seen further than others, it was by standing on the shoulders of giants.[21] One of these great figures was surely Jeremiah Horrocks.

During the Victorian era, there was a revival of interest in Jeremiah Horrocks, and a chapel dedicated to the remarkable young astronomer was built in St Michael's Church in Hoole. In the chapel, a marble tablet and a stained glass window commemorate the young astronomer who consolidated Kepler's revolution and laid the foundations for Newton's even greater revolution.

**Figure 34** Stained glass window showing Horrocks in St Michael's Church, Hoole.

Chapter Four

# VOYAGING THROUGH STRANGE
# SEAS OF THOUGHT

'Sir Isaac Newton, renowned inventor of the milled-edge coin and the catflap!'

'The what?' said Richard.

'The catflap! A device of the utmost cunning, perspicuity and invention. It is a door within a door, you see, a . . .'

'Yes,' said Richard, 'there was also the small matter of gravity.'

'Gravity,' said Dirk with a slightly dismissed shrug, 'yes, there was that as well, I suppose. Though that, of course, was merely a discovery. It was there to be discovered.' . . . 'You see?' he said, dropping his cigarette butt. 'They even keep it on at weekends. Someone was bound to notice sooner or later. But the catflap . . . ah, there is a very different matter. Invention, pure creative invention. It is a door within a door, you see.'

Douglas Adams, *Dirk Gently's Holistic Detective Agency*

## A Discussion over Coffee

Following a meeting of the Royal Society in January, 1684, three of England's leading intellectuals – Christopher Wren, Robert Hooke and Edmund Halley – retired to a London coffee house to continue their discussions. All three men would be remembered for their contributions to science. On this evening, their deliberations concerned the force that keeps the planets in orbit around the Sun. In particular, they were considering the laws of planetary motion derived by the German mathematician Johannes Kepler and what their implications were for the force of gravity between the Sun and the planets.

In the early years of the century, Kepler had undertaken a painstaking analysis of the most accurate observations of the planets ever made. These had been compiled over the course of several decades by the astronomer Tycho Brahe. Kepler's conclusions could be summarised in his laws describing how the planets move around the Sun, as summarised on page 80.

The three Royal Society fellows could see that Kepler's Third Law, which relates the period of a planet's orbit to its distance from the Sun, might be the key to the problem, as it seemed to suggest that gravity becomes weaker as the distance between the Sun and a planet grows. More precisely, they believed that it implied that the force of gravity falls as the inverse square of distance, which means that at twice the distance, the force falls to a quarter of its original value; at three times the distance, to one-ninth of its original value, and so on. But their proposal was quite tentative, as they did not have the necessary mathematical tools to demonstrate this conclusively.

Wren realised that the case for the inverse square law would be clinched if it could be demonstrated that this force law would produce elliptical orbits, as described by Kepler's First Law. So he offered a prize to anyone who could prove this relationship. Hooke claimed that he had a proof, but he was unable to produce it and no-one else could find a solution. So, in August 1684, Halley travelled to Cambridge to consult the Lucasian Professor, Isaac Newton, in his rooms in Trinity College.[1]

### I Have Calculated It!

The mathematician Abraham De Moivre has left us an account of this momentous meeting:

> After they had been some time together, the Dr asked him what he thought the curve would be that would be described by the planets, supposing the force of attraction towards the Sun to be reciprocal to the square of their distance from it. Sir Isaac replied immediately that it would be an ellipse. The Doctor, struck with joy and amazement, asked him how he knew it. Why, saith he, I have calculated it. Whereupon Dr Halley asked him for his calculation without any farther delay. Sir Isaac looked among his papers but could not find it, but he promised him to renew it and then to send it him ... [2]

Newton duly wrote up his proof and sent it to Halley in November of that year. When Halley read the letter, he was astonished. It was clear that Newton had developed a whole system of mechanics but had told nobody about it. Halley realised the significance of Newton's discoveries and knew that they had to be published. He set about persuading Newton to write up a complete description of his system. Halley agreed to pay for the publication, and Newton plunged himself into the task. The publication in 1687 of Newton's *Philosophiæ Naturalis Principia Mathematica* (*The Mathematical Principles of Natural Philosophy*), usually known simply as the *Principia*, would trigger the birth of modern science.

It is unlikely that Newton ever claimed the prize offered by Sir Christopher Wren, which was a book worth forty shillings. But he did win undying fame with the publication of the *Principia*, a book whose value is beyond calculation.

### *Isaac Newton*

How did Newton produce the answer to the question that had defeated all the other great minds of the 17th century?

Isaac Newton was born on Christmas Day, 1642, by the reckoning of the old Julian calendar that was still in use in England at the time. He was born in the hamlet of Woolsthorpe, near Grantham in Lincolnshire. Newton's father had already died by the time he was born. Soon he would effectively be motherless as well, as his mother moved in with a new husband and left the infant Isaac to be raised by her parents. From this unpromising start in life, Newton would become one of the greatest mathematicians of all time and arguably the greatest scientist who has ever lived. He would trigger a scientific revolution that would transform the world, and devise an approach to science that remains at the heart of engineering and the physical sciences today.

In 1661, Newton went to Cambridge University and entered Trinity College. At this time, Cambridge was something of an intellectual backwater, but Newton had access to the books of Galileo, Kepler, Descartes and Gassendi. Unlike many of his predecessors, Newton was not satisfied with vague philosophical explanations of the workings of Nature. He was a very practical man, combining a willingness and ability to perform experiments with a rigorous mathematical outlook on the world. In later life, Newton described the years 1665–1666 as his most productive. As he put it:

> For in those days I was in the prime of my age for invention & minded Mathematicks & Philosophy more than at any time since. [3]

This included a period when he returned to Woolsthorpe, as the university was closed due to an outbreak of the plague. During this time, when Newton was in his early twenties, he invented calculus, which is one of the three most important inventions in the history of mathematics. [4] He also worked out many of the principles of mechanics that would eventually form the basis of the *Principia*.

Many years later, Newton told the story that it was at this time, when he was sitting in the garden of his family home, that the fall of an apple inspired him to think about gravity and ponder the possibility that the apple was attracted to the ground by the same force that holds the Moon in orbit around the Earth. Newton would illustrate this idea in the *Principia*. He asked his readers to imagine a cannon ball fired from a mountaintop. The cannon ball would travel along an arc until it hit the Earth's surface. If it was fired with a greater velocity, it would disappear over the horizon, but would eventually curve back to the ground some way around the Earth's circumference. Newton argued that if the cannon ball were fired with sufficient velocity, it would travel the whole way around the Earth before hitting the ground – it would be in Earth orbit, just like the Moon.

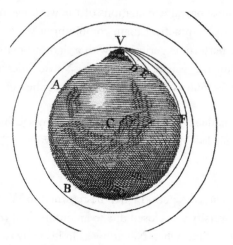

**Figure 35** Diagram from Newton's *Principia* showing the trajectory of a projectile lauched from a mountain top. If the launch velocity of the projectile is sufficiently great it will enter Earth orbit.

270 years after the publication of the *Principia*, in 1957, the Russian satellite Sputnik was launched into orbit by the USSR to become the first artificial satellite of the Earth. There are now thousands of satellites in orbit with a multitude of applications: television transmission, telephone communication, military surveillance, weather monitoring and even Google Earth.

### The Pattern of the Skies

> Lo, for your gaze, the pattern of the skies!
> What balance of the mass, what reckonings
> Divine! Here ponder too the Laws which God,
> Framing the universe, set not aside
> But made the fixed foundations of his work.

The *Principia* is a model of logic and rigour. Newton's language is altogether less flowery than Halley's ode that opens the *Principia*, as sampled above. Newton begins by setting down the fundamental principles of how objects move. These are his three laws of motion:

### Newton's First Law of Motion

*All bodies move with a constant speed in a straight line unless acted upon by an external force.*

This is the definition of natural or inertial motion. It is by no means obvious. (Newton credited the philosopher and mathematician René Descartes with the first correct statement of this law. However, the system of mechanics that Descartes derived from the law was rather confused and certainly incorrect.)[5] To an Earth-based observer, it might appear that, unless a force is acting, then a body will soon come to a halt. We all know that if we are pushing a heavy load, it will stop moving as soon as we stop pushing. A sailboat will stop when the wind ceases to blow. Even in situations where there is little friction – on ice, for instance – we know that an object skimming over the ice, such as a curling stone, will eventually slow down and stop. Examples such as these led Aristotle to base his system of mechanics on the idea that a force is required to keep a body in motion, and this misconception persisted for over two thousand years. In fact, in an environment such as outer space, where there is no friction, objects will continue travelling in a straight line indefinitely if they are not subject to any force.

Next, Newton asked how the natural motion of an object changes, and he defined this as a force. Newton was the first to give a precise understanding to this term, which had previously been used in many different ways. Newton's critical insight was that force is directional. It is not sufficient to say that the application of a force will change the speed of an object, as Descartes thought. What matters is that a force always acts on an object in a particular direction, and the velocity of the object will change in this direction. All this is encapsulated in Newton's Second Law, which defines what the effect of a force will be on the body to which it is applied.

### Newton's Second Law of Motion

*Force equals mass times acceleration.*

In other words, the application of a force changes the velocity of a body, and this change is in the same direction as the force. Equivalently, the acceleration (or change in velocity) that a body undergoes when a force is applied is equal to the size of the force divided by the mass of the body. This means that the greater the mass of the body, the less its velocity will change due to the application of the force. This seems quite reasonable. We all know that it is easier to push a light object than a heavy one. A golfer could not propel a cannonball from the tee as easily as a golf ball. Newton's Second Law defines what is meant by a force and encapsulates the fact that a more massive body has greater inertia.

Galileo had recognised the role of inertia in the motion of projectiles moving close to the Earth's surface. Prior to Newton, however, no-one realised that the concept of inertia is also crucial to understanding how a force that is directed towards the Sun results in circular or elliptical motion around the Sun. Kepler thought that the force emanating from the Sun must sweep the planets around like a broom. Descartes imagined that space was filled with a system of cosmic whirlpools or vortices carrying the planets around in their circular motions. Other researchers believed that there must be at least two forces acting on a planet to keep it in its orbit – one directed towards the Sun, and another pushing the planet around its orbit.

Newton's Third Law, which was certainly original to him, states that a force cannot act in isolation on a single body.

### Newton's Third Law of Motion

*To every action there is an equal and opposite reaction.*

This law can be illustrated in many ways. Imagine two ice dancers; when they push against each other, they move off across the ice in opposite directions. It would be impossible for one of the ice skaters to push against the other and race off while the second ice skater remains stationary on the ice.[6]

The shooting of a gun provides another example. When the gun is fired, the force on the bullet is exactly matched by the force on the gun that operates in the opposite direction. There is inevitably a sharp kick when the gun is fired and the bullet leaves the muzzle. The bullet races off at a much higher speed than the gun recoils, because the mass, and therefore the inertia, of the gun is much greater than that of the bullet.[7]

## *The Universal Law of Gravity*

Others had considered gravity before Newton. Horrocks had recognised that the attraction between the Sun and planets was mirrored by similar attractions between other celestial bodies.[8] Hooke had argued that, just as the Earth is bound together by its gravity, so is the Moon – which is why it is spherical.

What appears to be completely new with Newton is the critical idea that gravity is universal. It acts between any two pieces of matter in the universe. This means that the total force between two objects is produced by summing the forces between all their constituent parts. This sounds horrendously complicated. Newton was the only person with the necessary mathematical skills to make headway with such an idea. He proposed that the gravitational force between two material particles decreases as the inverse square of the distance between the particles, such that the force between *any* two material particles can be expressed as the universal gravitational law:

$$F = \frac{Gm_1 m_2}{r^2} \ ,$$

where $F$ is the force of gravity, $m_1$ is the mass of the first particle, $m_2$ is the mass of the second particle, and $r$ is the distance between them. $G$ is a constant that determines the fundamental strength of gravity. It is known as Newton's constant.

Newton then proved the far from obvious fact that, in the case of a spherical mass, the total gravity of the mass is exactly the same as if the entire mass were located in a single point at its centre. Which means that, with regard to gravity, two massive spheres can be treated in exactly the same way as two massive point particles. This offers an enormous simplification when considering physical problems, because many of the material objects of interest, such as stars and planets, are spherical to a very good approximation.

Therefore the gravitational force between two celestial bodes can be expressed by exactly the same inverse square law as the universal law. For instance, the force between the Sun and the Earth is:

$$F = \frac{GMm}{r^2} \ ,$$

where now, $M$ is the mass of the Sun, $m$ is the mass of the Earth and $r$ is the distance between the centre of the Sun and the centre of the Earth.

Gravity is intrinsically a very weak force, which is why it requires a huge accumulation of mass in an object like the Earth to produce any significant gravitational force. Mathematically, this is represented by the fact that $G$ is small. Newton did not have a precise figure for the size of $G$, as he did not know the mass of the Earth or of any other astronomical body.

Remarkably, the universal gravitational law, coupled with Newton's three laws of motion, is sufficient to explain the operation of the entire solar system and much else besides. This was the key to Newton's great breakthrough. The motion of the planets could now be understood from first principles. Newton could show that, with his force law, each planet will move in an elliptical orbit around the Sun, just as Kepler had deduced from Tycho's observations, and just as he had demonstrated in his letter to Halley.[9]

The precision with which deductions made from this small set of ideas matched observations would prove to be extraordinary. Nothing like this had ever been possible before. The *Principia* offered a quantitative and causal understanding of the clockwork of the Heavens.

Outside a spherical mass the gravitational force is described by an inverse square law. This is the cumulative effect of the gravity of all the matter forming the sphere. But, other configurations of matter can produce an overall force that is very different to the inverse square law. The most dramatic instance of this is the gravitational field inside a hollow spherical shell of matter.

## *Return to the Hollow Planet*

The American science fiction writer Edgar Rice Burroughs is most famous for his Tarzan stories. He also wrote a series of novels set in the land of Pellucidar, which is located within the Earth. In these stories, the Earth is imagined to be a hollow shell about 500 kilometres thick, and the inner world is reached by airship through a passage at the North Pole.

---

**Puzzle 6**

What gravitational force would be felt within a hollow planet? Would the inhabitants be pulled toward the centre of the inner void? Would they be held to the inner surface? Or would gravity act on them in some other way?

---

Imagine taking a trip to the Hollow Planet. Prior to our arrival, we might not even know that the planet is hollow. As the planet is spherical, outside the planet the gravitational force produced by all the mass forming the planet will be the same as if the entire mass of the planet were located in a point at the centre of the planet. The force will be an inverse square law force, just as it would for any other spherically symmetrical distribution of matter. When approaching the planet, we might be surprised that the gravitational force of the planet appears to be very weak, but we might assume that the planet is very low in the heavier elements. Perhaps, unlike the Earth, it might not have an iron core. But we would not be able to tell that the planet is actually hollow.

Only if we managed to make our way into the interior of the Hollow Planet, like the visitors to Pellucidar, would we discover the reason for the planet's low mass. So what would we feel when we were on the inside of the planet? Would we stick to the inside of the shell and be able to walk around, as we do on the surface of the Earth? No; rather surprisingly, there would be no gravitational force whatsoever within a spherical shell of matter.

---

**Answer to Puzzle 6**

The force of gravity completely cancels within a spherical shell of matter, so there would be no gravitational force at all.

---

At the exact centre of a hollow shell of matter, we would expect the gravitational forces from the surrounding material to cancel out completely. The attraction of the material to one side is balanced by the attraction of an equal amount of material at the same distance on the other side. This would be true whatever the force of attraction but, in the case of gravity, we can move away from the centre and the forces will still balance to leave no overall force. This is because gravity is due to the sum of forces from each piece of matter, and these forces diminish as the inverse square of distance. Only in this case does the force from a region on the near side of the shell balance the force from a region on the far side of the shell.[10]

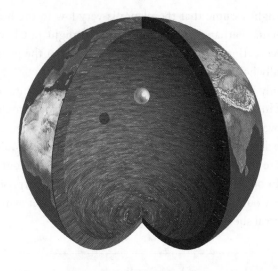

**Figure 36** Within a hollow planet there would be no gravity. Any freely moving object within the planet would travel at a constant velocity, as no force would be acting on it.

## *Journey to the Centre of the Earth*

Now, the Earth certainly isn't hollow, but we can imagine taking another science fiction journey, towards the centre of the Earth in the footsteps of the characters of Jules Verne. If we were to build a tunnel through the centre of the Earth, how would gravity vary as we pass through the tunnel? For the purposes of answering this question, we can consider the material from which the Earth is formed to be divided into two parts. When we are beneath the surface of the Earth, there is a spherical shell of material that is further from the centre of the Earth than we are. There is also a ball of material that is closer to the centre than we are. As we have seen, the spherical shell above us will have no gravitational effect on us.

The gravitational attraction on us will be due solely to the sphere of material beneath us. The strength of the force will be the same as if all this mass were located at the centre of the sphere. As we approach the centre, the sphere beneath us will shrink in size. This means that, as we fall from the surface of the Earth, the force of gravity diminishes gradually as we get closer to the centre. At the centre, we are within the entire Earth and the force of gravity will have completely disappeared.[11]

How will this be reflected in our journey through the tunnel? In freefall through the tunnel, we will be accelerated downwards towards the centre, where we will reach our maximum velocity. After passing the centre, we will be decelerated and we will come to a halt as we reach the surface on the far side of the Earth. If we are unhindered, we will oscillate back and forth from one side of the Earth to the other, just like a giant pendulum bob.[12]

If such a tunnel were drilled through the Earth, how long would it take to reach the antipodes? We will seal the tunnel and remove all the air, so that we are travelling through a vacuum. We step into the cable-free antipodes elevator, strap ourselves into our seats, then the robot driver takes off the handbrake and the elevator plummets like a stone into the shaft. Forty minutes later, we have arrived. We come to a gentle halt and the robot driver puts the handbrake back on – just in time, as a moment later we would have been racing on our way back home. Remarkably, we have travelled around 12,000 kilometres in under an hour and we haven't felt a thing; we have been weightless all the way (it did get rather hot, though!). As we passed through the centre of the Earth, we were travelling at around eight kilometres per second.

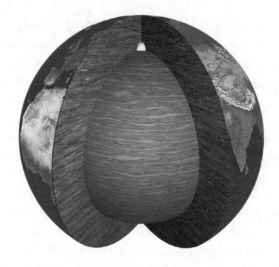

**Figure 37** The gravitational attraction of the shell of material above the white capsule (shown cut away) cancels completely, so the white capsule is only attracted by the sphere of material beneath its position within the Earth (shown as the inner sphere).

## *The Moon and the Tides*

> Once upon a perfect night, unclouded and still, there came the face of a pale and beautiful lady. The tresses of her hair reached out to make the constellations, and the dewy vapours of her gown fell soft upon the land. This lady, whom all mortals call the Moon, danced a merry dance in the pathless sky, for she had fallen in love, and the object of her devotion was the Sun.
>
> Kit Williams, *Masquerade*

Kepler believed that the Moon must somehow cause the oceans to flow thereby generating the tides, but Galileo ridiculed this idea and accused him of invoking occult influences to explain physical phenomena. Galileo had his own theory, in which the tides were produced by the oceans sloshing around as the Earth rotates. This was one of Galileo's main arguments for the Earth's rotation, but unfortunately it is completely wrong. Newton provided the correct explanation in the *Principia*. His definitive explanation of the tides is one of his most celebrated results. The gravitational force between two objects decreases with distance. This means that the pull of the Moon is greater on the side of the Earth facing the Moon than it is at the centre of the Earth, and the pull on the centre of the Earth is greater than the pull on the side of the Earth facing away from the Moon. If the Earth were completely fluid, then the difference in the pull of the Moon on the different parts of the Earth would stretch the Earth in the direction of the Moon.

Now the Earth is not completely fluid, of course, but the oceans are. The solid Earth is distorted by the pull of the Moon, but not enough for us to notice it, whereas the oceans flow. On the side of the Earth facing the Moon, the oceans flow because the pull of the Moon on them is greater (because they are closer to the Moon) than the average pull on the bulk of the solid Earth. On the opposite side of the Earth, the oceans flow because they are pulled less by the Moon than the bulk of the solid Earth (because they are further away from the Moon).

The Earth rotates once every twenty-four hours. As it rotates, the region of the Earth facing the Moon moves, and so the position of the bulges facing towards and away from the Moon changes. Twice every twenty-four hours, we will be in the vicinity of a bulge. As the oceans are so much more fluid than the land, we notice this as a high tide, which

**Figure 38** This diagram is a schematic illustration of the forces acting on the Earth due to the gravitational pull of the Moon. The large arrows show the Newtonian force, which decreases with distance from the Moon. Forces 4 and 5 represent the net forces acting on opposite sides of the Earth. Force 4 is equal to force 1 minus force 2. Force 5 is equal to force 3 minus force 2 (Force 5 points in the opposite direction to the other forces, because force 2 is bigger than force 3). These differential forces are known as tidal forces. They cause the tides to rise.

occurs once every twelve hours or so[13] (clearly, there will also be a low tide that occurs every twelve hours as well, midway between the high tides).[14]

For a more precise understanding of the details about the tides, there are a few more facts that need to be taken into account, but they do not alter the fundamental principles that are at work. The first thing to note is that, although the Moon is the most important body with regard to the generation of the tides, the Sun is also important, even though it is much further away. This means that the shape of the Earth and, more importantly, that of the oceans, is also distorted by the pull of the Sun. The result is that the tides are greatest when the Sun and Moon are aligned in the same direction, so that the distortions from the two bodies add up. The Earth, Sun and Moon are in a line at both New Moon and Full Moon, and this is when the highest tides occur. The tides are smallest when the Sun and Moon are in perpendicular directions when viewed from Earth. These are the times when we can see half the face of the Moon (known to astronomers, for dubious reasons, as 'First Quarter' and 'Last Quarter'). At these times, the distortions the Sun and Moon produce in the shape of the Earth and its oceans partially cancel out.

To determine the exact timing of the tides at a particular place, we must take into account the fact that the Earth is spinning and the oceans are dragged around with it. This means that the bulge in the ocean due to the Moon's pull is constantly being carried around as the Earth spins, and the oceans must continually flow back towards the position beneath the Moon, which takes time. This produces a small time difference between the time expected for high tide due to the position of the Moon and when it actually occurs.

Over geological epochs, it has also had a rather dramatic effect on the Earth-Moon system. When the Moon formed, early in the Earth's history, the Earth would have been spinning much faster (a day might have been as short as about three hours), and the Moon would also have been much closer than it is now. Consequently, the tides were much bigger in the distant past. These tides would have produced a drag on the Earth's rotation, gradually slowing it down. Simultaneously, the Moon would have gradually drifted further away from the Earth. This effect is much weaker now, but the tides are still slowing the Earth's spin and the Moon is still receding.

## Britannia Rules the Waves

> There is no drop of water in the ocean, not even in the deepest parts of the abyss, that does not know and respond to the mysterious forces that create the tide.
>
> Rachel Carson, *The Sea Around Us.*

The other factors that affect the timing and size of the tides are geographical. For instance, the shape of the Bristol Channel funnels the tides into the Severn Estuary, and this produces the Severn Bore and some of the highest tides in the world.

Calculating the precise time and size of the tides at a particular place is complicated. Among other things, it depends on predicting the position of the Moon, which is not easy. The Moon feels a strong gravitational attraction towards both the Earth and the Sun, and this makes its motion very difficult to analyse. To a good approximation, the Moon's orbit is elliptical, but the axis of the ellipse changes direction, as Jeremiah Horrocks realised even before Newton's time. There are other important periodic variations in the Moon's orbit, such as the size of the eccentricity of the orbit and the degree of tilt of the orbit relative to the Earth's equator. Although each of these variations is regular, they all change at different rates, so the overall trajectory of the Moon does not repeat itself in a regular way. Before the age of the computer, this made any calculation of the position of the Moon and the corresponding prediction of the tides an extremely lengthy and arduous undertaking.

In 1872, Kelvin realised that it would be possible to construct a mechanical device that would perform the calculations by adding all the periodic variations together to give the height of the tide at any particular time and anywhere throughout the world. Within a year, Kelvin had completed his first ingenious design for such a machine. The machine contains dials that are used to set the oceano-graphic data for a particular harbour and the astronomical data for the starting time. It consists of several pulleys attached to assemblies, whose gearing is set to sum the various contributions to the tides in the appropriate pro-portions. When the handle is cranked, the gears are driven and the height of the tides is computed and plotted on a roll of paper. In around four hours, the machine will calculate the tides for a full year.[15] Kelvin's original tide predicting machine is shown in Plate 6.

Kelvin's machine was the basis for tide calculators that were used for the following century, until the advent of dig-ital computers. These machines produced extremely valuable information for a maritime nation such as Britain, with its overseas empire. A single machine was used to calculate tides for the whole of India.

## *Mortals Rejoice!*

Towards the end of his life, Sir Isaac Newton mused:

> I do not know what I may appear to the world, but to myself I seem to have been only like a boy playing on the seashore and diverting myself in now and then finding a smoother pebble or a prettier shell than ordinary, whilst the great ocean of truth lay all undiscovered before me.

On Newton's tomb in Westminster Abbey, there is a Latin inscription which translates as:

> Here is buried Isaac Newton, Knight, who by a strength of mind almost divine, and mathematical principles peculiarly his own, explored the course and figures of the planets, the paths of comets, the tides of the sea, the dissimilarities in rays of light, and, what no other scholar has previously imagined, the properties of the colours thus produced. Diligent, sagacious and faithful, in his expositions of nature, antiquity and the holy Scriptures, he vindicated by his philosophy the majesty of God mighty and good, and expressed the simplicity of the Gospel in his manners. Mortals rejoice that there has existed such and so great an ornament of the human race! He was born on 25th December 1642, and died on 20th March 1726.[16]

Newton's mastery of the universe had a profound impact on the psychology of the British.[17] In the century following the publication of the *Principia*, Newton's discoveries were popularised in numerous books. They were presented in lectures and discussed widely.[18] The new science was made available to the whole of society, in books such as Voltaire's *The Elements of Sir Isaac Newton's Philosophy* (1738) and Francesco Algarotti's *Newtonianism for Ladies* (1737). It became generally accepted that a scientific understanding of the laws of nature was not only possible, but extremely useful in developing new technologies that could generate huge wealth.

The publication of mathematics textbooks increased to meet the demand for access to the new science. Engineers such as John Smeaton undertook experiments to test the efficiency of mechanical devices. In 1759, Smeaton published *An Experimental Enquiry Concerning the Natural Powers of Water and Wind to Turn Mills and Other Machines Depending on Circular Motion*, in which he compared the efficiency of various types of water wheel. This was the world in which engineers such as Matthew Boulton, Thomas Newcomen and James Watt grew up. Within a few generations, steam engines would be powering Britain's factories and the nation would be opened up by major engineering projects. Newton and his Royal Society contemporaries developed an understanding of science that would transform Britain into the world's first great industrial power.

Alongside the early stirrings of British industry, Newton's ideas would be applied throughout the physical sciences. For over 200 years, Newton would reign supreme.


## *Celestial Mechanics*

If this is the best of possible worlds, what then are the others?

Voltaire, *Candide.*

In 1755, Lisbon, the mighty capital of the Portuguese Empire, was demolished in a catastrophic earthquake. The magnitude of the earthquake was about 9.0, making it one of the biggest shocks in recorded history. The earthquake struck on the morning of 1 November – All Saints Day – when most of the population of 200,000 were attending church. Tens of thousands died in the earthquake and the subsequent tsunami, and it has been estimated that a fifth of the population may have perished. This devastation prompted the philosopher Voltaire to write his most famous work, *Candide*.

**Figure 39** Earthquake at Lisbon, 1755.[19]

John Michell was also deeply affected by the Portuguese disaster and turned his attention towards the physical mechanisms behind earthquakes. Although Michell is now almost forgotten, he was one of the leading scientists of his day. He taught at Cambridge University and made many important scientific discoveries, and he deserves to be much more well-known.[20] Following the Portuguese earthquake, Michell suggested that earthquakes spread out as waves through the solid Earth and are related to the faults in geological strata. His book on the subject would establish seismology as a modern science. Michell was rewarded by his election to the Royal Society in 1760. In 1767, at the age of 42, Michell was appointed rector to the village of Thornhill, near Dewsbury in West Yorkshire, where he would continue his scientific investigations.

Michell constructed his own telescopes, the largest being an impressive ten-foot instrument with a thirty-inch mirror. But it is his astronomical ideas that are most significant. Michell was the first to apply statistics to astronomy. He showed that if stars were scattered randomly throughout the sky, then it was extremely unlikely that we would see clusters of stars such as the familiar Pleiades or Seven Sisters. This implied that star clusters must be genuine clumps of stars that are gravitationally bound together. Michell also demonstrated that there are far too many pairs of stars in the sky for them all to be due to chance alignments. His conclusion was that most such pairs must be orbiting each other in double-star systems.[21]

These enquiries led to even more astonishing speculations.[22] Michell expanded the realm of gravity beyond the solar system by showing that it is possible to determine the mass of a star in a binary system by studying the motion of its companion star. His analysis of this problem led him to consider the possibility that there might exist stars that are invisible because light cannot escape from them.

When a ball is thrown upwards, its speed will gradually decrease before falling back to Earth. But, a projectile that is hurled upwards fast enough may escape the Earth's gravity and disappear into space. The escape velocity of the Earth is around 11 kilometres per second, while the escape velocity of the Sun is 600 kilometres per second. This is the speed that a missile or other projectile must reach in order to be released from the Earth's or the Sun's clutches. Michell considered a remarkable question: how massive must an object be if its escape velocity is to exceed the speed of light? His conclusion was that we would not be aware of any star with the density of the Sun but 500 times its diameter, as 'its light could not arrive at us'. He then suggested that it might be possible to detect these dark stars in binary systems through the motion of their companion stars. We now know that a dark star such as Michell was imagining 250 years ago would collapse under its own gravity. It would be a black hole.[23] We will soon be taking a much closer look at these mysterious objects.

Michell's final project was to determine the intrinsic strength of gravity. This might sound simple; after all, we measure the force of gravity every time we weigh ourselves. But, we cannot really answer the question in this way unless we know the mass of the Earth. Michell designed an experiment that would measure the gravitational force between two metal balls in the laboratory. The mass of both balls could then be determined, so measuring the force between them would enable Michell to work out the value of the constant $G$ in Newton's force law. Indirectly, this would also give him the mass of the Earth. Michell constructed the apparatus for the measurement but unfortunately, in 1793, he died before he could perform the experiment. After Michell's death, his apparatus was given to another leading scientist, Henry Cavendish, who would complete the task.[24]

## The Silent Man

Henry Cavendish was the son of Lord Charles Cavendish. He was an aristocrat and one of the richest men in England, as well as a leading scientific figure of the 18th century. Although he was totally dedicated to science, he was also excruciatingly shy and found conversation agonising. According to one contemporary, he 'uttered fewer words in the course of his life than any man who lived to fourscore years, not at all excluding the monks of La Trappe'.[25]

Cavendish performed his experiments in his house in central London, where he communicated with his servants through written messages. He once happened to bump into one of his cleaners on his staircase and was so flustered by the experience that he had another private staircase built in his house so that he should never suffer this ordeal again. Despite his ill-ease with company, he rarely missed the weekly dinner of the Royal Society at the Crown and Anchor on the Strand. Although Cavendish was highly respected by his colleagues, he published very little, so he was not always given the credit he deserved for his scientific enquiries. He was a meticulous experimenter who made significant advances in chemistry and physics, decades before others who would receive the acclaim. Many of his discoveries were only revealed a century later, when James Clerk Maxwell studied his notebooks.

By the time Cavendish obtained the apparatus built by Michell to determine the strength of gravity, its wooden frame had warped, so Cavendish had to have it substantially rebuilt. He also made other modifications to the equipment before performing the measurements that Michell had devised. Cavendish gave Michell full credit for its design, but it is usually known today as the Cavendish Experiment.

The measurements were completed in 1798. Cavendish quoted the results of the experiment as a determination of the average density of the Earth, which he revealed to be 5.48 times the density of water. This is within about 1% of the modern accepted figure. An incredible achievement for such a difficult experiment, performed in Cavendish's front room over two centuries ago. From his result, it is straightforward to calculate the value of Newton's constant $G$, which encapsulates the fundamental strength of the force of gravity.

Cavendish died in 1810. Half a century later, his relative William Cavendish, 7th Duke of Devonshire, gave an endowment to Cambridge University in honour of his scientific research. This money was used to build the university's physics laboratory. It was named the Cavendish Laboratory by James Clerk Maxwell, who would be the first Cavendish Professor. The Cavendish Laboratory would be the home of world-changing research, from the discovery of the electron to the structure of DNA.

## The Music of the Spheres

William Herschel was born into a musical family in Hanover on 15 November 1738. William's father Isaac was a member of the regimental band of the Hanoverian Guards and, as a youth, William joined him in this occupation. At this time, the crown of Hanover was united with that of Britain under the reign of George II. In 1756, the Seven Years War broke out and France invaded Hanover. The Hanoverian forces were overwhelmed at the Battle of Hastenbeck. Although William was not injured, he spent the night sheltering in a ditch – an experience that convinced him that he was not suited to the life of a soldier. Without waiting to be discharged from the Hanoverian forces, William managed to find his way to England to build a new life as a musician.

By 1766, Herschel had obtained the position of organist at the Octagon Chapel in Bath. He also became the Director of Public Concerts in this fashionable spa town, composing and performing many concertos and symphonies. However, despite his obvious musical talents, William Herschel is not remembered for his music. In 1773, he took an interest in astronomy and started grinding lenses and building his own telescopes. With the help of his sister Caroline, Herschel began to make systematic observations of a variety of astronomical objects, including the planets and double-star systems and comets. His interest developed to the extent that he would spend sixteen hours a day on the tedious job of grinding the lenses of his astronomical instruments. The obsession with perfecting his optical equipment grew to the point where Caroline would read to him while he laboured at the grinding and even spoon-feed him while he continued with this laborious task. But it was worth it; Herschel's telescopes would prove to be better than any in Britain, including those of the Astronomer Royal at Greenwich.

In March 1781, while searching for double stars, Herschel came upon a new object that appeared as a disc through his telescope. This clearly could not be a star, as stars are so distant that even the biggest appear point-like through a telescope. Herschel initially thought that it must be a comet – but it was a very unusual comet, as it appeared to be circular and it did not have a tail. Herschel monitored the object over the next few nights and recorded that it was moving slowly against the background stars. From the rate of its motion, it was clear that this object was more distant than Saturn.[26]

Herschel wrote to a circle of leading astronomers, announcing his discovery. Soon it became clear that the object within Herschel's sights was not a comet, it was a far more sensational discovery: a new planet, the first new planet to be discovered in recorded history. Herschel proposed that the new planet should be called 'Georgium sidus', the Georgian star, after the Hanoverian monarch. Fortunately, this name soon fell out of favour. We now know the planet by the classical name Uranus, the Greek god, father of Saturn and the Titans. Herschel went on to make many other discoveries, including two satellites of Uranus. His sister Caroline was a great astronomer in her own right and is one of the greatest comet finders of all time.

Uranus is just about bright enough to be visible to the naked eye, so it is rather surprising that it was not discovered until over 170 years after the invention of the telescope. Astronomers soon realised that it had been observed on several occasions over the years, and even plotted on star maps by astronomers, who had assumed that it was just another fixed star. The distant Uranus moves quite slowly against the background stars, completing a full orbit in 84 years, so these early sightings of the planet proved to be very useful for determining its precise orbit. William Herschel died in his 84th year in August 1822, living almost long enough for his planet to complete one full orbit of the Sun.

## An Embarrassing Episode

By the early years of the 19th century, it was becoming clear that Uranus was not keeping to the path predicted by the astronomical tables. Every attempt to pin down an elliptical orbit for the planet seemed to work for a period of time but, within a few years, the planet would drift from its expected position. This became known as the Uranus problem. The issue was all the more glaring, as Newton's celestial mechanics was supposed to represent the perfection of the exact sciences. The orbital gyrations could be predicted in exquisite detail with regard to all the other planets, but Uranus would not behave.

In 1828, observations of Uranus were taken under the supervision of George Biddell Airy, Cambridge Professor of Astronomy. They indicated a discrepancy of 12 seconds of arc when compared to the data in the best current astronomical tables. This is a small error – about 150th of the diameter of the Moon – but it was certainly significant when compared with the accuracy of the predictions for the other planets, and was well beyond what would be expected from observational errors in the early part of the 19th century. By 1829, the error had grown to 23 seconds of arc, and the following year it reached 30 seconds of arc. Something was clearly wrong with the astronomical tables.

As Airy pointed out in his 1832 *Report on the Progress of Astronomy*, Uranus seemed to be unwilling to conform to an elliptical orbit. A number of unconvincing suggestions were put forward to explain the anomaly. Perhaps Uranus had collided with a comet and this had affected its trajectory. Perhaps Newtonian gravity needed to be modified over distances as large as that between the Sun and Uranus.

In 1841, a young undergraduate called John Couch Adams[27] came across Airy's report in a Cambridge bookshop and set out to solve the puzzle. Adams could see at once that the most likely explanation was the existence of another planet orbiting the Sun beyond Uranus. The unknown planet would tug on Uranus, causing the deviations in its orbit. This possibility had already been suggested by others, but no-one had tackled the problem mathematically and shown that such a solution would work. Given the existence of an extra planet with a known orbit, it would be relatively straightforward to calculate the effect of its gravitational pull on each of the other planets. Working in the other direction, however, would present difficulties on a totally different scale.

Part of the problem was that a very massive planet orbiting at a great distance from Uranus would have a similar effect to a less massive planet orbiting close to Uranus. Furthermore, the new planet's orbit might be circular but, on the other hand, it might be a very eccentric ellipse that would see the planet receding into the depths of space. It was certainly a problem that no-one had ever solved before. Indeed, no-one had even contemplated such a problem before. But Adams was a very capable mathematician, with exactly the right skills for the task.

Adams undertook the arduous calculations and, by September 1845, he had computed the position of the hypothetical planet and derived clear instructions for where astronomers should look to find it. He wrote up his findings and sent them to Airy, who by now was director of the Royal Observatory at Greenwich. Airy was a meticulous man who ran his observatory like clockwork. He instructed his employees never to throw away any paper. Everything had to be documented before being stowed away for safekeeping. A colleague joked that, 'if Airy wiped his pen on a piece of blotting paper, he would duly endorse the blotting paper with the date and particulars of its use, and file it away amongst his papers.'[28]

In Airy's view, the mission of the observatory was clear. It was the precise measurement of the heavens, in order to regulate the time and to aid navigation between Britain and her dominions. The observatory lay at the heart of the Empire, with the express purpose of regulating its pulse and maintaining its smooth running and commerce. Naturally, there was no place for speculative searches after new discoveries. Airy received the letter from Adams and promptly filed it away.

Meanwhile, on the other side of the channel, the French mathematician Urbain Le Verrier had reasoned in the same way as Adams and had made his own calculations of the position of an unseen planet that might be pulling Uranus out of line. Through the summer of 1846, Le Verrier made several attempts to persuade French astronomers to look for his planet, meeting with no more success than Adams. Finally, on 18 September, he wrote to Johann Gottfried Galle, an assistant at the Berlin Observatory who received the letter five days later. The director of the observatory, Johann Franz Encke, was unimpressed by the suggestion of a new planet, but Galle was keen to take up the challenge. Encke gave his permission and, along with his colleague Heinrich D'Arrest, Galle started the hunt that very night. The pair set out on a systematic search of the region of sky that Le Verrier had indicated. They compared the position of each star that they could see to an up-to-date map of the heavens. Within just half an hour they spotted a point of light that was not on the map – the planet Neptune had been found.

The following night, the excited Galle showed the planet to Encke. They confirmed that it had moved slightly since the previous night by the amount that would be expected for a planet at that distance, and that it appeared through the telescope as a small disc rather than a mere point of light. Encke wrote to Le Verrier: 'Allow me, Sir, to congratulate you most sincerely on the brilliant discovery with which you have enriched astronomy. Your name will be forever linked with the most striking proof imaginable of the validity of the Law of Universal Gravitation'.[29]

The news soon reached London, where it was heralded as one of the most embarrassing episodes in the history of British astronomy. While Britain and France were vying to carve up the Earth, the French had stolen a whole new world from under the noses of the British.

**Figure 40** Cartoon from the 7 November 1846 issue of the French magazine L'Illustration, showing Adams looking for Neptune in the wrong direction before finding it in Le Verrier's notebook.

## *The Search for Planet Vulcan*

> Spock: Check!
>
> Kirk: Checkmate!
>
> Spock: Your illogical approach to chess does have its advantages on occasion, Captain.
>
> Kirk: I'd prefer to call it inspired.
>
> Spock: As you wish.

*Star Trek*, episode Charlie X (1966)

Following his triumph with the planet Neptune, Le Verrier drew up plans for an in-depth analysis of the entire solar system, taking into account the mutual gravitational influences between all the planets. In 1854, he was appointed director of the Paris Observatory, where he combined his theoretical analysis with an observational survey of the motion of the planets. With this data, he was able to account for the orbital characteristics of each planet. Every orbit fitted his calculations perfectly, with just a single exception – the planet Mercury – the messenger of the gods, racing around the Sun on the innermost path in the solar system.

Mercury has the most eccentric of all the planetary orbits. Observations showed that Mercury's orbit precesses. More precisely, the direction of the axis of its orbit rotates by 574 seconds of arc, or just under one sixth of a degree, per century. In around 225,000 years, Mercury traces out a complete orbital rosette. Le Verrier calculated that the gravitational attraction of Venus, the planet that approaches Mercury most closely, has the biggest effect on Mercury's orbit. It accounts for a shift of 277 seconds of arc per century. The giant planet Jupiter adds another 153 arcseconds; the Earth chips in 90 arcseconds; and the rest of the planets add about 11 arcseconds per century. These contributions amount to a total of 531 arcseconds, which leaves 43 seconds of arc unaccounted for.[30]

Le Verrier assumed that the wanderings of Mercury must have a similar cause to those of Uranus. Following his successful prediction of the existence of the planet Neptune, he proposed that there must be another unknown planet within the orbit of Mercury that was responsible for producing the unexplained shift in its position. Mercury is close to the Sun, which can make it quite difficult to see. Although it is very bright, it tends to be lost in the glare of the Sun, as it is only visible in the twilight of sunset or sunrise. A planet within the orbit of Mercury would be even more difficult to spot, so

Le Verrier's suggestion of another hidden planet could not be ruled out without further investigation. The hypothetical planet was named *Vulcan* after the metalworking smith of the gods baking in the heat of his forge.

Even though Vulcan would be very hard to find under normal circumstances, during a total eclipse it should be visible close to the Sun. Nineteenth century astronomers were on the lookout and there were several reported sightings in the second half of the century. Le Verrier died in 1877, no doubt convinced that his proposal was correct, but none of the sightings could be confirmed, for the very good reason that Vulcan does not exist. It was not until 1915 that the puzzle of Mercury's wanderings was solved. The solution was remarkable and totally different from the explanation of the discrepancies in the orbit of Uranus. It involved a discovery that was even greater than the discovery of a new planet. The mystery would be solved by Albert Einstein.

In the 1780s, one century after the publication of Newton's *Principia*, William Wordsworth was a student at the college next to Newton's in Cambridge. Wordsworth's poem *The Prelude* looks back to his days at St. John's College, ending with Wordsworth dreamily surveying Trinity's Great Court from his rooms:

> And from my pillow, looking forth by light
> Of Moon or favouring stars, I could behold
> The antechapel where the statue stood
> Of Newton with his prism and silent face,
> The marble index of a mind for ever
> Voyaging through strange seas of Thought, alone.

Chapter Five

# THE GREAT OCEAN OF TRUTH

Light thinks it travels faster than anything else, but it is wrong. No matter how fast light travels, it finds the darkness has always got there first, and is waiting for it.

Terry Pratchett, *Reaper Man*

In 1862, James Clerk Maxwell published a set of equations that tied electricity and magnetism together and united them in his theory of electromagnetism. The electric and magnetic forces would henceforth be seen as two faces of a single coin. Maxwell's theory was the mathematical expression of the results of many experiments performed by Michael Faraday and other earlier researchers over the course of several decades in the first half of the 19th century.[1]

145

The most important results of these investigations were that a changing or moving electric field would generate a magnetic field, and that a changing or moving magnetic field would generate an electric field. For instance, an electric current is produced by the movement of electrically charged particles, usually electrons. The flow of these electrically charged particles will inevitably produce a magnetic field, so a magnetic field will always be present around an electric wire when a current is flowing through the wire. Conversely, moving a bar magnet near a wire will produce an electric field, and this electric field will cause the electrons in the wire to move and, thereby, produce an electric current. This interplay between the two aspects of the electromagnetic force is at the heart of the electricity industry and the electrical devices that we are so familiar with. Maxwell's equations capture the interrelationship between electricity and magnetism in a neat and concise fashion.

Maxwell's equations offered an added bonus. The equations could be combined into an equation describing the propagation of an electromagnetic wave. This wave is formed from an electric field and a magnetic field oscillating in perpendicular directions. As the electric field changes, it generates the magnetic field and, as the magnetic field changes, it generates the electric field in a mutually self-sustaining manner. The wave propagates in a direction perpendicular to the directions of oscillation of the electric and magnetic fields.

In one of Faraday's experiments, he had passed a beam of polarised light through a magnetic field and showed that the magnetic field affects the polarisation of the light. This experiment hinted at a hitherto unknown connection between light and electromagnetism. Faraday tentatively suggested such a link, but he was unable to prove it to his own satisfaction.

When Maxwell worked out from his equations the speed at which his electromagnetic waves would be transmitted, it all fell into place. The speed was to within a very small margin equal to the most up-to-date measurements of the speed of light. Maxwell visited Faraday on his deathbed and told him that once more he had been correct, but Faraday was already too ill to understand the significance of his words.

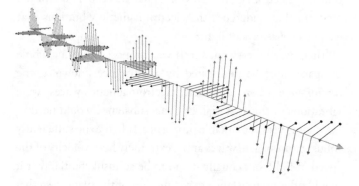

**Figure 41** An electromagnetic wave. The darker arrows represent the electric field and the lighter arrows represent the perpendicular magnetic field.

In the second half of the 1880s, the German physicist Heinrich Hertz provided a direct confirmation of Maxwell's identification of light as an electromagnetic wave. Hertz generated radio waves from a spark produced by passing an electric current across a spark gap, just like the spark plugs in a car engine, which sometimes produce radio interference. Hertz detected the radio waves on the opposite side of his laboratory. He measured the wavelength of the waves and determined their velocity to confirm that it was the same as the speed of light. Radio waves are identical to light, but with a much longer wavelength.

It was now clear that the light that we receive from the stars is electromagnetic in origin. But, if light rays are simply electromagnetic waves, what is it that is waving? This question perplexed Victorian scientists. Sound travels through the air as pressure waves. It is formed by regular variations in the pressure of the air – a sequence of compressions and rarefactions. But space is a total vacuum; it is empty, so how could it transmit electromagnetic waves? What was the nature of the medium that undergoes the electromagnetic vibrations that we perceive as rays of light?

There was no easy answer. It was proposed that the whole of space must be permeated by a substance known as the *luminiferous ether*, and that electromagnetic waves were vibrations in this material. But this substance would need to have some very remarkable properties. It had to be sufficiently robust to propagate waves at the extremely high velocity of the speed of light, but equally it had to be so insubstantial that it would offer no resistance to the motion of the planets, so that they could continue in their orbits indefinitely in accordance with Newtonian physics and would not rapidly spiral into the Sun. There were some who argued rather unconvincingly that the ether was proof of the existence of God, as only God could make a substance with these impossible properties.

### Making Waves in the Ether

What was needed was an experiment that would provide incontrovertible evidence of the existence of this extraordinary medium with such miraculous qualities. It was assumed that the ether provided a stationary background through which the Sun, planets and stars were moving. If the motion of the Earth through this background could be detected, then this would clearly demonstrate its existence. It seemed obvious that the speed of light emitted in the direction of the Earth's motion must be affected by this motion. What was required were two measurements of the speed of light – one in the direction of the Earth's motion and one in a perpendicular direction.

The American physicist Albert Michelson worked for many years on techniques for accurately measuring the speed of light. From 1882 onwards, Michelson perfected the design of an interferometer, a device that could measure distances with great precision. It worked by splitting a beam of light, reflecting each half-beam numerous times between pairs of mirrors along two arms of the device to increase the length of the paths travelled by the light, and then recombining the beams to produce interference fringes. In 1887, Michelson collaborated with Edward Morley in an attempt to detect the motion of the Earth through the ether. In order to reduce the effect of any vibrations or thermal variations and increase the sensitivity of their interferometer, they assembled it on top of a large block of sandstone in the basement of a stone dormitory.

The interferometer was floated on a bath of mercury, so that it could be rotated with minimum friction. As the device was turned, each arm would point in a direction parallel to the Earth's motion twice during every complete rotation. The interference fringes could be watched continuously as the interferometer turned. The device was so sensitive that the Earth's motion should easily have been seen as a shift in the position of the fringes. But, to the amazement of Michelson and Morley, they could not detect any such shift at all. In subsequent years, a number of physicists attempted to account for the Michelson-Morley results, but their explanations always seemed rather contrived and unnatural.

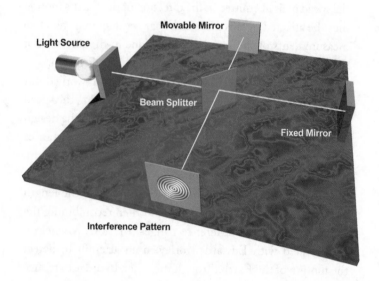

**Figure 42** A schematic representation of the Michelson-Morley Experiment. A beam of light is shone through a half-silvered mirror which splits the beam into two perpendicular beams. These beams are reflected back through the half-silvered mirror and on to a screen where they form an interference pattern. One of the mirrors is fixed, the other is movable so that the path length can be varied. The whole apparatus can be rotated, so that the orientation of the beams changes with respect to the Earth's motion through space.

In 1905, a patent clerk (technical expert third class) working in a patent office in the Swiss capital, Bern, wrote a paper that would supply the correct explanation of the experiment. This obscure patent clerk was Albert Einstein, and his paper *On the Electrodynamics of Moving Bodies* offered the world a new system of mechanics known to physicists as *special relativity*.

## *The Birth of an Einstein*

Einstein was born in the German city of Ulm on 14 March 1879. No-one could have foretold that, in the not-too-distant future, his name would quite deservedly be synonymous with genius. Einstein was smart – very smart. This might seem obvious, but Einstein is often portrayed as being slow at school. In fact, Einstein's school record was very good. Einstein was introduced to philosophy during his teenage years. He taught himself calculus and became deeply interested in the ideas of thinkers such as David Hume, Immanuel Kant and Ernst Mach. He would develop into the most philosophical of all great physicists.

As early as the age of sixteen, Einstein would muse about physics by imagining ideal situations, such as sitting on a beam of light. Einstein turned the analysis of such 'thought experiments' into an art form. The concept of the thought experiment was not new, but Einstein emphasised its central role in the development of his ideas. It was a laboratory in the mind, where he could test his understanding of the physical world. In many respects, it was a refinement of the traditional approach of the philosopher, in which the philosopher would stretch an idea into unfamiliar territory and draw some conclusion from the possibly absurd repercussions.[2] The novelty of Einstein's use of philosophical arguments was that he united them with a thorough understanding of physics, and this enabled him to give his thought experiments a critical place in the construction of new theories of physics. In Einstein's hands, the thought experiment became an incredibly powerful tool.

## *The Cosmic Speed Limit*

Einstein was adamant that the Michelson-Morley experiment was not a major influence on him. Rather, it was the structure of Maxwell's equations that inspired him to develop a system of mechanics that was capable of describing motion at speeds approaching that of light. As we have seen, Maxwell's equations predict that electromagnetic waves travel at the

**Figure 43** Einstein, photographed when he was a patent clerk.

speed of light, which was exactly why physicists were able to identify light as an electromagnetic wave. The equations give a precise figure for this speed, and no indication that the rate might vary in the manner expected by Michelson and Morley. Einstein argued that we should accept the message that Maxwell's equations were sending us, even if this meant there were flaws in our understanding of motion.

According to Einstein, Maxwell's equations implied that Newtonian mechanics is unable to describe motion at speeds approaching the speed of light. He therefore set out to construct a new system of mechanics that would reduce to Newtonian mechanics for velocities that were small compared to the speed of light, but would also correctly account for motion at much higher speeds.

Einstein based the new mechanics on just two fundamental principles. The first of these is the principle of relativity. This principle gives its name to the new system of mechanics, but it was not really new with Einstein. Newton's First Law of Motion states that unless acted on by an external force, a body will move in a straight line at a constant speed. This establishes a notion of natural motion. This law applies to the motion of all objects: when no force is acting, they all move in the same way, i.e. in a straight line at a constant speed.

This implies that there is no absolute way to determine the speed at which an object is travelling. If we throw a ball into the air, we can define its speed relative to the ground. We know that the Earth is moving around the Sun, so we could work out the speed of the ball relative to the Sun. We also know that the Sun and planets are moving around the galaxy, so we could work out the speed of the ball relative to the centre of the galaxy. Which of these speeds is the correct speed of the ball? They are all equally valid – although the speed relative to the ground gives far and away the most convenient description of the motion of the ball. There is no absolute velocity; velocity is a relationship between two objects, so the velocity of one object only makes sense when defined relative to another object. When applied to Newtonian mechanics, relativity is usually referred to as 'Galilean relativity', since it is closely related to the concept of inertia, as first understood by Galileo.[3]

Following in Galileo's footsteps, Einstein rested his first principle on the assumption that there is no experimental way to determine absolute velocity. In other words, whatever the velocity of our laboratory, as long as the velocity does not change, the outcome of any fundamental physics experiment will be identical; we cannot distinguish between different constant velocities. It is not possible to define a state of absolute rest, as Einstein pointed out at the start of his first paper on special relativity:

> The introduction of a 'luminiferous ether' will prove to be superfluous inasmuch as the view here to be developed will not require an 'absolutely stationary space' provided with special properties.[4]

Einstein's second principle was completely new. This principle states that there is a maximum possible speed for the transmission of any interaction and this speed is the speed of light in a vacuum. With this second principle, Einstein sliced through the Gordian knot of Michelson and Morley's experiment. According to Einstein, the Michelson-Morley experiment could never detect the Earth's motion by measuring the speed of light, because light would propagate at exactly the same speed, irrespective of the Earth's motion. Einstein summarised the two building blocks of special relativity in this way:

We will raise this conjecture (the purport of which will hereafter be called the 'Principle of Relativity') to the status of a postulate, and also introduce another postulate, which is only apparently irreconcilable with the former, namely, that light is always propagated in empty space with a definite velocity c which is independent of the state of motion of the emitting body.[5]

---

### Puzzle 7

As shown in the figure below, the positions of supernova A, supernova B and the observer V form an equilateral triangle in the plane of the galaxy, so that both supernovae, which are 1,000 light years distant, are seen simultaneously by the observer. A second observer sees supernova B at the same time as V, but sees supernova A 1,000 years later.

Where is the planetary system of the second observer located?

**Figure 44** Spiral galaxy showing the positions of supernova A, supernova B and observer V, which form an equilateral triangle.

---

Einstein's principle of relativity had disposed of the notion of absolute space. Strict adherence to his second principle, the invariance of the speed of light in a vacuum, would mean that something else would have to give, and this would prove to be even more disturbing and counter to our everyday assumptions about the world. Accepting the speed of light as the cosmic speed limit implied that it was impossible to show unambiguously that two events are simultaneous. Information about the events would be transmitted at the speed of light; although the two events might appear simultaneous to one observer, they would not be simultaneous to a second observer. For instance, if there were two supernovae in our galaxy, separated by a distance of 1,000 light years, a civilisation situated midway between the two supernovae might witness them simultaneously, whereas a second civilisation in a different part of the galaxy might observe one supernova explosion 1,000 years before the other.

We might not be too concerned about giving up the notion of simultaneity but, as Einstein went on to point out, it affects our whole understanding of the nature of time:

> We have to take into account that all our judgments in which time plays a part are judgments of simultaneous events. If, for instance, I say that: 'A particular train arrives here at 7 o'clock,' I mean something like this: 'The pointing of the small hand of my watch to 7 and the arrival of the train are simultaneous events.' [6]

The only reasonable conclusion, according to Einstein, was that there could be no such thing as absolute time. In other words, the passage of time could not be measured by an eternal clock simultaneously ticking with the same beat throughout the universe. Our everyday notion that time was passing everywhere at the same rate, irrespective of the motion of the observer, would have to be abandoned.

### Answer to Puzzle 7

If a straight line from supernova A to supernova B is extended an equal distance beyond supernova B, we reach C, the position where the planetary system of the second observer is located. The light from supernova B will take 1,000 years to reach this point and the light from supernova A will take 2,000 years to reach this point.

**Figure 45** Spiral galaxy showing the positions of supernova A, supernova B, observer V and observer C.

## *Einstein's Bicycle*

The implications of Einstein's new system of mechanics would prove to be dramatic. Objects that travel at close to the speed of light do not behave as we might expect. We will illustrate this in the guise of a thought experiment.

Imagine Albert Einstein cycling past us at a steady rate of half the speed of light. He shines his torch in front of him. His bicycle is equipped with a device that will measure the speed of the light that is being emitted by his torch. This could be some sort of interferometer, but we will just refer to it as his light meter. Einstein measures the speed of light without falling off the bike and, as usual, the rays in the torch beam are receding at the speed of light.

In our back garden, we also have a light meter that can measure the speed of light and we decide to measure the speed with which Einstein's torch beam is moving relative to us. We might expect that the torch beam would be moving at a speed that is equal to the sum of the bicycle speed plus the speed of light. In other words, we might imagine that the light would appear to move at one and a half times its normal speed. Our commonsense expectations have been developed through our experience of living in a world in which the laws of Newtonian mechanics are obeyed to a very good approximation.

However, we only have direct experience of objects that move with very small relative velocities compared to the speed of light. It turns out that the obvious addition law of velocities that we take for granted is only approximately true. This approximation is an incredibly good one when we are considering objects moving at the low speeds that we are familiar with, but it becomes a very poor approximation as objects approach the speed of light. When we use our light meter to measure the speed of the beam emitted by Einstein's torch, we will find that it is moving at the speed of light. We know that this is the case, because this thought experiment is really the Michelson-Morley experiment in disguise.

As Einstein explained, there is only one way to reconcile these two measurements of the speed of the torch beam. If we look closely at Einstein's light meter, we will see that the clock attached to it appears to be running more slowly than the clock attached to our light meter. If we look at the ruler attached to his light meter, it will appear to have shrunk by comparison to the ruler attached to our light meter. It would seem that the laws of Nature conspire to ensure that any measurement of the speed of light in a vacuum will always produce the same result, irrespective of the motion of the experimenter. If this were not the case, then it would be possible to determine our speed relative to the background of space, simply by measuring the speed of light.

Incidentally, as Einstein races by, he will see us moving past him at half the speed of light. If he takes a look at our light meter, it will appear to him as though our clock is running slowly and as though our ruler has shrunk. This must be the case, as the motion is relative and we cannot determine that one of us is moving and not the other one, as encapsulated in Einstein's first postulate – the relativity principle.

## *Time Dilation*

The apparent slowing down of the passage of time for a body in motion relative to us, such as Einstein on his bike, is called *time dilation*, and it is built into the laws of physics. It applies to time as measured in any conceivable way: grandfather clocks, digital watches, atomic clocks, egg timers or the rate of stubble growth – it makes no difference. You might think that this is all academic, and it cannot have any real applications – nobody can cycle as fast as Einstein.

But, in fact, it is an every day occurrence. The first direct measurements of time dilation occurred in 1940. The electron has a heavy relative known as a muon. In many ways, the muon is very similar to an electron, but it is around 207 times as massive. It is also an unstable particle. Typically, it will survive for a mere two microseconds before decaying. Muons are produced when cosmic rays hit atoms in the upper atmosphere. The muons are travelling at close to the speed of light when they are created in these high-energy collisions. Even at such speeds, were it not for time dilation, the muons could not reach the ground before decaying. However, as Bruno Rossi and David Hall demonstrated in 1940, muons *do* reach the ground in just the proportions expected due to the increase in their lifetimes, as predicted by Einstein's theory.[7]

At CERN and other particle physics laboratories around the world, particles are routinely accelerated to within a whisker of the speed of light before being smashed into other particles. The resulting particle debris is then analysed in great detail. The electronics within the particle detector will determine the identity of each particle produced in the collisions, along with its direction and energy. Most of the particles produced in such collisions are short-lived, unstable particles. Physicists know how long each species of particle will typically survive when it is at rest. The newly created particles race away from the impact point at close to the speed of light, and physicists can calculate the time dilation at these velocities. Because of time dilation, the lifetimes of the high-speed particles are extended, but always in accordance with special relativity.

There are close to a billion collisions a second within the Large Hadron Collider, and each collision is a test of special relativity. Einstein's theory routinely passes these tests every time, and no-one expects it to fail in the near future.

## *Crossing the Light Barrier*

It is one thing to declare that the speed of light is a universal speed limit, but what happens if we just keep on pushing an object faster and faster? Whether it be a spaceship or a proton in the Large Hadron Collider, can we not just keep on accelerating until we reach a speed that exceeds the speed of light? The answer turns out to be a definite 'no'. As an object approaches the speed of light, it becomes ever more difficult to raise its speed any further. Effectively, the mass of the object increases as it approaches the speed of light, so when a force is applied, the change in speed becomes much smaller because of the corresponding increase in inertia. To accelerate the object all the way to the speed of light would mean that the mass of the object was pushed all the way to infinity and would require the input of an infinite amount of energy – which is, of course, impossible.

The consequences of this are dramatic, as Einstein soon realised. In another paper in 1905, Einstein used special relativity to work out a formula for how the inertia of an object increases as its speed increases. The formula emerged logically from the two postulates upon which he had built special relativity, so there was no doubting that it was correct if special relativity was correct. But the meaning of the formula was not immediately clear. Einstein's interpretation was typically brilliant and would introduce one of the most important unifying ideas in the history of physics. An approximate version of the formula looks something like this:[8]

Inertial mass $= m + \frac{1}{2} m (\frac{v}{c})^2 + \ldots$

where $v$ is velocity and $c$ is the speed of light. The dots represent a sequence of other, smaller terms.

On the left is the inertial mass; this is the quantity that, in Newtonian physics, determines the relationship between force and acceleration via Newton's Second Law. The bigger the inertial mass of an object, the less acceleration it will receive when a force is applied to it. The first term on the right is what we normally think of as the mass of the object and, in Newtonian physics, this corresponds exactly to the inertial mass. Following Einstein, physicists know this as the rest mass of an object.

All the other terms on the right hand side involve velocity. At low speeds, the second term is far and away the biggest of these; it is the kinetic energy, the energy of motion in Newtonian physics, divided by the speed of light squared. However, according to Einstein's new relativistic analysis, there is a whole sequence of additional terms on the right hand side. The higher terms represented by the dots are very small when the velocity is small compared to the speed of light. These are additional relativistic contributions to the kinetic energy.

Einstein argued that the best way to understand the formula is to postulate the complete equivalence of inertial mass with the total energy, so (after multiplying through by $c^2$) we can write the formula as follows:

Total energy $= mc^2 + \frac{1}{2} mv^2 + \ldots$

Once this identification is accepted, the picture becomes much clearer. As we accelerate a body, we are increasing its energy and, because of the equivalence of energy and inertial mass, this increases the inertia of the body, which makes it more difficult to increase its velocity further. Therefore, applying a force to a rapidly moving body will increase its velocity by a much smaller amount than applying the same force to a body moving at a much lower speed.

The punch line comes if we consider the meaning of the formula when applied to a body that is stationary. In this case, all the kinetic energy terms on the right disappear. This makes sense because the body is not moving and, if $v = 0$, then all these terms are multiplied by zero. So we are left with the statement that for a stationary body the total energy is equal to the rest mass of the body multiplied by the square of the speed of light.

$E = mc^2$

In Newtonian physics, a stationary object appears not to be carrying any energy, but Einstein's interpretation of this equation implied that, even when a body is stationary, it still contains an amount of energy equal to its rest mass multiplied by the speed of light squared. If Einstein was correct, then the amount of energy locked in the mass of material objects would be huge. And he most definitely was correct. This fact has had devastating consequences, but it is fundamental to modern physics.

If mass is just another form of energy, then the law of conservation of energy needs to be modified, since any change in mass must be accounted for and included in the balance. The amount of energy released in chemical reactions is very small compared to the amount of energy locked in the mass of the reacting atoms and molecules. It is so small that it had never been noticed before Einstein's bombshell. Nuclear and particle physics was in its infancy but, as these subjects matured, it became clear that nuclear reactions involve much larger amounts of energy, so the equivalence of mass and energy must be taken into consideration.

This is why particle physicists talk in terms of the energy of the particles that they are accelerating around their machines, rather than their speed. Particle physicists quote the energy of a particle in the convenient unit of the electron Volt (eV). One electron Volt is the energy gained by an electron or other charged particle when it moves through a one Volt circuit. The equivalence of mass and energy means that this is also the best unit in which to specify the rest mass of a particle. For instance, the rest mass of a proton is just under 1 GeV, where GeV means one billion electron Volts.

When a proton is accelerated around the Large Hadron Collider, its speed barely changes but its energy steadily increases. A proton with an energy of 1 TeV (1,000 GeV) in the Large Hadron Collider will be travelling around the machine within a whisker of the speed of light. To be precise, its speed will be 99.999% of the speed of light. After a few more minutes whirling around the LHC, the energy of the proton will have doubled to 2 TeV, but its speed will have barely increased at all. It will now be 99.9999% of the speed of light. The forces that are applied to the proton increase its energy, but its speed hardly changes. This is a perfect demonstration of the dramatic increase in the inertia of material bodies as their speed approaches the speed of light.

Some of the consequences of the existence of a speed limit for interactions take a bit of getting used to. In many respects, however, the cosmic speed limit leads to a much more consistent and philosophically satisfactory physics. One of the main criticisms faced by Newton was that his theories seemed to imply the existence of instantaneous action-at-a-distance. It seems philosophically implausible that one object, such as the Sun, should act on another object that is a great distance away, such as the Earth, without any time lag for the operation of the force. This is what Newtonian physics appears to suggest. Newton's response was that his theories describe how the universe functions, but they do not explain why it works in the way that it does. Following Einstein, if interactions between two bodies are limited by the speed of light, then the manner in which forces operate seems much more amenable to rational interpretation. But as soon as we accept that there is a maximum speed of interaction, then Einstein's theory of special relativity, with all its surprising consequences, follows with a relentless logic.

## The Fourth Dimension

Filby became pensive. 'Clearly,' the Time Traveller proceeded, 'any real body must have extension in four directions: it must have Length, Breadth, Thickness, and Duration. But through a natural infirmity of the flesh, which I will explain to you in a moment, we incline to overlook this fact. There are really four dimensions, three which we call the three planes of Space, and a fourth, Time. There is, however, a tendency to draw an unreal distinction between the former three dimensions and the latter, because it happens that our consciousness moves intermittently in one direction along the latter from the beginning to the end of our lives.'

H.G. Wells, *The Time Machine* (1895)[9]

We have direct experience of living in three-dimensional space. It is intuitively obvious that there are three perpendicular directions to the space that our bodies occupy, and we could construct a coordinate system with three perpendicular axes. In addition, we have a sense that we are passing through time. We can imagine that time forms a continuum and, as our clocks tick, the universe passes forwards in time along a fourth temporal dimension.

Imagine a fly in a cubic room. We could set up a coordinate system in which the $x$ axis increases along one wall, the $y$ axis along a second perpendicular wall, and the $z$ axis runs from the floor to the ceiling. At each moment in time, we could specify the position of the fly in terms of four coordinates. The $x$, $y$ and $z$ coordinates determine the position of the fly in the 3D space and the fourth coordinate is the time at which it is located at this position. The four coordinates will change in a continuous way as the fly buzzes around the room.

In this way, the four dimensions of space and time form the stage on which the drama of the universe is acted out. This intuition rests at the core of Newtonian mechanics. Newton did not describe physics in terms of four dimensions, but the idea that time could be considered as an extra dimension predates relativity. Treating time as a fourth dimension is not, in itself, a product of Einstein's revolution. Although it is famously part of relativity, it does not feature in Einstein's earliest formulations of the theory. The idea of uniting space and time as they are found in special relativity was first proposed in 1907 by the mathematician Hermann Minkowski, who had been one of Einstein's teachers.

The views of space and time which I wish to lay before you have sprung from the soil of experimental physics, and therein lies their strength. They are radical. Henceforth space by itself, and time by itself, are doomed to fade away into mere shadows, and only a kind of union of the two will preserve an independent reality.

Hermann Minkowski, *Space and Time*[10]

Einstein initially dismissed the idea, possibly because he felt that it added unnecessary baggage to the theory, but he would soon recognise its tremendous potential for advancing the theory. The relationship between space and time is much more intimate in special relativity than in Newtonian physics. As we will see, the concept of a unified spacetime becomes very powerful. Unfortunately, Minkowski, who died in 1909, did not live long enough to see the full fruits of his idea.

## *Another New Theory*

Einstein realised that the cosmic speed limit, which was a foundation stone of special relativity, would demand an even bigger upheaval in physics – a new theory of gravity. Newton's theory of gravity had been a cornerstone of physics for over two hundred years and it had scored success after success, but there is a feature of Newton's theory that was incompatible with special relativity. The theory contains no mention of the time taken for the gravitational interaction to occur. Effectively, it assumes that the gravitational force is transmitted instantaneously. This feature of Newton's theory had been questioned when it was first published, and Newton himself was well aware that it was philosophically untenable, but the theory worked so well that the need for a better theory had not arisen. With the arrival of special relativity, built on the principle that no information can be transmitted faster than the speed of light, the need for a new theory of gravity became obvious. This was simply a question of consistency.

The route to a new and improved theory of gravity was far from obvious. One possibility might be to start with Newton's theory, which had been so successful for so long, and to modify it in line with special relativity to take account of the various effects that might arise as objects approach the speed of light. In addition to the Newtonian inverse square law term, there might be new terms to account for each relativistic effect. These might include: a term that would represent the delay in the application of the gravitational force due to its transmission being limited by the speed of light; a term that would represent the fact that mass and energy are equivalent and that the changing velocity of a body would change its energy and therefore also its mass; a term that would represent the energy in the gravitational field; a gravitomagnetic term that would be the gravitational equivalent of magnetism in electromagnetism; and so on.

In many branches of physics, the inclusion of additional terms to account for specific effects is the best approach to the construction of a model.[11] But, this would not be Einstein's approach to gravity. Einstein believed in working from fundamental physical principles, and this would mean discarding the entire apparatus of Newtonian gravity and starting from scratch. The end result would be a theory of physics that was like nothing ever previously constructed in the history of physics. It is almost as though the world was given the scientific theory of an alien civilisation, or the physics of the 21st century conceived a century ahead of its time.

## *A Happy Thought!*

In 1907, Einstein had an idea that he would later describe as the happiest thought of his life. Einstein recalled that: *'for a few days I was beside myself with joyous excitement.'*[12] He explained the idea as a thought experiment. He imagined being in a lift whose cable had snapped. As the lift fell in the Earth's gravitational field, the occupants of the lift would feel weightless, just as though the Earth's gravitational field did not exist – they would not feel the force of gravity. The reason that they would feel nothing is that the lift and everything in it, including every part of the body of each occupant, would fall with the same acceleration.

In a sense, there was nothing new about this idea; it is a feature of Newton's theory. According to Newton's Second Law of Motion, the acceleration produced by a force is equal to the size of the force divided by the mass of the object being accelerated. What this means is that a massive object resists being accelerated. We know this property as inertia. The bigger its mass, the greater the force required to change its motion. We have an intuitive understanding of this – it is much easier to throw a small stone than it is to hurl a large boulder.

Now, in most cases where a force might be applied to an object, the size of the force will be completely independent of the mass of the object. For instance, the strength of the electromagnetic force on an object is proportional to the electric charge that the body carries (a very massive object might not feel any electromagnetic force if it is not electrically charged). But gravity is different. According to Newton's theory, the gravitational force that an object feels is proportional to its mass. In other words, a more massive object weighs more than a less massive object. Overall, the result is that, although a more massive object feels a greater gravitational force, it will also have a greater inertia, and this means that it will undergo the same acceleration in a gravitational field as a less massive object. The increased gravitational force due to the larger mass will exactly cancel with the increased inertia due to the larger mass. So, what Newton's theory predicts is that all massive objects will undergo the same acceleration in a gravitational field, with the result that Einstein's imaginary occupants in the plummeting lift will feel weightless.

In Newton's theory, this feature of gravity seems almost accidental. What Einstein realised was that he could use this unique attribute of gravitation as a fundamental building block for a new theory. The name that Einstein gave to it is the Equivalence Principle – the equivalence of gravitational and inertial mass. Einstein could see that by using the Equivalence Principle as the basis for a new theory, the notion of a force of gravity could be dispensed with altogether. Gravity would become a force without a force.

In the absence of any forces, all objects travel in the same way; they continue in a straight line at a constant speed. In a gravitational field, but in the absence of all other forces, all objects will still travel in the same way, because gravity affects all objects in the same way. Einstein realised that it would be more economical to discard the idea of a force of gravity acting on all objects in the same way and take the view that a massive object distorts the shape of spacetime and that other bodies then follow the straightest paths through this warped spacetime. Without gravity, spacetime is flat and objects travel along the shortest paths, which are straight lines; with gravity, spacetime is curved, and objects still travel along the straightest paths through this curved spacetime.

To make use of this idea, it would be necessary to encapsulate it mathematically. Prior to this time, Einstein had always assumed that it should be possible to describe fundamental physics using fairly elementary mathematics. It was the ideas underpinning the physics that mattered. Einstein had a single-minded determination to understand the physical universe and was not interested in mathematics for its own sake. Indeed, his teacher Minkowski is reputed to have referred to him as a 'lazy dog' because of his attitude to mathematics. Clearly, this judgement was more than a little harsh. Einstein's neglect for his mathematical studies was more a reflection of his general rebellious nature and the focus of his attention on physical problems. Now, with the need to develop a new theory of gravity, Einstein knew that he would require some sophisticated mathematics. In the next chapter, we will see how Einstein moulded a new universe out of the geometry of curved space.

Chapter Six

# LET'S DO THE TIME WARP AGAIN

Of meridians and parallels
Man has weav'd out a net, and this net throwne
Upon the Heavens, and now they are his owne.

John Donne, *First Anniversary*

## *Cartography*

Medieval European maps were little more than schematic diagrams, without any pretence of representing the Earth realistically. As European nations extended their domination of the world during the 16th and 17th centuries, so did the demands for accurate map-making skills. The principles of cartography were established as an essential aid to navigation and to demarcate the newly-found territories. Foremost among the explorers and the map-makers were the Dutch, whose wealth increased as they opened up trade routes around the world.

There is a fundamental difficulty in producing an accurate map of the world. The Earth is a globe, so it has a curved surface, whereas a map is a flat piece of paper. If the surface of the Earth were a cylinder, there would be no problem, because a cylindrical map of its surface could be unrolled to lie flat without any difficulty. But, there is no way to consistently take the features of a spherical surface and place them onto a flat map without some distortion. As long as we accept this, then there are many ways to create a map and each has its own characteristics. The particular construction chosen by a cartographer depends on the purpose of the map, and which features of the map are considered most important. This may be as much a matter of politics as science.

**Figure 46** Albrecht Dürer woodcut showing the projection of the image of a lute onto a flat canvas.

The techniques used by cartographers are similar to those used by artists since the Renaissance for producing realistic perspective in their paintings. The artists' canvas may be thought of as like a window looking out on the scene that is being represented.[1] The painting is constructed by imagining rays of light travelling straight from each point in the scene to the artist's eye or the viewpoint of the painting. The place at which the ray crosses the plane of the canvas is the position at which its image is painted, as shown in the illustration on the previous page, which is an engraving by the great Renaissance artist Albrecht Dürer. The imaginary rays form a projection of the object being depicted which, in this case, is a lute. The canvas slices across the projection, so that the image on the canvas is a cross-section of the projection.

Just as projection can be used to represent an object such as a lute on a two-dimensional canvas, so projection can be used to represent a spherical globe on a map. Cartographers have devised various methods to achieve this. For instance, the United Nations flag is shown below. We can picture it as being drawn on a flat plane that rests on the North Pole of the globe. Lines are drawn from the South Pole through the globe to the plane of the map. The points at which these lines cut the globe are projected onto the points where the lines reach the map. The result is a map in which the Arctic region, in the centre of the map, appears without much distortion, but the southern hemisphere is stretched outwards. As we move radially from the centre of the map, equal distances on the globe correspond to increasing distances on the map. The southern land masses look huge compared to the northern continents. Antarctica is completely missing from the map, as it would stretch right around the perimeter.

**Figure 47** The United Nations flag.

The most familiar world maps use a projection that was invented by the Flemish cartographer Gerardus Mercator, who coined the name *atlas* for his collection of maps of the world, after the giant Atlas who bore the heavens on his shoulders in classical mythology. Mercator's maps use a type of cylindrical projection. They are constructed by wrapping the cylindrical map around the globe, then projecting from the point at the centre of the globe through each point on the surface and onto the map at the position where the point is to be plotted. The cylinder is then unrolled to produce a flat map. This type of projection was first used on Mercator's world map, published in 1538. Maps using the Mercator projection are accurate near the equator, but regions far from the equator appear abnormally enlarged, so Greenland appears to be about the size of South America even though, in reality, it has only one-ninth of the area.

**Figure 48** In the Mercator projection, features on the surface of the globe are projected onto a cylinder that touches the globe at the equator. The cylinder is then unrolled to produce the map.

## Geometries Old and New

In the 3rd century BC, the Greek mathematician Euclid wrote *The Elements*, in which he proved the most important results of geometry. These theorems, as they are called, were built up step by step from a small set of axioms that were taken as irrefutable truths. Euclid began with simple results, such as a proof that the angles of a triangle add up to 180 degrees, to more complicated results about the structure of the regular solids. For thousands of years, the notion of geometry meant the geometry of Euclid. There was a universal belief in the existence of a direct correspondence between Euclid's geometry and the structure of the real world. It was considered so obvious that the results of Euclid must hold in all circumstances that it was never questioned.

### Puzzle 8

A sphere can be divided into eight equal parts by three circles. If we take one circle as the equator, then the other two circles go through the poles, but are rotated by 90 degrees relative to each other, as shown in the figure below. Each of the eight equal parts is a spherical triangle. What is the sum of the angles of one of these triangles?

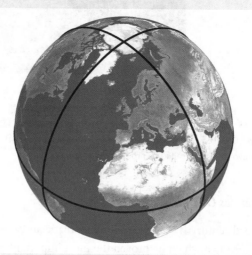

**Figure 49** A sphere that has been divided into octants by three great circles.

However, the geometry of Euclid is not valid on a sphere. As the above puzzle illustrates, on a sphere, the angles of a triangle do not add up to 180 degrees. The geometry of a sphere is quite different to the geometry of Euclid because one of Euclid's

**Answer to Puzzle 8**

Each of the three angles of the spherical triangle is a right angle. The sum of the angles is therefore 270 degrees.

axioms – the parallel postulate – does not hold true on the sphere. According to the parallel postulate, if we take a straight line and a point that is not on the line, then we can always draw a unique line through the chosen point that is parallel to our line. This sounds quite reasonable, or at least it did for two thousand years. In fact, this axiom holds on a flat surface, but not on a curved surface such as a sphere. If we take two lines of longitude, they look parallel at the equator but they meet at both the North and South Poles. There are no parallel lines on a sphere.

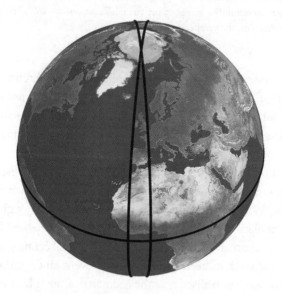

**Figure 50** Two lines of longitude. They appear parallel at the equator, but meet at the North and South Poles.

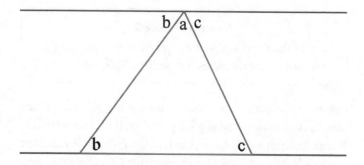

**Figure 51** To prove that the angles of a triangle sum to 180°, we can proceed as follows. Extend the base of the triangle with a straight line that extends to infinity. Draw a line parallel to this line through the third vertex of the triangle. Then the two angles labelled b in the diagram are equal. The two angles labelled c are also equal. The sum of angles a, b and c is 180°, because they form a straight line. But these are also the three angles of the triangle. Therefore the angles of the triangle must sum to 180°. The proof clearly relies on the parallel postulate.

Because this axiom does not hold for the geometry on a sphere, Euclid's results that rely on this axiom will not hold on a sphere. This is the case with his proof that the angles of a triangle sum to 180 degrees. Euclid's geometry is actually a very special geometry; it is the geometry of flat space.

It is perhaps surprising, but mathematicians did not discover the existence of non-Euclidean geometries until the early years of the 19th century and, even then, it was not through the contemplation of spherical geometry. Geographers had been producing accurate maps of the globe for several centuries, and astronomers had been mapping the heavens since antiquity, yet no-one had realised that the geometry of the sphere could be constructed in a manner that was comparable, but distinct from, the Euclidean geometry that describes flat space.

There were mathematicians who had refused to give the parallel postulate the same status as the other axioms of geometry. Several had devoted their lives to fruitless attempts to prove that it was not truly independent, by showing that it could be derived from the other, simpler axioms. One such mathematician was the Hungarian Farkas Bolyai. When his son Janos also began to take an interest in the problem, Farkas warned him:

> For God's sake, please give it up. Fear it no less than the sensual passion, because it, too, may take up all your time and deprive you of your health, peace of mind and happiness in life. [2]

However, Janos did not heed his father's advice. In the early 1820s, three mathematicians saw the problem differently from all their predecessors. Janos Bolyai was one of those to make the breakthrough that would rock the world of mathematics. A young Russian mathematician called Nikolai Lobachevsky independently made the same monumental discovery. Carl Friedrich Gauss was widely recognised as the world's leading mathematician at the time, and is now considered to be one of the three greatest mathematicians ever. When Gauss was informed about Lobachevsky's results, he revealed that he had also arrived at the same conclusions, but had chosen to keep quiet.[3] Each of these mathematicians realised that if the parallel postulate is abandoned, then a new type of geometry becomes possible. This geometry is known as hyperbolic geometry. It was invented as an abstract mathematical exercise, but it corresponds to the geometry of a saddle or a curved funnel. In this geometry, the angles of a triangle always add up to less than 180 degrees.

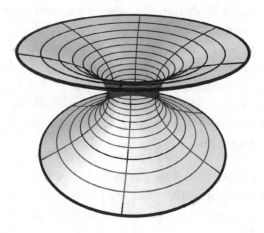

**Figure 52** Hyperbolic geometry is the geometry of a saddle or curved funnel. This hyperbolic surface is known as a catenoid.

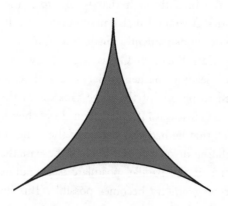

**Figure 53** An example of a triangle in hyperbolic geometry. Each of the angles of this particular triangle is less than 60 degrees, so the sum of the angles is less than 180 degrees.

## Curvaceous Figures

We have an intuitive understanding of the distinction between a flat surface and a curved surface. We can make these ideas more precise by considering a region of a hyperbolic surface embedded in three-dimensional space, as shown in the illustration below. At every point, the surface curves in two perpendicular planes. The illustration shows a representative point with two perpendicular curves drawn through the point. The centres of curvature are in opposite directions, as indicated by the arrows. This is known as negative curvature,[4] and it is the defining feature of hyperbolic geometry. The curvature is negative at every point on a hyperbolic surface, such as the one shown in the figure below.

**Figure 54** The arrows indicate the directions towards the centre of curvature at a point on the hyperbolic surface.

Now consider the more familiar example of a spherical surface. In the illustration below, two perpendicular curves are drawn through a representative point on the surface. In this case, the centres of curvature are both in the same direction, which is the centre of the sphere. This means that, whereas a hyperbolic surface has negative curvature, the sphere has positive curvature.

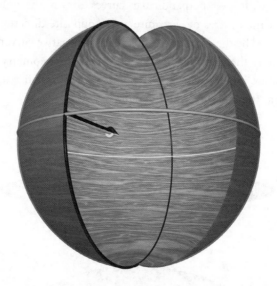

**Figure 55** The arrows indicate the directions towards the centre of curvature for a point on a sphere.

## *What is the Shape of Space?*

The existence of these new geometries raised the question of the true geometry of space. Euclidean geometry could no longer be accepted without question. In the 1820s,

Gauss organised an expedition to investigate the geometry of space in the Earth's locality. His idea was to measure the angles of a triangle formed by three of Germany's most prominent peaks. Taking the summits of the Brocken, Hohenhagen and Inselberg mountains as the vertices of the triangle, the survey measured the angles between its three sides[5] (note that Gauss was not attempting to measure the curvature of the Earth's surface – he was searching for any possible curvature in the three-dimensional space around the Earth).

To within the accuracy of the measurements, Gauss concluded that the sum of the angles in his triangle was 180 degrees, as expected in flat space. The matter might have appeared settled, but the measurements were simply too crude to reveal the curvature of space that would be predicted by Einstein's theory a century later.

The German mathematician Bernhard Riemann was a pupil of Gauss in the 1850s. Riemann was born and lived in poverty. His life was filled with tragedy, and he died of tuberculosis in 1866 at the age of just 39. Despite this, he was one of the truly great mathematicians of the 19th century. Most mathematicians tread very carefully and have a rather cautious approach to their subject, but Riemann was very different. He had the vision to open up sweeping new vistas of mathematics. Riemann realised that the invention of hyperbolic geometry was only the beginning of a revolution that would transform geometry. What was needed was a systematic method of describing surfaces that curve in arbitrary ways and similar techniques for analysing geometry in more than two dimensions.

Riemann's key to a general understanding of arbitrary surfaces was closely related to cartography. As we have seen, there are many ways in which to create a map of the world.

Each relies on a projection of the features of the globe onto a flat surface, and each projection produces its own distortion of the features on the globe. What a navigator requires is a set of instructions that indicate how the distortion has come about. They need to know that distances in one region of the map might represent different lengths on the globe than distances in another region of the map, so that they can compensate for the distortions. In effect, as the navigators' rulers are moved over the map, they must imagine that their length is constantly changing.

For instance, in Mercator's maps, regions near the poles appear comparatively much larger than regions near the equator. With the Mercator projection, we know that our rulers effectively change length as they are moved around the map, and the ruler will be longer at the poles than it is near the equator. One hundred kilometres might be represented as one centimetre close to the equator, but it could be represented as three centimetres towards the poles. Riemann adopted a similar approach to the analysis of arbitrary curved surfaces in any number of dimensions. He devised a method by which the surface could be projected onto flat space (with the same number of dimensions), along with a recipe for how the distance between any two points in the surface could be calculated.

All the necessary information about distances is encapsulated in a mathematical object known as the metric. For instance, the metric of flat space is different from the metric of a sphere, which is different from the metric of hyperbolic space. These ideas were developed further by other mathematicians in the later years of the 19th century, following Riemann's early death.

**Figure 56** The entire infinite hyperbolic plane can be mapped into a disc.[6] The illustration shows a tessellation of triangles in the hyperbolic plane. Each triangle has the same area, but the projection onto the disc distorts the size of the triangles, just as Mercator's projection distorts the area of the continents.

---

**Puzzle 9**

What is the sum of the angles of each of the triangles in the hyperbolic tessellation in the disc shown in the figure above?

HINT: It is a regular tessellation. Consider the puzzle about tessellations in chapter 2.

---

**Answer to Puzzle 9**

The angles that meet at each point must sum to 360 degrees. Eight triangles meet at each vertex in the tessellation (four black and four white). Each triangle in the tessellation is identical to the rest, therefore as 8 × 45 = 360, the eight angles that meet at each vertex must each be 45 degrees. The sum of the angles of each triangle is therefore 3 × 45° = 135°.

## *Back to Einstein*

Galileo had demonstrated the counterintuitive fact that all objects fall with the same acceleration under gravity, irrespective of their mass. In Newtonian physics, mass has a double role: it is responsible for our inertia and, thereby, diminishes our acceleration when a force is applied, but it also generates the force of gravity. The cancellation between these two properties of mass means that all objects are affected by gravity in exactly the same way, irrespective of their mass, and this accounts for Galileo's observation. Newton accepted that mass plays this dual role without comment.

Einstein saw it differently. He thought that this equivalence was so striking that it must be a fundamental principle of the universe, not just a lucky coincidence. As we have seen, Einstein realised that, when falling under gravity (such as in a lift whose cable has snapped), if no other forces intervene, then we will not feel any force at all. Every part of our body and everything else around us falls in exactly the same way. The laws of physics operate in just the same way as they would in empty space, far from the gravitational effects of any massive objects. For this reason, Einstein believed that it must be possible to describe gravity without using Newton's concept of a gravitational force.

The novelty of Einstein's approach would be the introduction of spacetime curvature into physics. Minkowski had shown the potential impact that geometry could have on physics by sewing space and time together into four-dimensional spacetime. In Einstein's special relativity, spacetime was the flat background on which physics was played out. Einstein now intended to incorporate gravity into the theory by transforming this background into a dynamic part of the theory. The idea was that matter would shape spacetime, and then spacetime would determine how matter would move. In Newton's theory, the motion of a projectile is determined by the force of gravity. Einstein could see that any object that was launched with the same velocity would follow the same path. It was more economical to view spacetime as curved and see the projectile as following a straight path through curved space, than to imagine that a force is acting on the projectile.

A straight path through curved space sounds like a contradiction, but it is fairly easy to generalise our flat space notion of a straight line. In flat space, a straight line is the shortest path between two points. Similarly, we can determine the shortest path between two points on a curved surface. These paths are known as geodesics and, when space is curved, they are the equivalent of straight lines. The Mercator maps of the world that we are familiar with distort our perception of distance on the globe. Lines of longitude and latitude both appear straight on these maps but, whereas lines of longitude are the shortest paths between the points that they connect, lines of latitude (other than the equator) are certainly not the shortest routes. Lines of longitude are geodesics, but lines of latitude are not.

For instance, the shortest route when flying from London to Tokyo is to follow a great circle route that takes an aircraft well into the Arctic, even though Tokyo is much further south than London, as shown in the figures below.

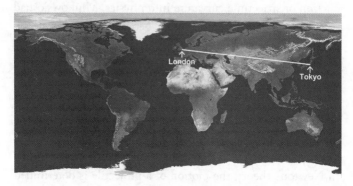

**Figure 57** Map of the Earth. What appears to be a straight line between London and Tokyo is actually a much longer route than that shown in the figure below.

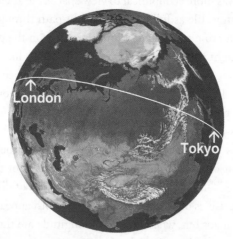

**Figure 58** The shortest path between London and Tokyo follows a great circle route that goes via the Arctic. (A great circle is one that divides the Earth into two equal hemispheres.)

Einstein proposed that bodies falling freely in a gravitational field could be treated as though they were following a geodesic in curved spacetime. This would update the idea of Newton's natural inertial motion to the context of Einstein's new theory. According to Newton's First Law, if no forces are acting, objects will continue to move at a constant velocity in a straight line. In Einstein's theory, inertial motion also includes motion in a gravitational field. According to Einstein, if no forces are acting other than gravity, then objects will continue to move along a geodesic in spacetime.

### Blowing Bubbles

Einstein's aim was to somehow replace Newton's gravitational force with spacetime curvature. This sounds like an outlandish idea. How could curvature play an equivalent role in physics to a force? An everyday analogy will show that this is not really as crazy as it might seem. If two rings are placed together in soapy water until they are covered in a soapy film and then gradually separated, a bubble may emerge, stretching between the rings. The bubble will form a hyperbolic surface known as a catenoid.

The shape of the bubble is determined by the surface tension in the soapy water. At each point on the surface, the surface tension generates forces that act towards the centres of curvature. On a hyperbolic surface, the centres of curvature at each point are in opposite directions, as shown in Figure 54 on page 183. This means that the surface tension forces can exactly balance at each point, as they must if the surface is to be stable, which is why the bubble forms this particular shape.

A second example is even more familiar. When we blow soap bubbles into the air, they form spheres. The direction

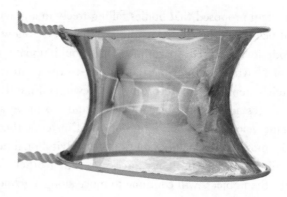

**Figure 59** A soap bubble that stretches between two rings. The bubble is a hyperbolic surface.

towards the centre of curvature at each point on the surface is now towards the centre of the sphere. This means that the surface tension is producing an inward force at each point on the spherical bubble. The inward force squeezes the air within, raising its pressure until the air inside the bubble exerts a force that is sufficient to resist any further contraction of the bubble. This is why bubbles sink: the air within the bubble is denser than the air outside. The difference in the air pressure between the inside and outside of the bubble balances the inward pressure due to the surface tension of the bubble. (When producing the hyperbolic bubble, the rings were open at each end of the surface. This allows air to circulate freely, so the air pressures on the inside and outside of the surface are the same.)

Einstein's attempts to relate curvature to forces made sense, as the bubble analogy shows. What Einstein needed was a recipe for calculating the metric of curved spacetime – an

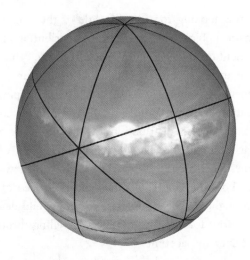

**Figure 60** A spherical bubble.

equation that encapsulated how a massive object would warp the spacetime region that surrounded it. But to formulate his new theory, Einstein would first need a better understanding of curved space and a thorough grounding in the mathematical machinery developed by Riemann and other geometers. This was an arcane subject that was unfamiliar to physicists at the beginning of the 20th century. Fortunately, one of Einstein's close friends, Marcel Grossmann, was a mathematician who was an expert in Riemannian geometry. Einstein spent several years in Zurich working with his friend to master the intricacies of the subject.

## *The Messenger of the Gods Dances a Jig*

Einstein announced the final form of general relativity to the world in November, 1915. He had found the equation that he was looking for. On one side of the equation is a mathematical object that describes the distribution of energy and momentum in a region of space.[7] On the other side is a mathematical object that encodes the curvature that the mass generates in this region of space.[8] It is as simple as that. The equation is known quite naturally as Einstein's equation. Given a particular distribution of matter, it determines how spacetime will be warped. A solution of the equation determines the metric of spacetime. In other words, it describes how the length of rulers and the speed of clocks varies throughout spacetime. This, in turn, would determine the trajectories followed by an object travelling through the region of curved spacetime.

The solar system had been used as a laboratory to test Newtonian gravitation for several hundred years, and Newton's theory had scored a long sequence of triumphs. If general relativity were to be a viable theory, then, as Einstein well knew, it would have to reproduce these great successes. However, solving Einstein's equation is easier said than done. The equation is actually ten coupled equations that must all be simultaneously satisfied. Solving Einstein's equation for a general distribution of matter is still beyond the mathematical technology of today. By contrast, it is much easier to find approximate solutions, and this is perfectly adequate for testing the theory in situations where gravity is not too intense and for objects that are moving slowly compared to the speed of light – such as within the solar system, where Newton's theory had scored its greatest successes. In making these approximations, it is natural to convert the esoteric picture of objects following geodesics through curved spacetime into the more familiar imagery of Newtonian mechanics.

Einstein could see when he undertook these calculations that, to a first approximation, general relativity looked exactly the same as Newtonian gravity – which was good news. According to the theory, objects that were not too dense would act on each other with a force that diminishes as the inverse square of distance, just as Newtonian gravity says. This meant that all of the great successes of Newton's theory would also automatically apply to general relativity. This was a great first step, but simply reproducing all the results of an already successful theory would not, in itself, be accounted a great achievement. What was needed was to examine the theory beyond this Newtonian approximation to find results that differed from the Newtonian predictions, so that the two theories could compete head-to-head in their explanation of the physical universe.

When the analysis of general relativity goes one step further, there is a small additional term that is equivalent to a force that diminishes as the inverse fourth power of distance. This represents a clear distinction from Newtonian gravity, where the force of gravity corresponds to an inverse square law and nothing else. Therefore, this new term derived from general relativity offers the possibility of testing the theory in what is known as the post-Newtonian approximation.

As Newton proved, an exact inverse square law will result in elliptical orbits and, in this way, Newton's theory of gravity accounts for Kepler's First Law of Planetary Motion, a purely descriptive law that Kepler derived from Tycho's observations. The effect of the small additional force would be to cause the direction of the axis of the ellipse to change gradually. In other words, the orbit would precess. This was clear without making any detailed calculations. But what Einstein needed to know was how big this effect would be. How fast would the axis of the ellipse precess? In the solar system, the effect of this extra term is largest in the case of Mercury, because Mercury is closest to the Sun – which means that Mercury is deeper in the Sun's gravitational well. Mercury is also travelling fastest, and so will be subject to greater relativistic effects than all the other planets. Einstein performed the calculation. His analysis showed that the additional term due to general relativity would cause Mercury's orbit to precess by just 43 seconds of arc per century.

This was the moment when Einstein knew that his theory was a phenomenal success. The size of the precession produced by these relativistic effects precisely matched the known discrepancy in Mercury's orbit – the discrepancy that Le Verrier had attempted to plug by hypothesizing the existence of the inner planet Vulcan. Now Einstein knew the real reason for the precession of Mercury's orbit. It was nothing to do with an invisible planet, but simply the consequence of the curvature of spacetime predicted by his revolutionary new theory of gravity. In the words of his friend and biographer, Abraham Pais: 'This discovery was, I believe, by far the strongest emotional experience in Einstein's scientific life, perhaps in all his life. Nature had spoken to him.'[9]

## Heroism on the Eastern Front

Karl Schwarzschild was a mathematician and astrophysicist with wide-ranging interests, who was forty years old and a professor at Göttingen, Germany's most prestigious university, when the First World War broke out in August, 1914. Despite his age and his unsuitability for military conflict, he immediately volunteered for military service. Initially, he was put in charge of a meteorological station in Belgium. He was then stationed with an artillery unit in France, calculating missile trajectories before being posted to the Eastern Front and the conflict with Russia. On the Eastern Front, Schwarzschild began to suffer from a rare and extremely painful autoimmune disease of the skin, known as pemphigus.

Somehow, amidst the insanity of war, deafened by the roar of shells and with painful, blistering skin, Schwarzschild was able to focus his mind on Einstein's general relativity published in November, 1915. Einstein's new theory was highly original, as we have seen, and employed ideas and mathematics that had never previously been used by physicists. Furthermore, the fundamental equations of the theory were very complicated and difficult to solve exactly. Einstein had only been able to find approximate solutions, which he had used to calculate the precession of the orbit of Mercury.

Schwarzschild wrestled with the equations in the isolation of the trenches and, despite the novelty of the mathematics, within a few weeks he had found the most important solutions of Einstein's equation. Schwarzschild had dramatically simplified the mathematical analysis by considering a very symmetrical situation, a spherically symmetrical mass. His solutions describe the shape of spacetime inside and outside a perfectly spherical body, such as a star or a planet. On 22 December 1915, he wrote to Einstein to tell him of his discovery. Schwarzschild's concluding remarks demonstrate his incredible courage in the most desperate of circumstances: 'As you see, the war treated me kindly enough, in spite of the heavy gunfire, to allow me to get away from it all and take this walk in the land of your ideas.' [10]

Einstein was taken aback by the solution that Schwarzschild had found. He replied: 'I have read your paper with the utmost interest. I had not expected that one could formulate the exact solution of the problem in such a simple way.' [11]

Schwarzschild's skin condition worsened and in March, 1916, he was removed from the front. Two months later, on 11 May, Schwarzschild died.

## *Total Eclipse*

On 11 November 1918, the guns finally fell silent on the Western Front. The British mathematician and astrophysicist, Arthur Eddington, promoted the idea of an expedition to test one of the predictions of Einstein's theory of general relativity. Eddington, who was a Quaker, felt that the expedition would offer a great opportunity for reconciliation after the horrors of the First World War. British scientists would be testing a theory by a German scientist that could overthrow the theory of gravity devised by the greatest of all British scientists. According to general relativity, the path of a beam of light should bend when passing through the warped space close to a massive object such as the Sun. This would imply that the position of a star would appear to shift very slightly when it was close to the edge of the Sun's disc, as the Sun's gravity would bend the path taken by the star's light. However, viewing the positions of the stars close to the Sun is nearly impossible, as they are drowned out by the intensity of the Sun's light. Fortunately for us, on Earth there are occasions when just such an observation is possible – a total eclipse of the Sun.

In the 19th century, solar eclipses had given astronomers the opportunity to confirm Newton's theory of gravity by searching for the elusive planet Vulcan. Now, in the 20th century, astronomers could take advantage of a solar eclipse in the hope of overturning Newton by confirming the new theory of Einstein. Eddington travelled to the island of Principe, off the west coast of Africa, to photograph the region around the Sun during the total solar eclipse of 29 May 1919. When analysed, the photographs showed a small shift in the positions of the stars close to the Sun. The light-bending power of gravity had been witnessed. Eddington heralded the results as a triumph for science and announced to the world's press the sensational confirmation of the theory of general relativity. From this moment on, Einstein's life would change completely. For the rest of his life, he would be feted worldwide as the greatest intellect on the planet.

In reality, the eclipse results were not very accurate, and their agreement with general relativity was not as conclusive as Eddington may have suggested. Nonetheless, he was correct. We now have beautiful pictures that offer a dramatic illustration of this remarkable feature of gravity and its interpretation by Einstein. The figure below shows the effect of gravitational lensing, as it is called. A cluster of galaxies warps the space around it to such an extent that the light from much more distant galaxies bends around the intervening cluster. We see distorted images of these remote galaxies surrounding the central cluster. There may be more than one image of the same distant galaxy.

As an added bonus, gravitational lensing offers a great way to measure the amount of mass within the object that is responsible for bending the light. This has given astronomers a valuable new tool to work out the mass of a cluster of galaxies. The results are rather surprising, as they indicate that there is far more matter in the universe than we can see. We will return to this issue in a later chapter.

**Figure 61** The galaxy cluster Abell 2218 is shown in this picture taken by the Hubble Space Telescope. The immense gravitational field of the cluster bends the light from much more distant galaxies into wispy arcs, which may include multiple images of the same galaxy. The distant galaxies are magnified, brightened and distorted by the curved space around the cluster. The curved space acts like a lens and is, indeed, referred to as a gravitational lens. (© HST, NASA.)

**Figure 62** Left: Schematic diagram of a gravitational lens. The light from a distant object bends around a very massive intervening object such as a galaxy or a cluster of galaxies. From Earth multiple images of the more distant object are seen. If the alignment is perfect the object will appear as a ring around the intervening mass.

Right: The image of a distant galaxy is almost warped into a ring around a galaxy at an intermediate distance. (Image of LRG 3-757, © HST, NASA/ESA.)

## *Let's do the Timewarp Again!*

According to general relativity, mass not only curves space – it also warps time. How do we measure the passage of time? One way is to use the regular pulse of an electromagnetic wave. By measuring the frequency of a beam of light, it is possible to keep track of time, and this is the basis for a classic experiment that tested Einstein's prediction that time is warped in a gravitational field.

When an atomic nucleus undergoes nuclear decay by emitting a gamma ray photon, the nucleus will recoil, in accordance with Newton's Third Law of Motion. In 1958, Rudolf Mössbauer discovered that, in some circumstances, when the nucleus is in an atom that is bound in a crystal lattice, it is possible for the recoil to be shared throughout the lattice. This means that the decaying nucleus effectively suffers no recoil at all. The Mössbauer effect, as it is called, produces gamma rays of a very sharply defined frequency. Robert Pound and Glen Rebka realised that this would provide the perfect tool for testing the distortions in time predicted by general relativity.

In 1959, Pound and Rebka fired gamma rays from a radio-active iron source down Harvard University's twenty-metre Jefferson Tower.[12] At the bottom of the tower was a second thin piece of iron, beneath which was a gamma ray detector. Gamma rays with just the right frequency would be mopped up by the nuclei in the iron absorber. Each gamma ray photon emitted by an iron nucleus at the top of the tower would have exactly the right energy to excite another iron nucleus at the bottom. However, according to general relativity, falling in the Earth's gravitational field should change the frequency of the gamma radiation. The radiation should undergo a blue shift on its journey to the bottom of the shaft. (Another way to look at this is that the photons will gain energy as they fall in the gravitational field and, as the energy of a photon is proportional to its frequency, this increase in energy translates into an increase in frequency.)

A small shift in the frequency, as predicted by general relativity, would mean that the gamma rays would have the wrong energy to be absorbed by the iron nuclei at the bottom. They would therefore travel straight through the iron and be detected below it. If the theory was wrong, then no shift would occur. In this case, the gamma rays would be absorbed in the iron and they would not be detected below. The really clever feature of the Pound and Rebka experiment was that the iron absorber could be driven upwards or downwards at a slow velocity, to produce a tiny Doppler shift in the gamma radiation. When the velocity was just right, it would exactly compensate for the gravitational shift in frequency, producing a peak in the amount of radiation absorbed by the iron absorber and therefore a trough in the number of gamma ray photons hitting the detector below. This ingenious arrangement enabled Pound and Rebka to detect the tiny gravitational blue shift and to make a very accurate measurement of its size.

The shift in the frequency of the radiation measures the distortion in the passage of time due to the Earth's gravity. It provides a measure of part of the metric of spacetime in the vicinity of the Earth. Pound and Rebka concluded that the predictions of general relativity were satisfied to within the accuracy of their experiment. The effect is tiny in the Earth's relatively weak gravitational field; the shift in frequency is around one part in a thousand trillion ($10^{-15}$).

In the 1970s, the gravitational distortion of time was verified more directly by taking atomic clocks around the world on aeroplanes. When these high-flying clocks were reunited with their stay-at-home earthbound counterparts, they confirmed that a different amount of time had elapsed for the different clocks. Again, these differences precisely matched those expected due to the effects of relativity.

## *Where Are We?*

The difference between the predictions of Newtonian gravity and general relativity are tiny in the vicinity of the Earth – so small that we might not expect to ever need to take account of the relativistic corrections to Newton's theory. It is rather surprising, therefore, that we rely on an everyday technology that is dependent on general relativity for its accuracy; the use of satellite navigation systems in mobile devices is now commonplace. The original system developed by the United States is built around a constellation of 24 satellites in high Earth orbit. The altitude of their orbits is about 20,000 kilometres. Each satellite carries an atomic clock, and these clocks are synchronized several times a day with updates from even more accurate ground-based clocks. From any point on Earth, at least four GPS satellites are above the horizon at each moment in time. Triangulation using the time taken for signals to arrive from four satellites can be used to determine the position of any point on Earth to an incredible precision of less than two metres. In order to achieve such accuracy, the system must keep time to within about six nanoseconds.[13]

This means that two relativistic effects must be taken into account. The satellites are travelling around the Earth at about 14,000 kilometres an hour, which introduces time dilation effects as described by special relativity. This causes the atomic clocks on board to lose around 7,000 nanoseconds per day, compared to Earth-based clocks. However, the satellites are much higher in the Earth's gravitational field than clocks on Earth. As Pound and Rebka demonstrated, this means that they will tick faster than clocks on the ground, deep in the Earth's gravitational well. This general relativistic effect means that the onboard clocks should gain about 45,000 nanoseconds per day. The net effect is that the GPS satellite clocks gain around 38,000 nanoseconds per day. However, the system is designed to compensate for this disparity in the flow of time. If it were not taken into account, the system would become unreliable in under a minute.[14]

## Is Einstein's theory better than Newton's?

In all the situations in which it has been tested, general relativity agrees with the experimental and observational evidence. In every case where it has been possible to measure a gravitational effect sufficiently accurately to distinguish between general relativity and Newtonian gravity, general relativity has come out on top. General relativity is, without question, a more accurate theory than Newtonian gravity. This is the primary reason for accepting it as the best theory of gravity that we have. However, there is more to the theory than this; general relativity is universally regarded as the most elegant of all theories of physics. It epitomises what physicists consider to be a beautiful theory. It is constructed from a few simple philosophical principles, which gives it very secure physical foundations.

When Newton published the *Principia*, he was criticised by philosophers and mathematicians such as Bishop Berkeley, Wilhelm Leibniz and Christiaan Huygens for introducing occult forces into the physical sciences. The force of gravity seemed to act at a distance, which left a bad taste in the mouth. In Einstein's theory, this issue is resolved. According to general relativity, the presence of matter curves spacetime in its vicinity, and this local curvature then spreads outwards at the speed of light. The shape of spacetime will determine the course of other bodies, but they cannot be affected until there has been time for the gravitational influence to reach their locality.

On 31 December 1999, Time magazine named Einstein as the person of the century.

## *The Schwarzschild Solution*

Schwarzschild solved Einstein's equation and found the shape of spacetime around a spherical object such as a star or planet. Schwarzschild also solved Einstein's equation for the shape of spacetime within a spherically symmetrical mass. Having seen that there is extremely good evidence that Einstein's theory offers a useful way to view gravity, we should take a closer look at Schwarzschild's solutions. Space is three-dimensional and we live inside it, so we cannot view the shape of space from outside. But we can get a good idea about the shape of space if we consider a two-dimensional slice through three-dimensional space. Our surface will look like a warped rubber sheet. (We must bear in mind that the passage of time is also distorted, but we will come back to that.)

Outside the mass, the curvature of space is negative, so the 2D slice through space looks like the hyperbolic surface that we saw earlier. The curvature decreases with increasing distance from the mass and gradually falls towards zero. At large distances from the mass, space will essentially be flat.

Our slice through space looks like a funnel that ends on an open circle. This is because, for the moment, we are

**Figure 63** The geometry of a 2D slice through space outside a spherical mass. The circle at the base of the diagram corresponds to where the slice passes through the surface of the spherical mass. For instance, this could be the equator of the sphere.

only considering the space outside the mass. The open circle represents a cross-section of the boundary of the spherical mass. It might be its equator, for instance. In the Newtonian description, the force of gravity falls off as the inverse square of distance from the centre of the mass in the region outside the mass shown in the figure above.

We can also consider the shape of space within the mass. The direction of curvature changes as we enter the mass. Inside the mass, the curvature is positive and, if the mass has uniform density, then the curvature inside will be constant and our 2D slice will look like a hemisphere. The space within the mass must join smoothly to the space outside, which means that our hemisphere can be sewn on to the circle at the bottom of the previous illustration; the resulting shape is shown in the figure below. To a good approximation, this is the shape of a 2D slice of space in and around any spherical mass.

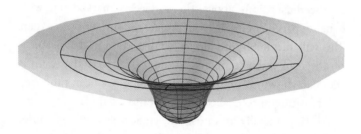

**Figure 64** A 2D slice through the space in and around a massive spherical body. Outside the body, space is negatively curved; inside the body, space is positively curved.

The spherically curved space inside the mass corresponds to the region of space where the Newtonian force grows in proportion to the distance from the centre of the mass. This means that the force falls off as we approach the centre, as described in Chapter 4, where we journeyed through the centre of the Earth. At the centre of the mass, the force disappears completely. In the figure above, this corresponds to the point at the bottom of the depression. As long as we remember that we are looking at a 2D slice through space, this is a good picture of how space is warped by the presence of a massive object.

In reality, an object such as a star will warp the whole 3D space that surrounds it. We have taken a slice through space, so that we can see it embedded in flat 3D space. When we do this, it is immediately obvious that the surface is curved. But imagine creatures confined within the 2D surface. How would space appear to them? They cannot see the surface from outside, as we have been doing. The curvature will appear to them as a distortion in the lengths of their rulers. In the illustrations above, the surface is marked out with equally spaced circles. We can project the surface onto a map. This will, inevitably, produce some distortion in the distances on the map when compared to the real surface. The result is the map shown in the next figure, which has been produced by projecting our 2D slice upwards onto a flat plane.

Moving radially inwards, the circles cluster ever closer together until we reach the edge of the mass. This corresponds

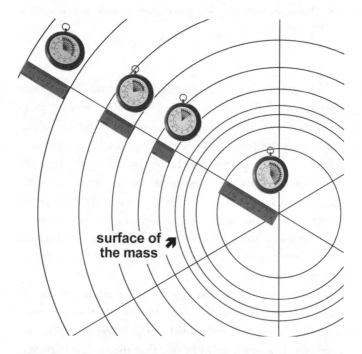

**Figure 65** Projection of a slice through Schwarzschild space in and around an extremely dense body. The distortion in the radial direction is shown as the stretching of a standard ruler. The distortion in time is depicted as a change in the rate at which the second hand on a watch moves.

to the negative curvature outside the massive body. As we enter the mass, the direction of curvature changes and the circles gradually become more spaced out again. The circles are bunched most closely where the rubber-sheet-like 2D slice plummets downwards at the edge of the mass. Creatures within the slice would see this as a distortion in the lengths of their rulers as they travel through the gravitational field of the mass. (Note that as the massive body is approached, rulers shrink, which means that the map understates lengths in the actual 2D surface. This corresponds to the stretching of space in the gravitational field.) Similarly, clocks slow down, as verified by Pound and Rebka, which indicates that time has been compressed in the gravitational field.

Our 2D slice is representative of all the possible slices through the space around a massive object. In each slice, space is stretched towards the mass in the same way. However, it is very difficult to draw all this information together and imagine the distortion of 3D space in its entirety. The problem is that, like the imaginary 2D creatures in our slice, we live within the 3D space that is being warped. The best that we can do is to pretend that we live within a flat 3D map and account for the warping of space from within. Like the 2D creatures, we can do this by considering the effect of gravity on the length of a ruler. The curvature of the 3D space in which we live can be mapped out by comparing the lengths of rulers to a standard ruler that is kept far from the mass. As shown in the figure above, outside a mass, our rulers shrink in the direction towards the mass. In three dimensions, there are two directions perpendicular to the radial direction. A ruler oriented in either of these directions would grow as we moved towards the mass. What this means is that space is stretched in the radial direction and squeezed in the two perpendicular directions.

## *Warping 3D Space*

Returning to the Newtonian description of gravity for a moment, the decrease in gravity with distance outside a massive object means that the gravitational force at two widely separated points may be different. The difference in the pull of the Moon on opposite sides of the Earth raises the tides and, for this reason, such differential forces are known as tidal forces. Einstein removed the need to invoke the Newtonian

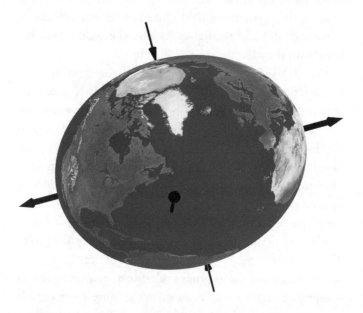

**Figure 66** The Newtonian picture of tidal forces is converted into a picture of spacetime curvature in Einstein's theory. The tidal forces produced by the Moon's gravity correspond to a distortion of the space around the Earth, and this is what causes the tides to rise. The distortion is enormously exaggerated in the illustration. The size of the actual distortion can be gauged by comparing the height of the tides to the radius of the Earth.[15]

inverse square law force to explain gravity, but tidal forces cannot be removed in this way. In fact, it is the tidal forces that correspond to spacetime curvature in general relativity. According to Einstein's theory, the Moon distorts the shape of space in its vicinity. This spatial curvature stretches the Earth in the direction of the Moon and squeezes the Earth in the perpendicular directions. In Einstein's description, it is this stretching and squeezing that generates the tides.

## Holes in Space

The universe contains objects that are far more massive and much denser than the Sun. It is close to these objects that the predictions of general relativity come into their own.

The curvature of space within a massive body has an effect that is quite similar to the spherical bubble in the analogy described earlier. The curved space squeezes the material within, raising its pressure and increasing its density until it exerts an outward force that prevents it from being compressed further. This outward force is produced by structural forces within the material body, such as those between atoms, that are ultimately electromagnetic in origin. (In the next chapter, we will see that there are also weird stellar remnants that are supported by nuclear forces.)

If a star is sufficiently massive, then the gravitational curvature generated by its mass may be so intense that eventually it completely crushes the star out of existence. The Schwarzschild solution predicts that once the size of an object has been squeezed within a distance known as its Schwarzschild radius, nothing can prevent further collapse. All that will remain is an extremely warped region of spacetime that we call a black hole. The boundary of such an object is a spherical region known as its event horizon, from within which not even light can escape. The Schwarzschild radius of the Sun is just 2.9 kilometres,[16] so the entire mass of the Sun would have to be squeezed within this radius to create a black hole. The Schwarzschild radius of the Earth is less than a centimetre. No known force is capable of transforming the Earth or even the Sun into a black hole, but there can no longer be any doubt that black holes really do exist. The figure below shows a 2D slice through the space around a black hole. The event horizon is circular in the illustration, and spherical in the true 3D picture. In the next chapter, we will take a closer look at these celestial monsters.

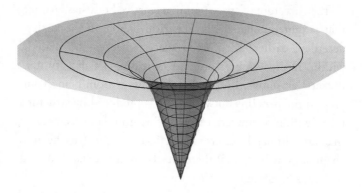

**Figure 67** A 2D slice through the Schwarzschild space around a black hole.

Chapter Seven

# A BRIEF HISTORY OF BLACK HOLES

On my ship, the Rocinante
Wheeling through the galaxies,
Headed for the heart of Cygnus
Headlong into mystery

The x-ray is her siren song
My ship cannot resist her long
Nearer to my deadly goal
Until the Black Hole
Gains control . . .

Rush, *Cygnus X-1*

## *This is Nonsense, Stephen!*

Stephen Hawking's greatest triumph came in 1974.[1] He made his breakthrough public at the Rutherford Appleton Laboratories' winter meeting, where he announced the results of his latest research to an audience of theorists. Hawking was already using a wheelchair and was on the stage. As he came to the conclusion of his talk, he broke the news of his momentous insight into fundamental physics. There was a stunned silence. The audience of experienced physicists were shocked. Finally, Professor John Taylor of King's College, London, who was acting as chairman for this session of the meeting, stood up angrily, saying, '*This is nonsense, Stephen!*' before rushing from the lecture theatre – apparently intending to write a paper to demolish Hawking's idea. This is not the usual response to a fundamental physics seminar, which is more likely to end with a polite handclap and a couple of yawns from those who began to doze as the speaker conjured up the more technical details of their latest research. So what did Hawking say that was so shocking to his colleagues? I will reveal all after a quick tour of the cosmos.

## *Apocalypse Now!*

Stars are huge balls of hydrogen and helium. However, despite their almost identical composition, their ultimate fate can be surprisingly different. The real action within a star takes place in its core, where conditions are so intense that atomic nuclei merge to form heavier nuclei. The energy released in this way supports the star against the crush of its own gravity. But eventually, the fuel runs out and the nuclear reactor in the star's core is turned off. Once the energy supply is exhausted, the star collapses under its own gravity.

The final result depends on the mass of the star. Stars of greater mass have higher temperatures in their core, which means that the nuclear reactions proceed faster. Very massive stars burn their nuclear fuel at a prodigious rate and race through their life much faster than lower-mass stars. The Sun will continue to shine for around ten billion years. A megastar with around twenty times the mass of the Sun would use up its nuclear fuel in around ten million years – a cosmic blink of the eye. Twenty times as much fuel is burnt in one thousandth of the time, which means that energy is being released at 20,000 times the rate of the Sun and, therefore, the star will shine 20,000 times as bright as the Sun. Fortunately, these stars are all much further away than the Sun, so we only see them as tiny pinpricks in the night sky.

When a star has converted most of the hydrogen in its core into helium, its outer layers swell up to form a bloated red giant. In five billion years' time, the Earth will be engulfed by the outer layers of the Sun as it approaches the end of its life. In a star such as the Sun, these outer layers will eventually disperse into space to reveal the star's core as an extremely dense glowing ember, about the size of the Earth. The nuclear reactions in the core will have ceased, and the core will gradually cool as it radiates its heat into the depths of space. These cosmic cinders are known as white dwarf stars.[2] They are extremely hot, but very faint, as they are so small compared to normal stars. The nearest white dwarf is in orbit with Sirius, the brightest star in the night sky, but it is not visible without a large telescope.[3]

The really massive megastars have a more spectacular future to look forward to. When the hydrogen runs out, their temperature rises and new nuclear processes begin. Helium is converted into carbon and oxygen, then even heavier atoms are cooked up. Eventually, no new nuclear reactions are possible and the final collapse begins. The collapse of the star releases so much gravitational energy that the star blasts itself apart in a supernova explosion, which may be as bright as an entire galaxy composed of hundreds of billions of stars. It was the sudden appearance of a brilliant supernova where no star had previously been seen that shocked Tycho so much in 1572. Plate 7 shows an artist's impression of a supernova explosion. When the smoke clears, the core of the star may have been transformed into an object around thirty kilometres across – the size of a major city – but with the density of an atomic nucleus. These remarkable objects are known as neutron stars.

In 1930, Subrahmanyan Chandrasekhar was awarded a graduate scholarship by the Indian government to continue his studies in physics at Trinity College, Cambridge. While on the voyage to England, Chandrasekhar realised that there was a limit to the mass of a star that could exist as a white dwarf. He calculated the maximum mass to be just under one and a half times the mass of the Sun. This is now known as the Chandrasekhar limit. A white dwarf with a mass greater than the Chandrasekhar limit will collapse to form a neutron star.[4] Chandrasekhar was awarded a Nobel Prize in 1983 for his research into the physics and evolution of stars.

## A Ticking Time Bomb

A large proportion of stars live in binary or multiple star systems, in which two or more stars are bound together and orbit around each other. When a white dwarf and a red giant are held in a gravitational embrace, the result can be very interesting. The white dwarf is, in a sense, a dead star, as it is no longer undergoing nuclear fusion reactions. However, as it travels around the red giant, it can accumulate material from the outer layers of the red giant. This material is drawn to the surface of the white dwarf and is compressed by its intense gravity to form a shell around the white dwarf. Eventually, a critical density is reached and this shell detonates in a huge nuclear fusion explosion that is visible from the other side of the galaxy.

These events are seen quite regularly by astronomers. Suddenly a star appears as if from nowhere. It is known as a nova, meaning 'new star'. The nova will gradually fade and eventually disappear again. About ten novae are seen in the Milky Way galaxy each year (another thirty or so are thought to be hidden from our view by dust and gas clouds). The process leading to the nova will repeat as the white dwarf continues to draw material from its companion star. The period between eruptions is typically several thousand years, but it may be as short as a decade or two. For instance, the star RS Ophiuchi lit up in 1898, 1933, 1958, 1967, 1985, and 2006. Over time, the mass of the white dwarf will increase. Eventually, it will reach the Chandrasekhar limit, the point at which its mass can no longer be supported. The white dwarf will then undergo its terminal collapse into a neutron star. This cataclysmic event produces a conflagration that may be as much as 100,000 times brighter than the earlier novae – the star has gone supernova.

We have now described novae and their big brothers – supernovae. In fact, we have seen two ways in which a supernova may be produced. When very massive stars have used up all their nuclear fuel, they end their lives with a bang. These explosions are known as Type II supernovae. Also, greedy white dwarfs in orbit with another star may accumulate so much extra mass that they collapse to form neutron stars. These explosions are known as Type Ia supernovae. These two processes are quite different, and the characteristics of the resulting supernova explosions are different. They were classified before their origin was understood.

## Little Green Men

> It is an interesting question – if one thinks one may have detected life elsewhere in the universe how does one announce the results responsibly? Who does one tell first?
>
> Jocelyn Bell Burnell, *Little Green Men, White Dwarfs or Pulsars?*

Towards the end of 1967, Jocelyn Bell was analysing the signals detected by a new array of radio receivers constructed in Cambridge, under the guidance of her PhD supervisor Anthony Hewish.[5] Bell noticed within the data a signal that repeated with metronomic regularity every 1.3 seconds.[6] Such regularity had no obvious explanation. After ruling out a terrestrial origin for the signal, the next possibility to consider was that the Cambridge astronomers had found the first sign of an extraterrestrial civilization. The radio source was whimsically designated LGM-1, where LGM stands for 'Little Green Men'.

On Christmas Eve, Bell found another example pulsing away in a different part of the sky, and this was followed by two more examples after the Christmas holiday. Clearly, the sky could not be full of extraterrestrials that were all attempting to attract our attention in the same way. The identity of this strange new class of celestial objects, now known as pulsars, was provided by the astrophysicist

**Plate 1** Mural of Dante painted in 1465 by Domenico di Michelino in Florence Cathedral. The sinners pass downwards into Hell. In the background is the nine-tiered Mount Purgatory and in the sky are the nine crystal spheres of the heavens. The cathedral itself is shown in the middle ground.

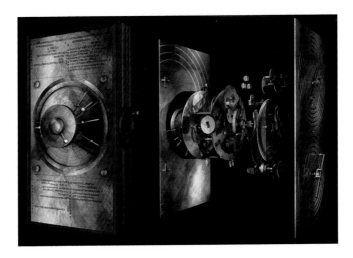

**Plate 2** Exploded Reconstruction of the Antikythera Mechanism.
(© 2012 Tony Freeth, Images First Ltd.)

**Plate 3** The Anatomical Man from the Très Riches Heures du Duc de Berry created by the Limbourg Brothers.

**Plate 4** Tycho's quadrant partially surrounds a mural depicting Tycho seated in front of a cross-section of the Uraniborg observatory. In the basement of the observatory is Tycho's alchemical laboratory, above which is a library containing the giant globe and on the upper floor are Tycho's astronomical instruments. In the mural, Tycho points towards a narrow opening in the wall. In the foreground, Tycho is using the quadrant to measure the altitude of an object viewed through the opening. An assistant reads the time from a collection of clocks, while a second seated assistant records the observation.

**Plate 5** Galileo and his last disciple Viviani by Tito-Giovanni Lessi.

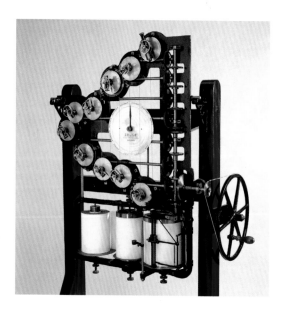

**Plate 6** Kelvin's first tide predicting machine, 1872.

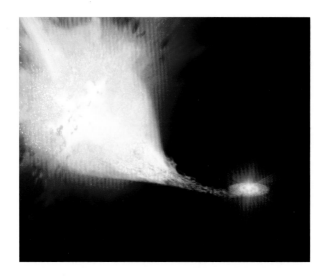

**Plate 7** Artist's impression of supernova SN 1993J. On the left, the red supergiant is exploding after having transferred about 10 solar masses of hydrogen to the blue companion star. (© ESA and Justyn R. Maund, University of Cambridge.)

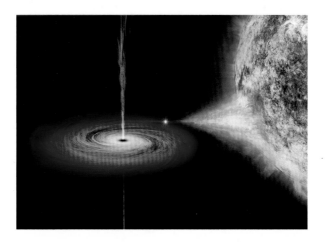

**Plate 8** Artist's impression of the Cygnus X-1 system. Material from the blue star is being drawn towards the black hole to form an accretion disc swirling around the black hole. There is a bright spot where this material hits the accretion disc. (© NASA/CXC/M.Weiss.)

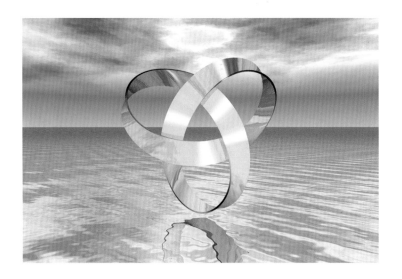

**Plate 9** Immortality by Nicholas Mee and John Robinson.

**Plate 10** Gordian Knot by Nicholas Mee and John Robinson.

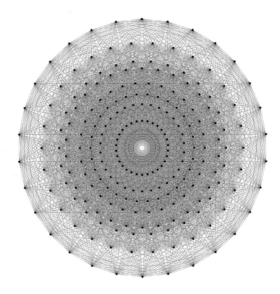

**Plate 11** With an $E_8$ symmetry group fundamental particles would come in sets of 248, with each particle carrying its own combination of 8 charges. (© J. Gregory Moxness)

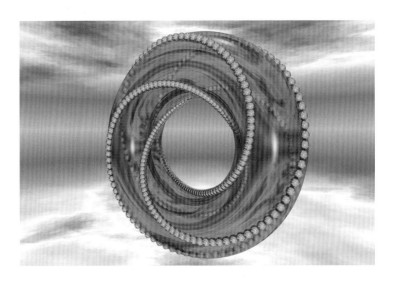

**Plate 12** String of golden beads wrapped around a torus to form a torus knot.

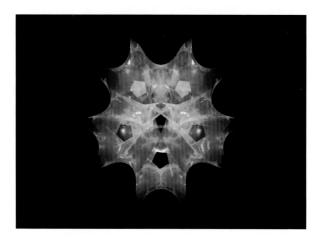

**Plate 13** A projection of the quintic hypersurface – one of the first Calabi-Yau hypersurfaces to be considered as a model for string compactifications.

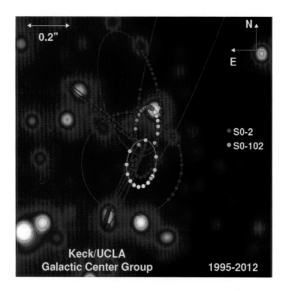

**Plate 14** Stars orbiting Sgr A*, the centre of the galaxy where a supermassive black hole is presumed to reside. (© Keck/UCLA Galactic Center Group.)

Tommy Gold, who suggested that pulsars must be the tell-tale signs of neutron stars. His arguments were very persuasive and were accepted by the physics community almost immediately.

Neutron stars are like cosmic lighthouses. They are outlandish ultra-dense objects, with the mass of a star compressed into a sphere that is a mere thirty kilometres or so in diameter – the remnants of a star that has undergone a supernova explosion. Neutron stars spin at an unbelievable rate, typically completing a full rotation in a fraction of a second. This generates a huge magnetic field that is thought to cause the emission of two intense beams of radiation from their poles. These pulsar beams are not perfectly aligned with the axis of the neutron star so, as the star spins, the beams sweep across the heavens. On Earth, radio astronomers detect a pulse of radio waves once every rotation when the pulsar beam points in our direction, which may be several times a second.

In 1974, astronomers Joseph Taylor and Russell Hulse searched systematically for pulsars with the giant Arecibo radio telescope in Puerto Rico, and they found many examples of these remarkable objects. Amidst the data was one whose behaviour seemed unusual. The pulses from pulsar beams are received with incredible regularity, but this one example was curiously different. The intervals between the pulses would increase for a while and then decrease again. There was a regular pattern to this behaviour, which would repeat every seven and three-quarter hours.

Hulse and Taylor had found one member of a *binary* neutron star system. The system consists of two neutron stars orbiting around each other, and the pulsar belonged to one of these neutron stars. As this neutron star approaches the

Earth, the interval between the arrival of its pulses steadily decreases then, as the neutron star recedes from Earth, the interval increases again. This is the well known Doppler effect that we often hear with moving sirens. Incidentally, if the other neutron star also has a pulsar, it never points in our direction, as it has not been detected.

The binary neutron star was a great find, because its regular pulses have enabled astronomers to study the motion of the neutron stars and measure their properties with great precision. We know that the two neutron stars have about the same mass, which is around one and a half times the mass of the Sun. They complete one orbit every 7.75 hours. This means that the orbit is quite small by cosmic standards. At their closest, the distance between the neutron stars is slightly more than the radius of the Sun. At their furthest, it is almost five times this distance. It is amazing to have such detailed information about the paths followed by objects that are an immense 20,000 light years away, which is about a billion times further away from us than the Sun.

But the Hulse-Taylor neutron star has much more to offer. The solar system is quite a sedate home. The planets serenely orbit the Sun, and Newton's theory of gravity explains their motion to great accuracy. Only in the case of Mercury was there a small hiccough that required a better theory than Newton's. As we have seen, the resolution was provided in 1915 by Einstein's theory of general relativity. Einstein's theory gives different predictions for the shape of planetary orbits, but the differences are tiny unless the planets are moving rapidly in a very strong gravitational field. As Mercury is the closest planet to the Sun, the relativistic corrections are much bigger than for the other planets – but the effect is still very small.

## *The Laboratory at the End of the Universe*

The Hulse-Taylor neutron star system is a much more extreme gravitational environment than the solar system, so the relativistic effects are expected to be much greater. And the pulsar offers us a built-in precision time-keeper. This gives astronomers a great physics laboratory in which they can put Einstein's theory to the test. When the paths of the two neutron stars were mapped out in detail, as expected their highly eccentric orbit was shown to be precessing, so it did not quite match the Newtonian prediction, but it agreed with Einstein's theory exactly. This was a great confirmation of our modern understanding of gravity, and it is still one of the greatest triumphs of Einstein's theory of general relativity. Even so, this effect had already been seen with Mercury many years earlier, so it was not quite headline news.

But there was something else that was even more exciting. Einstein's investigations that led to his theories of relativity were initially triggered by his desire to provide a better understanding of electromagnetism. His general theory of relativity, which explains gravity as the warping of space and time by massive objects, has many features that are analogous to electromagnetic effects. For instance, when an alternating current is passed through an aerial, the electrons in the aerial, which is just a long thin piece of metal, will move rapidly up and down. The acceleration of the electric charges of the electrons generates electromagnetic waves that we know as radio waves. This effect was first observed in the laboratory by Heinrich Hertz in 1887. We perform the same experiment every day when we turn on the radio or television or use our mobile phone.

## *Ripples in the Fabric of Space*

In Einstein's theory of gravity, mass plays a similar role to electric charge. One of the surprising predictions of the theory is that if large masses are whirled around vigorously, then gravitational waves will be emitted. As the theory explains gravity in terms of the warping and curvature of space, gravitational waves are simply ripples in the fabric of space that emanate away from the gravitating system. (A schematic representation of how this comes about is shown in the figure below.)

**Figure 68** Schematic representation of the shape of space around two very massive compact objects in orbit around each other.

Gravity is incredibly weak compared to electromagnetism. This might seem surprising, but think of a fridge magnet. A tiny magnet such as this can defy the gravity of the entire Earth. The weakness of gravity means that an enormous mass must be given an almighty shaking to produce even the tiniest ripple of a gravitational wave.[7] For this reason, physicists have

**Figure 69** The passage of a gravitational wave. The positions of test particles change as a gravitational wave passes through space. The test particles are arranged in a circle. As the gravitational wave passes, space is squeezed in one direction and stretched in the perpendicular direction. The illustration shows a single cycle of the wave. (The direction of the wave would be into or out of the page.) The stretching and squeezing is greatly exaggerated.

so far been unable to construct instruments that are sensitive enough to detect gravitational waves.

However, the Hulse-Taylor binary neutron star system has provided astronomers with a remarkable laboratory. As mentioned above, the orbital period of these neutron stars can be measured with great precision. It is about seven and three-quarter hours, but it is decreasing by 76.5 microseconds every year. General relativity provides the explanation. As the two neutron stars whirl around each other at high speed, they generate gravitational waves. The energy that is radiated into space in this way causes the orbit of the neutron stars to shrink. When physicists calculated the rate at which the orbit of the neutron stars would decrease due to the emission of gravitational waves, the prediction of general relativity matched the observations to perfection. So, although physicists have never detected gravitational waves, their existence has been confirmed by this extraordinary star system. Einstein's theory has been proved right again.

The size of the neutron stars' orbit is shrinking by a few metres every year, due to the emission of gravitational waves. In a mere 300,000 years the two neutron stars are scheduled for a close encounter. This meeting is sure to be an incredibly violent one.

## *A One-way Trip to Oblivion*

There is a maximum mass for a neutron star but, as the physics of these weird objects is so exotic, this limit is not known with the same certainty as it is for white dwarfs. But it must be in the range of two to three times the mass of the Sun. A neutron star with a mass greater than this would have an even stranger fate. It would inevitably collapse to form a black hole – a spherical region of space from which no matter or even light could escape. The name *black hole* was coined by the American physicist John Archibald Wheeler. Nothing can escape from within the black hole, not even light; hence the name. To evade the clutches of a black hole, a particle would have to be travelling faster than the speed of light, and one of the fundamental assumptions upon which relativity is constructed is that this is impossible.[8] But can such objects really exist? Even Einstein had his doubts.

In 1970, NASA placed its first X-ray telescope in Earth orbit. The satellite lifted off from a launch site in Kenya on 12 December, the seventh anniversary of Kenyan independence from Britain. NASA gave it the name *Uhuru*, Swahili for freedom, in honour of their Kenyan hosts.[9] The telescope was designed to explore a new region of the electromagnetic spectrum. X-rays correspond to electromagnetic radiation of short wavelength and high energy, and would only arise in violent events in very energetic environments (fortunately, we are shielded by the Earth's atmosphere from high-energy radiation from space, which is why X-ray astronomy is only possible from Earth orbit). Like any pioneering journey into the unknown, when the satellite was launched, no-one was sure what it might find.

One of the first discoveries made by Uhuru was a powerful X-ray source in the constellation of Cygnus the Swan. This object is known as Cygnus X-1. It would prove to be a very interesting celestial object. The X-ray source was soon identified as a star that could be examined in visible light with earth-based telescopes. Astronomers have now been studying Cygnus X-1 for forty years with a variety of observatories, detecting light at a range of wavelengths – radio, optical and X-ray. The best data has been produced by the NASA satellite Chandra launched in 1999. It is named after the Indian astrophysicist Chandrasekhar and is home to an X-ray telescope. Assessment of the most up-to-date information has enabled astrophysicists to draw up a quite detailed picture of the object producing the X-rays.

Astronomers believe that the Cygnus X-1 system began as a binary star system consisting of two very massive stars bound together by their mutual gravitational attraction. The heavier of the two exhausted its nuclear fuel first and underwent a supernova explosion, in which the remnants of the star collapsed into a black hole. The original star would have been millions of kilometres in diameter, but the black hole is tiny, with a diameter of only a few tens of kilometres. The black hole remains gravitationally bound to its companion star, and they have continued to perform their orbital dance.

Using the National Radio Observatory's Very Long Baseline Array, the distance to Cygnus X-1 has recently been determined to be 6,070 light years. This accurate new figure has improved the precision with which the features of the black hole are known. It appears that the black hole was born just six million years ago, from the terminal collapse of a super-massive star that imploded after consuming its supply of nuclear fuel. The mass of the black hole is a whopping 14.8 times the mass of the Sun,[10] and it is spinning at a phenomenal 800 times per second – close to the maximum rate possible.

The second star is a brilliant blue supergiant. The black hole and the supergiant star dance around each other in a tight embrace, with each orbit taking just over five and a half days. The outer layers of the star are dispersing into space. Some of the material accumulates around the black hole, to form a disc rotating in the plane of the black hole's equator. This material is known as an accretion disc. There are no stable orbits close to the black hole, so the material forming the inner edge of the accretion disc gradually spirals into the black hole. A huge amount of gravitational energy is released as the material falls towards the black hole and this is converted into heat by friction in the swirling disc. The accretion disc glows so hot that it emits X-rays, and this was the distinctive clue that revealed the existence of Cygnus X-1.

The black hole is tiny by cosmic standards, with a diameter that is much smaller than the thickness of the accretion disc. Intense magnetic fields are generated in the accretion disc, and in this highly energetic and turbulent environment, not all of the material finds its way into the black hole. Some of it misses and is propelled outwards in the form of two oppositely aligned jets that spew hot matter into the depths of space from near the poles of the black hole. An artist's impression of the Cygnus X-1 system is shown in Plate 8.

The black hole should not be thought of like a hole in the ground or a plug hole – it is a spherical region of space. The point of no return is a sphere known as the *event horizon* of the black hole. Anything that finds itself within the event horizon is on a one-way trip to oblivion. Once inside, an object would have to travel faster than light to escape. As this is impossible, nothing can get out, not even light. The event horizon of the black hole in Cygnus X-1 is thought to be just 80 kilometres in diameter.

## *A Blast From the Past*

The Nuclear Test Ban Treaty was signed in 1963. To monitor compliance with the treaty, the United States launched a series of satellites in 1967 that could detect gamma rays, which are the unmistakable signatures of nuclear explosions. These satellites soon began to detect occasional flashes of gamma rays, or Gamma Ray Bursts, as they are known. These mysterious events were immediately put under investigation.

By 1973, it was clear that the gamma rays originated in deep space, so the research was declassified by the military. Since this time, astronomers have worked steadily to uncover their secrets. As the Gamma Ray Bursts typically last just a few seconds, this has proved quite a challenge. Success has depended on the rapid deployment of telescopes to study the lingering afterglow of a burst following its detection by instruments aboard a satellite.

It is now clear that these events are the product of the most violent cataclysms in the universe. They are rare, but the events are so powerful that we can detect them from the other side of the universe, thousands of millions of light years away. Gamma Ray Bursts have been divided into two categories. Most of the events last for a few seconds and are known as long Gamma Ray Bursts. The other category consists of the short Gamma Ray Bursts that last for less than two seconds.

## *Last Tango in Deep Space*

The long Gamma Ray Bursts are thought to be due to the gravitational collapse of a huge star into a black hole at the end of its life. As the star collapses, it spins ever faster, such that when the black hole forms, it is just a few kilometres across and spinning at almost the speed of light. Black holes are often portrayed as gaping like the jaws of Hell. It is certainly true that, once inside, it is impossible to escape. But getting inside in the first place may not be that easy. Black holes are very messy eaters. They are tiny by cosmic standards, so squeezing an entire star into one proves to be difficult. Much of the material shoots out at the poles of the black hole, rather than entering the abyss. This material is compressed beyond nuclear densities and focused into two beams that shoot outwards at almost the speed of light. Much of this material is converted into intense gamma ray beams that race across the universe. A civilization on the other side of the universe that happens to be looking down the barrel of this gamma ray-gun may eventually pick up a brief trace of radiation signalling the death of a mighty star and the formation of a black hole.

Short Gamma Ray Bursts have proved to be even more difficult to study, because they are so short-lived and much less powerful. Recently, however, there has been an important breakthrough. On 3 June 2013, the gamma ray telescope aboard NASA's Swift satellite picked up a Gamma Ray Burst that lasted just a tenth of a second. Nine days later, the Hubble Space Telescope took up the search for the origin of the gamma radiation. Hubble found a faint glow in a galaxy four thousand million light years distant, so the Gamma Ray Burst had been produced in an event that occurred when the Earth was in its infancy.

Analysis of Hubble's images has shown that the short Gamma Ray Burst was generated by a type of stellar explosion called a kilonova, so named because they are around a thousand times as bright as a nova. Nevertheless they are just a hundredth to a tenth of the brilliance of a supernova. What sort of drama produces a kilonova, you might ask? They are generated by the merger of two neutron stars that have reached the climax of their cosmic dance. In 300,000 years time, this will be the ultimate fate of the binary neutron star system discovered by Hulse and Taylor.

### A Black Hole Has No Hair!

In 1963, Roy Kerr, a mathematician from New Zealand, discovered a remarkable solution of Einstein's equation. It describes the shape of spacetime around a rotating spherical mass. The Kerr solution reduces to the solution found by Schwarzschild when the spin falls to zero. The Kerr solution is particularly important for describing spacetime around a black hole, as black holes are the most extreme gravitational environments and are expected to spin at a phenomenal rate. In a lecture in 1975, Chandrasekhar told his audience that in his entire scientific life: 'The most shattering experience has been the realization that an exact solution of Einstein's equations of general relativity, discovered by the New Zealand mathematician Roy Kerr, provides the absolutely exact representation of untold numbers of massive black holes that populate the universe.'[11] Kerr's discovery has many important consequences. It began a golden age in the analysis of general relativity and black holes.

Planets come in all shapes and sizes. Each of the eight planets in the solar system has its own particular character and the same is no doubt true of the many others that are being found in planetary systems throughout our galaxy. Similarly, stars come in numerous varieties – red giants, brown dwarfs, neutron stars, white dwarfs – and each will have a slightly different composition. Some contain more carbon than average, some contain more of other elements. Black holes, by contrast, have at most three features, so they can be completely defined by just three numbers: their mass, the rate at which they spin and their electric charge. Of these, the third is unlikely to be important in the real universe, as matter is usually electrically neutral and there is no known mechanism for giving a star or black hole a significant electric charge. This means that a real black hole can be described exactly, simply by determining its mass and its rate of spin. It can have no other features whatsoever. Physicists refer to this fact as the 'no-hair theorem'. A black hole has no hair.

## Hawking's Area Theorem

The radius of the event horizon of a black hole is determined by its mass – the greater the mass, the bigger the hole. As material falls into a black hole, its mass increases and, therefore, its size will also increase. Nothing can get out of the black hole so, as time passes and the black hole feeds on its surroundings, it will inevitably grow in size. One way of putting this is to say that the area of the event horizon of the black hole will necessarily increase with time.

Just as neutron stars collide from time to time, so black holes must be undergoing similar mishaps throughout the universe. The merger of two black holes to form a single black hole would be an extremely violent event that would generate large gravitational waves. Hawking noticed an important consequence of such mergers. He proved that whatever the details of the encounter, the area of the event horizon of the final black hole would be greater than the sum of the areas of the event horizons of the two original black holes. Hawking then showed that in any process whatsoever, according to general relativity, the total area of black hole event horizons must always increase. This is Hawking's Area Theorem. It is a very abstract result that Hawking proved using very sophisticated mathematical techniques. It sounds like a quirky fact without much physical significance but, as we will see, it opened the door to a profound re-evaluation of the role of gravity in the universe.

## *The Two Cultures*

In 1959, the scientist and author C.P. Snow gave the Rede Lecture at the Senate House in Cambridge. The lecture was subsequently published under the title: *The Two Cultures and the Scientific Revolution*. In the lecture, Snow decried the gap that had opened up between scientists and artists in the 20th century. Harking back to earlier centuries, Snow observed that science and art were considered to be two complementary ways to view the world and that an educated person was expected to be conversant with both:

> A good many times I have been present at gatherings of people who, by the standards of the traditional culture, are thought highly educated and who have with considerable gusto been expressing their incredulity at the illiteracy of scientists. Once or twice I have been provoked and have asked the company how many of them could describe the Second Law of Thermodynamics. The response was cold: it was also negative. Yet I was asking something which is the scientific equivalent of 'Have you read a work of Shakespeare's?' [12]

So what is the Second Law that C.P. Snow was so concerned about?

Physics and technology have long had a mutually stimulating effect on each other. The two are so closely intertwined that it is often difficult to disentangle the direction of these influences. One branch of physics that certainly owes a lot to technology is thermodynamics, a subject that grew out of the analysis of steam engines and how to improve their efficiency. As we demonstrate every day in a variety of ways, from boiling an egg to driving a car, energy can be converted from one form into another, and this is what thermodynamics is all about.

The First Law of Thermodynamics states that if all forms of energy are taken into account, including heat, then the sum total of the energy at the start of a process will equal the sum total of the energy at the end of the process.[13] It is also known as the Law of Conservation of Energy. This law clearly has important industrial applications. It means that we can convert energy from a form where it cannot be conveniently used, such as that contained in a lump of coal, into a more convenient form, such as the energy in an electric current, but energy cannot be created out of nothing. Following Einstein's relativistic revelations at the beginning of the 20th century, the Law of Conservation of Energy was updated to include the fact that mass and energy are inter-convertible. In effect, mass is just another form of energy.

There are many processes that would be allowed by the First Law of Thermodynamics that are never observed in the real world. For instance, heat never flows from a cold object, such as a lump of ice, into a warm object such as a cup of tea. If this were possible, we could imagine adding ice to the tea in such a way that the ice becomes colder and the tea rises in temperature. This would not violate the First Law, because the total energy could be conserved. But we know that it does not happen – we cannot boil a cup of tea by adding any amount of ice to it. The Second Law of Thermodynamics was devised to account for the fact that such processes are never observed. It can be stated succinctly in terms of a quantity known as *entropy*, which equals heat divided by temperature. In terms of entropy, the Second Law can be expressed as: *in all physical processes, the total entropy of the universe will increase.*

One consequence of this law is that, when energy is converted from one form into another in a power station, there will always be a portion of the total energy that will be emitted as heat. It is not possible to convert all the energy in a lump of coal into electricity or some other usable form; it is inevitable that some energy will be lost as heat. Another consequence is that the bigger the temperature difference between the turbines in a power station and the surrounding environment, the lower the proportion of energy that is lost as heat, and so the greater the efficiency of the power station. So this law has very important real-world applications.

### Anyone For Iced Tea?

Why is it not possible to heat up your cup of tea by putting ice cubes in it? This suggestion is so obviously ridiculous that it takes a bit of thought to work out what the question actually means. We know from our lifelong experience of interacting with the world around us that if we put ice in our tea, it will always cool the tea down and will never warm it up. However, the ice cubes that we take from our freezer contain plenty of heat – they are much warmer than a winter's day in Siberia, for instance. Perhaps some of this heat could be liberated from the ice and added to the tea, thereby warming the tea and cooling the ice further. Although this would conserve energy, we know that it never happens.

The impossibility of this process was codified in the middle years of the 19th century. To clarify what is happening, it helps to define a new quantity, S, that is equal to an amount of heat Q at a specified temperature T:

$$S = \frac{Q}{T}$$

We call this quantity entropy. It might appear quite abstract and unfamiliar, but it plays a very important role in physics. Changes in entropy determine which processes happen and which are forbidden by the laws of physics. For instance, our observation that heat always moves from hot objects to cold objects, and never from cold objects to hot objects, can be captured in terms of entropy.

For a given amount of heat, the entropy is smaller at a high temperature than at a low temperature. If $T_{high}$ represents a high temperature and $T_{low}$ represents a low temperature, then

$$\frac{Q}{T_{high}} < \frac{Q}{T_{low}}$$

(Because $T_{high}$ is bigger than $T_{low}$, when we divide by $T_{high}$ we are dividing by a bigger number.) If $S_{high}$ represents the entropy at the higher temperature and $S_{low}$ represents the entropy at the lower temperature, then:

$$S_{high} < S_{low}$$

This means that if an amount of heat Q is transferred from a hot object to a cold object, the total entropy will increase. If heat were transferred from a cold object to a hot object, the entropy would decrease. We are very familiar with the first of these processes, but our teatime experiments tell us that the second type of process never happens. We can capture this feature of the universe in the statement that, in any allowed process, the total entropy must increase. This fact was first recognised by the French engineer Sadi Carnot in an analysis of steam engines in the 19th century. It is now known as the Second Law of Thermodynamics.

Conservation of energy is quite a familiar idea and one that is readily understood. There are many other conservation laws in physics; the conservation of electric charge, for example. The Second Law of Thermodynamics is unusual in that entropy is not conserved. It can increase, but it can never decrease. This means that entropy determines the direction in which processes occur. (Compare the analysis of a conserved quantity such as energy. If state A has the same energy as state B, then state A might evolve into state B or vice versa. The law of energy conservation would allow either.)

Entropy increase gives a direction to processes that occur within the universe. It determines how the universe will evolve. In other words, it is closely related to the passage of time and our perception of the direction of time. Although the Second Law provides a succinct expression about which processes are forbidden, it does not tell us why these processes are not observed. They have simply been forbidden by fiat.

## Black Hole Dynamics

You might be wondering what a section about thermo-dynamics is doing in a book about gravitation and a chapter about black holes. Remarkably, there is a very strong connection between thermodynamics and black holes, and it came as a big surprise to physicists. The Israeli physicist Jacob Bekenstein had been concerned for some time that black holes seemed to offer a sink down which the universe could lose some of its entropy. Any material that fell into the black hole would be lost to the rest of the universe, along with the entropy that it contained. The event horizon of the black hole forms a one-way barrier. The inside of the black hole is inaccessible to the outside universe. This means that the entropy of the rest of the universe could be reduced by dropping stuff into the hole. The entropy of this matter would then no longer contribute to the total entropy. This seemed to violate the Second Law of Thermodynamics, so it was very puzzling.

By 1972, Bekenstein realised that there might be a way to resolve the dilemma. Any material that fell into the black hole would increase the mass of the black hole and, therefore, the size of the black hole would increase. In particular, the area of the black hole's event horizon would be enlarged. Hawking had recently proved that, according to general relativity, in all physical processes, the total area of black hole event horizons must increase. Bekenstein pointed out that there is a close similarity between Hawking's result and the Second Law of Thermodynamics. He then proposed a refinement of the Second Law of Thermodynamics that would encapsulate both the standard Second Law and the area law of black holes.

He combined Hawking's Area Theorem: *The total surface area of all the black holes in the universe can never decrease* and the Second Law of Thermodynamics: *The total entropy of the universe can never decrease.*

To produce the generalized Second Law of Thermodynamics: *The total entropy of the universe outside event horizons of black holes, plus the total area of all the black hole event horizons, can never decrease.*

This is a bit of a mouthful. But perhaps it could be made more succinct. There appeared to be a connection between the area of a black hole and the entropy of the black hole. The simplest conclusion was to accept a precise correspondence between these two quantities, such that a black hole's area was actually a measure of its entropy. This is what Bekenstein tentatively proposed. But how could this be? The area theorem of black holes was a geometrical result in general relativity, whereas the Second Law of Thermodynamics was a statistical law about heat.

Now this was a very strange idea. How could there be a link between gravity and a theory that was devised to explain heat engines? Furthermore, black holes were believed to be essentially featureless, being characterised simply by their mass, angular momentum and electric charge. How could they have any statistical properties?

Hawking's immediate response, when he heard about Bekenstein's proposal, was that it was a ridiculous idea. It could not possibly be true. He went to bed that night convinced that there must be a fundamental flaw in the argument. But he could not sleep; he lay awake, looking for a counterargument that would disprove this conjecture. It was clear to Hawking that if a black hole had entropy, then it must also have a temperature, and that was absurd. All objects with a temperature greater than absolute zero must emit radiation and, the hotter the object, the greater the intensity of the radiation. But black holes are inherently black, they cannot emit radiation because nothing – not even light – can escape a black hole.

Then Hawking had a revelation. He realised that there was a fatal flaw in his own argument and that Bekenstein's suggestion must be correct – the area of a black hole corresponds to the black hole's entropy. The black hole will behave like a body with a well-defined temperature, and the black hole will, indeed, emit radiation. Everything fitted together. There was no chance that Hawking would sleep now. Hawking's illness had progressed to the point where he could no longer get out of bed by himself, so he had to wait several hours for his nurse to arrive before he could put his ideas down on paper.

## *Hawking Radiation*

General relativity is the best fully formulated theory of gravity that we have. When a black hole is modelled using general relativity, its temperature is zero. This is because, although radiation could fall into the black hole, nothing could ever come out of the black hole, which means it could never give off any heat. It follows that, according to general relativity, a black hole is completely black. But general relativity is a classical theory and not a quantum theory, and this was at the heart of Hawking's revelation.

Although general relativity is a fantastically accurate theory, we know that the world is quantum mechanical, so the ultimate theory of gravity must include features of both general relativity and quantum mechanics. Hawking's analysis was based on applying quantum mechanics to black holes, which he was able to do in a consistent way, even though we do not have a fully formulated quantum theory of gravity. Although the temperature of a classical black hole must be zero, a quantum black hole has a non-zero temperature. This means that a black hole must emit radiation, and this was the shocking announcement that Hawking made to his colleagues in February 1974. The radiation emitted by a black hole is now known as Hawking radiation. It is, indeed, surprising that a temperature can be assigned to a black hole, which is why physicists were so taken aback by Hawking's proposal.

If you fell into a black hole, you would be crushed and stretched and it would get pretty warm. In fact, you would be vaporised before you reached the centre of the black hole and would probably be transformed into an extra bit of warped spacetime (no-one knows what is going on right at the centre of a black hole). However, the temperature of the black hole referred to by Hawking is the temperature that would be measured by anyone outside the black hole. This is determined by the radiation – or, in other words, heat – that the black hole is emitting. So, despite whatever incredible violence might be going on inside the black hole, its temperature can be very low. A black hole with the mass of a star has a temperature that is unmeasurably low. Hawking's calculations showed that a black hole of ten solar masses would have a temperature of less than a ten millionth of a degree above absolute zero ($10^{-7}$ K).[14]

The temperature of a black hole is so low that it would inevitably absorb more radiation than it would emit. The universe is bathed in radiation that was produced shortly after the Big Bang. This radiation is known as the cosmic microwave background. It has a temperature that is very low – at around 2.7 degrees above absolute zero – but it is very high compared to the Hawking temperature of a black hole. Any black hole with a temperature lower than this must necessarily absorb more radiation than it emits.

### Mini Black Holes

One way to see the connection between the size of a black hole and its temperature is to consider the wavelength of the radiation that is emitted. In Hawking's quantum analysis of a black hole, the wavelength of the radiation emitted by the black hole is bigger than the size of the black hole's event horizon. You could call this quantum mechanical tunnelling, or uncertainty in the position of a photon associated with the wave, or simply say that the black hole is not big enough to contain a wave of this size. But the point is that long wavelength corresponds to low energy, and the temperature of an object that typically emits radiation with a wavelength several kilometres long must be incredibly low – just above absolute zero.

A black hole with an event horizon just a few hundred nanometres across would radiate visible light and its temperature would be correspondingly higher – typical of objects that emit radiation in this range. There is no known mechanism to produce such mini black holes, but Hawking speculated that they might have formed immediately after the Big Bang, when the universe was very dense. He suggested that, in the early universe, matter might have been quite lumpy, and that some of the denser regions would have collapsed to form black holes. These hypothetical mini black holes are known as primordial black holes. They might have a mass equal to that of an asteroid packed into a region that is smaller than an atom. Their temperature would be correspondingly higher – much higher than that of a stellar mass black hole. Being hot, the mini black holes would emit large amounts of radiation and thereby lose some of their mass. With this decrease in mass, their temperature would rise and this would increase the rate at which they radiate. This is a runaway process that can only end one way. The temperature of the mini black hole will rise dramatically in its final moments, and it will undergo a huge explosion in which it disappears as a huge blast of radiation.

If primordial black holes really were formed in the very early universe, then it might be possible for astronomers to detect them going pop as they disappear in a puff of gamma rays. The smallest such primordial black holes would already have exploded. Black holes with a mountain-sized mass of around five hundred million tonnes ($5 \times 10^{11}$ kg)[15] should currently be on the verge of detonation.[16] Slightly larger, and the mini black holes will continue emitting X-rays and gamma rays for many aeons to come. To date, none have ever been seen. If they do turn up, then Stephen Hawking will certainly be rewarded with the Nobel Prize in Physics.

Whether mini black holes exist or not, there is absolutely no doubt that the general principles of Hawking's theory are correct and that black holes do emit Hawking radiation. The combination of general relativity, quantum mechanics and thermodynamics mesh together so well that these ideas must play an important role in the fundamental structure of the universe. This was the first result that linked quantum mechanics to gravity, and this is one of the reasons why it is among the most profound ideas in the history of physics.

Stephen Hawking was appointed Lucasian Professor of Mathematics at Cambridge University in 1978. This was the post that had been held by Isaac Newton 300 years earlier. Hawking's illness had been diagnosed as motor neurone disease and was progressively worsening. The university expected his appointment to be a short-term stop-gap measure, as he was not thought to have long to live. Confounding the sceptics yet again, Professor Hawking retired in 2009 at the age of 67.

## *A Singular Solution*

What would it be like in the vicinity of a black hole? (We will consider an isolated black hole with no accretion disc, in order to avoid being roasted by radiation produced by material falling into the black hole.) The first thing to realise is that black holes are not cosmic vacuum cleaners. Far from the event horizon of a black hole, its pull would be no different from that of a star of the same mass. An orbiting planet would follow an elliptical orbit, just like the planets in the solar system. Closer to the black hole, the axis of a planet's orbit would show significant precession.

If we were in orbit around a black hole or falling towards the black hole, we would feel nothing – we would be weightless. Stars have a surface that limits the depth of their gravitational well and, once inside a massive body such as a star, the gravitational well starts to bottom out. But black holes are tiny by stellar standards, and they have no surface. There is no such barrier around a black hole. If we approach more closely, then we will start to feel uncomfortable. In the Newtonian picture, the gravitational pull of the black hole will be greatest on whichever part of our body is closest to the black hole. These tidal forces will gradually increase as we approach the black hole. In Einstein's picture, close to the black hole, space is stretched towards the mass of the black hole and simultaneously squeezed in the perpendicular directions.

The event horizon of a black hole that formed from the collapsing core of a giant star might be as small as ten kilometres in diameter. Once the star has collapsed within its event horizon, there is no escape. The relentless squeeze of gravity will inevitably crush the star out of existence. No particle within the event horizon can ever get out again. If we venture too close to the black hole, we will be torn apart before we reach the event horizon. The remains of our body and our starship may cross the event horizon but, once inside, there is no turning back. From this point on, all roads lead to the centre of the black hole.

According to general relativity, the collapsed star that formed the black hole and everything that subsequently falls into it is compressed into a single point at the centre of the black hole. The entire mass of the star is located here. Mathematicians refer to such a point as a singularity. At this point, the warping of spacetime, as described by the Schwarzschild or Kerr solutions, becomes so extreme that the curvature of spacetime becomes infinite. This is a point of infinite density, where the equations of general relativity break down, and it presents physicists with a serious problem.[17] Although the idea of infinity is very useful for mathematicians, who routinely play with it in their mathematical proofs, it is a highly abstract concept. It might be possible to define it logically and use it consistently in the realm of mathematics but, when taking a physical measurement, we cannot measure a value of infinity. There may be quantities that are extremely large and well beyond the capacity of our instrumentation but, in reality, no quantity can be infinite (the existence of an infinite quantity would lead to a whole range of logical paradoxes that would make all the laws of physics void).

Some physicists in the 1960s questioned whether the Schwarzschild and Kerr solutions were realistic descriptions of all black holes and, in particular, whether the singularity at the centre of the black hole will always arise. Might it be possible for a star to implode in such an asymmetrical and chaotic way that the infalling matter forms a structure without a singularity? Roger Penrose finally squashed these faint hopes for a non-singular salvation. He devised ingenious and very technical arguments that proved that, according to general relativity, there would always be a singularity within a black hole.

The singularity at the centre of a black hole is often discussed as though it has real physical existence. However, a singularity would be a point at which the laws of physics would break down – a point where the forces of nature could not be understood, even in principle. If such a point existed in reality, then anarchy would reign and the contagion would infect the rest of the universe. General relativity models the universe very accurately, but some care is required to interpret the meaning of the singularity at the centre of the black hole. The prediction of an infinite quantity in any theory of physics must imply that the theory has been stretched beyond the domain where it gives an accurate representation of reality. The singular point in the equations does not mean that there is a point of infinite density within a black hole, but simply that this is what general relativity predicts. The only saving grace for general relativity is that the singularity exists within the event horizon of the black hole, and so is isolated from the rest of the universe.

The mysteries within a black hole are shrouded from the rest of the universe by the one-way barrier of the event horizon. The possibility of a nonsensical Alice in Wonderland world down the gravitational rabbit hole might be defended by its inability to infect the rest of the universe. But physicists are seeking a unified description of the whole universe, including the innards of black holes, and to accept singular regions that do not conform to any rational interpretation is to give up prematurely. Furthermore, as we have seen, black holes are not quite the one-way trapdoors that Einstein's theory might suggest.

General relativity seems to have predicted its own limit. There is good reason to think that if general relativity were to be combined with quantum mechanics to produce a quantum theory of gravity, then the issue with singularities would be resolved. There are no stable atoms in classical physics. According to classical physics, the electrons orbiting an atomic nucleus would collapse into the nucleus in an instant. Quantum mechanics is required to explain the stability of atoms. Perhaps it is possible to stabilise the centre of a black hole in a similar way. The need for a quantum theory of gravity was recognised long ago.

## Spacetime Foam

Max Planck laid the foundations of quantum theory in the year 1900. He had been struggling for several years to explain laboratory measurements of the colour and intensity of light that is emitted from an object as its temperature changes. In deriving a formula that explained the experimental results, he had been forced to conclude that the vibrations of the atoms in solids come in lumps or quanta. Planck knew at once that his revolutionary proposal would have seismic consequences. It would lead to the biggest upheaval in physics since the days of Isaac Newton. The cornerstone of quantum theory was a new fundamental constant of nature that relates the frequency of a vibration to the amount of energy that it carries. We know this constant as Planck's constant. It is always represented by the letter 'h' and is a measure of the granularity of the universe. If Planck's constant were zero, then the universe could be correctly described by the classical physics of Newton and Einstein. Although it is not zero, it is very small and this means that classical physics works well as a description of the macroscopic world that we inhabit. However, when considering very short length scales – at the scale of atoms and below – quantum mechanics must be taken into account.

Planck realised that the existence of quantum theory would eventually demand a reconstruction of every branch of physics, including gravity. By combining his new constant with the other fundamental constants of nature, such as Newton's gravitational constant and the speed of light, Planck could estimate the length scale on which quantum effects would need to be included in a theory of gravity. This length is a mere $10^{-35}$ metres and is known as the Planck length. If we scaled ourselves down to the size of a proton and simultaneously scaled a proton down by the same factor, the rescaled proton would still be much larger than the Planck length. This incredibly short distance is the fundamental unit of length in our universe.

Similarly, it is possible to work out the fundamental unit of time in our universe. It is known as the Planck time and it is the length of time that it would take for a particle travelling at the speed of light to travel a distance equal to the Planck length. The Planck time is $10^{-43}$ seconds. On these minuscule scales, quantum mechanics and gravity are simultaneously relevant. We know that gravity is best described by the curvature of space and time. Quantum mechanics is a theory involving random fluctuations. No-one knows what space and time look like at Planck distances. Most guesses imagine that space and time turn into some sort of frothy foam. The American physicist John Archibald Wheeler, who developed these ideas in the 1950s, described this quantum foam as:

> spacetime stirred into the writhing turbulence of myriad multiply connected domains[18]

Of course, the reality could be quite different, and any genuine understanding of what goes on in the innards of the universe is yet to arrive.

In quantum theories, each particle is associated with a wave and, the higher the energy of the wave, the shorter its wavelength. In general, short distances correspond to high energies. We can use this relationship to work out the characteristic energy scale of the physics of quantum gravity. This energy is known as the Planck energy. The mass of a proton is around 1 GeV. The Large Hadron Collider (LHC) at CERN accelerates and collides protons with energies of several TeV, where 1 TeV equals 1,000 GeV. The Planck energy is $10^{19}$ GeV ($10^{28}$ eV). This is around ten thousand trillion ($10^{16}$) times the energy scale that is being probed by the LHC. For this reason, it is very unlikely that the physics of quantum gravity will be tested in the laboratory in the near future.

## *Quantum Jelly*

> Jelly on a plate
> Jelly on a plate
> Wibble Wobble
> Wibble Wobble
> Jelly on a plate!

Physicists have developed an incredibly accurate quantum picture of the world. Quantum mechanics and special relativity have been moulded together to produce remarkable theories of all the forces except gravity. The first of these quantum field theories, as they are called, was the quantum theory of electromagnetism, otherwise known as quantum electrodynamics or QED. To understand such theories, we have to imagine that for each fundamental particle, such as the electron, there is a quantum field that fills the whole of space. This field has been described as a quantum jelly.[19]

Like jelly, it wobbles incessantly. On top of this wobble, the jelly can be excited, and the excitations can travel, like pulses or ripples through space. We interpret these excitations as particles. For each type of matter particle: electrons, muons, neutrinos, each type of quark and so on, there is a field that extends throughout space, and each species of particle is a vibration in the corresponding field. The way that these particles interact electromagnetically is through the electromagnetic field, which also extends throughout space. The excitations of this field are known as photons, and they are the fundamental particles of light. According to QED, an electromagnetic interaction occurs when one charged particle, such as an electron, creates a disturbance or excitation in the electromagnetic field. In other words, it creates a photon, and this photon is passed on to a second charged particle – maybe another electron, maybe a muon or a quark – which then absorbs the photon. In this way, some of the energy and momentum of the first particle is passed to the second particle.

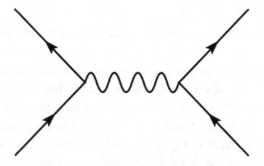

**Figure 70** Feynman diagram, showing two electrons exchanging a photon. The straight lines with arrows on are electrons. The wavy line is a photon.

The development of a quantum theory of gravity has long been a goal of theorists. Many of the pioneers of quantum field theory thought that the problem would soon be solved. If such a theory were to be realised, then it would mean that gravitational waves could be decomposed into particles known as gravitons and it would be the exchange of these particles that ultimately generates gravity. However, meshing quantum theory and gravity has proved to be incredibly difficult. This is perhaps not surprising, as quantum field theory and general relativity are built on fundamentally different and incompatible principles. In the case of gravity, the field that is wobbling is spacetime itself. But quantum field theories assume the existence of a fixed background spacetime. All direct approaches to turning this fixed background into a quantum jelly have so far proved unsuccessful, leaving theorists stranded at sea in the midst of a choppy spacetime ocean.

We might conceivably imagine particles adrift and buffeted by a fluctuating background space, but what would the corresponding fluctuations in time mean? No-one knows. The full unification of the two great theories of 20th century physics, general relativity and quantum mechanics, remains the goal of today's theorists. Finding a theory that incorporates both these theories will probably require a new understanding of the meaning of space and time, as well as new insights into the meaning of quantum mechanics. It should also answer some of our most profound questions, such as: '*How did the universe begin?*'

What seems clear is that the relationship between gravity and the other forces will need to be addressed if a quantum theory of gravity is to be achieved. In the next chapter, we will take a look at the other forces and the attempts that have been made to draw them all together into a single theory.

This is a prelude to the chapter that follows, in which we will look at a theory that purports to be the ultimate theory, combining all the forces including gravity into a single Theory of Everything.

Chapter Eight

# RINGING THE CHANGES

Oranges and lemons
Say the bells of St Clement's
You owe me five farthings
Say the bells of St Martin's
When will you pay me?
Say the bells of Old Bailey
When I grow rich
Say the bells of Shoreditch
When will that be?
Say the bells of Stepney
I'm sure I don't know
Says the great bell at Bow

A melodious peal of bells floating over the countryside is
quintessentially English. Cricketers on the village green and

the sound of church bells in the distance is the image of a beautiful English summer's day. Indeed, ringing the changes is a tradition unique to England, as observed by Dorothy L. Sayers in her novel of 1934, *The Nine Taylors*:

> The art of change ringing is peculiar to the English, and, like most English peculiarities, unintelligible to the rest of the world. To the musical Belgian, for example, it appears that the proper thing to do with a carefully tuned ring of bells is to play a tune upon it. By the English campanologist, the playing of tunes is considered to be a childish game, only fit for foreigners; the proper use of the bells is to work out mathematical permutations and combinations.

The study of symmetry is one of the most captivating branches of modern mathematics and, over the past century, it has become increasingly important for describing the underlying structure of the universe. The name given to this branch of mathematics is group theory. The origins of the subject are usually traced back to its codification by the British mathematician Arthur Cayley in the middle years of the 19th century – and beyond that, to his predecessors Niels Abel and Evariste Galois, who both died tragically young, in 1829 and 1832, respectively.

There is a rather lame mathematicians' joke that goes as follows: 'Why didn't Newton invent group theory?' The answer is: 'Because he wasn't Abel!'. However, though most mathematicians may be unaware of this, many of the ideas of group theory were anticipated by an English contemporary of Newton named Fabian Stedman, who was born in 1640, just two years before Newton and 150 years before Abel. Stedman was the son of the vicar of Yarkhill, in Herefordshire. He is known to campanologists as the father of their art. Bell-ringing had already been established in England for several centuries, but Stedman made a systematic study of the practice and codified it in two books on the subject, *Campanalogia* (1677) and *Tintinnalogia* (1668).[1] The frontispiece of the third edition of *Campanalogia* advertises the work as:

> Campanalogia Improved, or the Art of Ringing Made Easy
> By Plain and Methodical Rules and Directions, whereby the Ingenious Practitioner may, with a little Practice and Care, attain to the Knowledge of Ringing all Manner of Double, Triple and Quadruple Changes.
> With Variety of New Peals upon Five, Six, Seven, Eight and Nine Bells.
> As also the Method of calling Bobs for any Peal of Tripples from 168 to 2520 (being the Half Peal). Also for any Peal of Quadruples or Cators from 324 to 1140.

The ringing of church bells is distinctive, and does not have a counterpart in any other type of music. The bell tower of an English church typically contains six or more bells that are tuned to different notes. The bells are played in a sequence, then, instead of playing the same sequence of bells again, the order of the bells is changed. Hence the expression: 'ringing the changes'. The inertia of the heavy bells means that it is only practical to alter the position of a bell in the sequence by one place. Campanologists have therefore adopted the convention that from one line of bells to the next, the order in which consecutive pairs of bells is rung can be swapped, but no other change in order is allowed.

This is best illustrated with a simple example. We can take four bells and number them 1 to 4, such that the first sequence that is rung is the sequence: 1, 2, 3, 4. This is followed by a sequence in which the leftmost pair of bells are interchanged and the rightmost pair of bells are interchanged, to give the sequence: 2, 1, 4, 3. The next sequence is produced by swapping the middle two bells, to give: 2, 4, 1, 3. Next, the outer pairs are interchanged again. Continuing in this way, alternately swapping the outer bells and then the middle bells, after eight sequences of the four bells, the starting sequence 1, 2, 3, 4 is reached again. Bell-ringers always finish by playing the opening line a second time. This is the only line that is ever repeated. The full set of changes is shown below:

```
1 2 3 4
2 1 4 3
2 4 1 3
4 2 3 1
4 3 2 1
3 4 1 2
3 1 4 2
1 3 2 4
1 2 3 4
```

This simple example is known as 'plain lead on four bells'. Most churches have more than four bells, and correspondingly much longer sets of changes are possible. There are 5,040 different orderings of seven bells,[2] and it would take around three hours to play all these permutations as a sequence of changes. Any set with more than 5,000 rows is known as a peal (Stedman's frontispiece above alludes to a half peal of length 2,520). Ringing a peal of bells might be considered as the audible Christian equivalent of an elaborate Islamic tessellation. The regular pattern encapsulates the divine.

Group theory is an extremely rich subject that can be applied to any type of pattern. When discussing symmetry, the examples that usually come first to mind are the symmetries of regular geometrical objects, such as the Platonic solids or intricate tessellating patterns. But group theory can be used to describe the patterns formed by the possible rearrangements of any objects. These may be bells, corners of a square, suits in a pack of cards or whatever.

Plain lead on four bells described above only includes eight sequences of bells. If the four bells were to be played in every possible sequence, then there would be 24 different orderings of the bells, because there are a total of 24 ways in which any four objects can be ordered. The full set is known as the permutation group of four objects. The group of sequences that form plain lead on four bells is contained within the full collection of permutations. It is a subgroup of the permutation group. This is a very important feature of groups; they tend to be nested in hierarchies, one within another.

The symmetry group of a square is also a subgroup of the permutation group of four objects.

---

**Puzzle 10**

Including reflection and rotational symmetries, how many symmetries does a square have?

---

Each regular polygon is symmetrical under its own set of rotations and reflections. Together, these form the symmetry group of the polygon. By increasing the number of sides of the polygon indefinitely we reach, in the limiting case, a circle. A circle can be rotated through any angle around its centre and it remains unchanged. These rotations form a

**Answer to Puzzle 10**

The square is symmetrical under eight operations, as depicted in the figure below. The corners have been labelled to distinguish the different orientations of the square following the symmetry operations. At the top left is the starting position of the square. The square is symmetrical under rotations through multiples of 90° around its centre, as shown across the top of the diagram. It also has four reflection symmetries. The lines of reflection are shown as dashed lines. We can list the eight symmetries in the same way as for the bells: (1, 2, 3, 4); (4, 1, 2, 3); (3, 4, 1, 2); (2, 3, 4, 1); (2, 1, 4, 3); (4, 3, 2, 1); (1, 4, 3, 2); (3, 2, 1, 4).

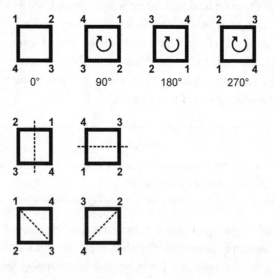

**Figure 71** Answer to Puzzle 10. The symmetries of the square. The top row are the rotational symmetries of the square. Below are the reflection symmetries. (The dashed lines represent the lines of reflection symmetry.)

continuous group – continuous because the rotation can be any angle between 0 and 360 degrees. Therefore, the symmetry operations can be expressed with a single continuous parameter.

**Figure 72** A circle is symmetrical under rotations around its centre. These rotations can be through any angle between 0° and 360°. The group consists of a single parameter representing this angle.

There are, of course, much bigger continuous symmetry groups, such as the symmetry group of a sphere. The symmetries of a sphere can be expressed in terms of three continuous parameters corresponding to rotations around three perpendicular axes, as shown in the figure below. (The symmetry group of a circle is a subgroup of the symmetry group of a sphere. It might consist of all rotations around the equator of the sphere, for instance.) Continuous groups such as these are known as Lie groups (pronounced 'Lee'), after the French mathematician Sophus Lie. They play a very important role in particle physics.

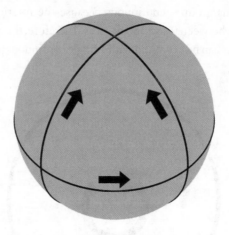

**Figure 73** A sphere is symmetrical under rotations around three perpendicular axes.

## *The Inner Structure*

> The universe is built on a plan, the profound symmetry of which is somehow present in the inner structure of our intellect.
>
> Paul Valery.

Group theory is the perfect tool to analyse the symmetries of physics. Many of the most important symmetries in physics are continuous symmetries. For example, physicists assume that empty space is identical at every point. If no force is acting, it is impossible to tell the difference between one point in space and any other point in space. This means that if we were in a starship deep in interstellar space and we moved our starship's laboratory from one point to another, it would be impossible to distinguish between the two points. A physicist would express this by saying that space is symmetrical under translations. The first of Newton's laws of motion is closely related to this fact. According to Newton, an object such as a starship will continue at a constant speed in a straight line unless it is acted upon by an external force. An alternative way of expressing this is to say that the starship's momentum will not change unless a force acts on it. In other words, the starship's momentum is constant.

The connection between the translational symmetry of space and the conservation of the starship's momentum becomes clearer if we imagine what would happen if there were a force acting. If a giant magnet suddenly appeared in space, the pull of the magnet would deflect the starship from its original course – its momentum would change. If we consider the situation from the viewpoint of symmetry, we can see that our region of space is no longer identical at all points – there is a whopping great magnet at one point and, in the neighbourhood of the magnet, the properties of each point in space are determined by their proximity to the magnet.

To summarise, when we have translational symmetry, momentum is conserved. When we do not have translational symmetry, momentum is not conserved. This is an example of one of the most important principles of modern physics.

*For each continuous symmetry, there exists a conserved quantity.*

The connection was first made in 1918 by a mathematician called Emmy Noether, who was studying Einstein's brand new theory of general relativity. This result is known as Noether's theorem. It lies at the heart of physics.

## *You Spin Me Right Round Baby, Right Round*

Empty space is spherically symmetrical, which means that it is symmetrical under rotations as well as translations. Noether's result implies that there must be a conserved quantity that corresponds to rotational symmetry. This quantity is called *angular momentum*. It is best illustrated on ice. A pair of ice dancers with outstretched arms and holding hands will twirl around an axis that lies about halfway between them. As they pull each other into a close embrace, they spin faster. Angular momentum is equal to the rate of spin multiplied by mass and by the distance from the axis, so although the ice dancers spin faster when close together, their angular momentum remains unchanged.

We have come across angular momentum before. In Chapter 2, we saw that Kepler's Second Law states that a planet sweeps out sectors of its orbit of equal area in equal periods of time, which means that the planet moves much faster when it is close to the Sun than it does when it is further away. This is conservation of angular momentum in action.

In the solar system, symmetry under translations is broken by the presence of the Sun and its gravitational field. The Sun's gravity pulls on a planet and bends the planet's path, so the momentum of the planet is not conserved. But the Sun's gravitational field is the same in all directions, which means that it is spherically symmetrical, so the angular momentum of the planet is conserved.[3]

## *Adding a New Dimension to Physics*

Einstein was the first person to appreciate the importance of symmetry for expressing the fundamental equations of physics. Gradually, the influence of Einstein's philosophy has seeped into the whole of physics. Symmetry has become the cornerstone of modern fundamental physics.

Einstein had an unquenchable thirst for the systematization of physics. Following his successful development of general relativity, his revolutionary theory of gravity, he felt that the next step in his programme had to be the quest for a theory that would combine both gravity and electromagnetism within the same formalism.

Maxwell published his theory of electromagnetism back in 1861. His equations encapsulate the interplay of electric and magnetic forces, and definitively establish that these two types of force are actually two sides of the same coin. Maxwell's equations were perfectly compatible with general relativity, so there was no disharmony or contradiction between the two theories, but this was not good enough for Einstein. The two theories treated gravity and electromagnetism as two completely different forces. Einstein believed that there must be a fundamental connection between the two, and he set out to find it.

In 1919, Einstein received a letter from a Polish mathematician, Theodor Kaluza, proposing a way in which general relativity might be extended to produce a geometrical theory of both gravity and electromagnetism. Kaluza considered his discovery to be very intriguing and of great significance. If it was correct, his theory would be an even greater triumph than general relativity. Einstein was immediately interested. Kaluza had been playing with Einstein's equation – the fundamental equation of general relativity – but rather than using the four dimensions of spacetime, he had formulated the equation in five dimensions. When he analysed the result, he discovered that, from a four-dimensional perspective, his equations looked exactly like the usual four-dimensional Einstein's equation, plus Maxwell's equations. This was remarkable. By starting in five dimensions, Kaluza appeared to have produced a theory that included both gravity and electromagnetism.

But what was the nature of this additional fifth dimension? The three dimensions of physical space are obvious to us all. A fourth time dimension is not too much of a stretch of the imagination. But how could there be a fifth dimension? This, Kaluza could not explain.

1925 was the year in which quantum mechanics came to maturity. From now on, particles were considered to behave like waves and, conversely, waves were considered to have a particle-like nature. Einstein had played a key role in the early development of quantum mechanics, but he could never reconcile himself to its full implications, as formulated by the work of Werner Heisenberg and Erwin Schrödinger. For the rest of his life, he would wage a guerrilla war against quantum theory. But despite the many alarming aspects of the theory, it worked incredibly well. Most physicists were prepared to just accept it as a powerful tool with which they could conquer wide areas of the physical world, without worrying about its philosophical implications.

With the new quantum mechanics in mind, Oskar Klein suggested an explanation for Kaluza's extra dimension. He proposed that the extra spatial dimension was rolled into a circle that was so small that it would be invisible in experiments. In addition to travelling through the three dimensions of space, particles would also move around this tiny circle. As we have seen, the translational symmetry of ordinary space leads to conservation of momentum. The new theory included another symmetry – symmetry under rotations around the tiny circular fifth dimension – and there must be an additional conserved quantity corresponding to this symmetry.

According to Klein, this quantity is what we experience as electric charge. This is quite a startling result. Momentum in a tiny curled-up extra dimension could be interpreted as electric charge. Conservation of electric charge would then be the analogue of conservation of momentum in ordinary space. The revised theory became known as Kaluza-Klein theory.[4]

**Figure 74** Three versions of an imaginary two-dimensional universe in which one dimension is rolled into a small circle. If the circle is small enough, then space would appear like a one-dimensional line, rather than a two-dimensional surface.

## Unified Field Theory

Despite its attractive features, there was no experimental evidence to support the idea of an extra spatial dimension, and physics was about to enter the most fertile period in its history. With the enormous progress made in applying quantum theory to explain whole swathes of the natural world from the mid-1920s onwards, the imaginative ideas of Kaluza and Klein, and the search for a unified theory of gravity and electromagnetism, were forgotten by almost everyone except Einstein. Einstein continued for the last thirty years of his life to seek his goal of a unified field theory that would incorporate both gravity and electromagnetism within a single structure.

By the 1930s, most physicists considered Einstein and his unification programme to stand well outside the main thrust towards comprehending the workings of the universe. Einstein, who had always thought of himself as an outsider, happily continued along his own course. Now an international celebrity, he pursued his work on unification in isolation from the rest of the physics community. His goal of unification also seemed to have been superseded by the discovery of two new forces that play vital roles in nuclear physics, These new forces are known as the strong nuclear force and the weak nuclear force – or, more usually today, simply the strong force and the weak force. Einstein was, of course, fully aware of the existence of the strong and weak forces, but he did not attempt to incorporate them into his unification scheme. He believed that these two new forces would turn out to be different manifestations of electromagnetism or, at least, closely related to electromagnetism. Rather surprisingly, he was at least partially correct in this view.

Einstein died in 1955. He was still scribbling the equations of possible unified theories on his deathbed.[5] The triumph of quantum mechanics had continued unabated. The quantum theory of electromagnetism, known as QED, was now established as an accurate theory that united special relativity with quantum mechanics in its description of the electro-magnetic force. But the mechanisms by which the weak and strong forces operate remained a mystery. The goal of total unification of the forces was a distant dream.

Einstein may have been an outsider in his later years, but much of his insight into the fundamental structure of physics remains at the heart of the drive to understand the universe. In particular, it was Einstein's theory of special relativity that first demonstrated the importance of symmetry in the laws of nature. Einstein's theories are built around the symmetries of the fabric of the universe. Special relativity is built on the symmetries of space and time, and of motion through them. General relativity goes much further and shows the relevance of sophisticated mathematics in describing the universe. The aim of modern theorists is to complete the programme that Einstein initiated in 1905.

Symmetry is a key component of all current theories of fundamental physics. The laws of physics must be expressed in terms of geometrical quantities. This is quite natural in the case of gravity because, in Einstein's formulation, the force is completely described in terms of the shape of space. But it is also true in the case of the other forces of nature. To see how this works, we will have to visit the world of elementary particles.

## *Quantum Identity*

Fundamental particles are naturally divided into two distinct categories. One category comprises the particles known as bosons. These are named after the Indian physicist Satyendra Nath Bose,[6] who was born in 1894 in Kolkata in West Bengal. In 1924, while at the University of Dhaka, Bose showed how the infant quantum theory could be used to derive Planck's formula for the amount of light emitted as the temperature of an object changes. However, Bose's original paper was rejected for publication, so he wrote to Einstein, who immediately saw its significance. Einstein translated the paper into German and submitted it to the German journal *Zeitschrift für Physik* on Bose's behalf.

Bose's argument was based on the fact that light is formed of particles known as photons. This proposal built on Einstein's work from 1905, in which Einstein explained an experimental result known as the photoelectric effect by treating light as being composed of photons. The critical idea introduced by Bose was that photons are indistinguishable particles – they are all identical. This is one of the most significant features of quantum mechanics. It means that it is not possible, by any manner whatever, to distinguish one photon from another.

In classical physics, we think of particles as akin to billiard balls. We can follow the trajectory of particle A as it collides with particle B, and it is always possible to track which is which. But this is not possible in quantum theory – even in principle – and this produces profound differences when considering the statistics of large collections of particles such as photons. It means that there is an enhanced probability that these particles will all be found in the same state as their fellow particles. This leads to collective behaviour that cannot be explained using classical physics, but you make use of it every time you play a CD or DVD.

Being bosons, photons like to be in the same state as their colleagues. A laser beam is a collection of vast numbers of photons with exactly the same wavelength, all vibrating together in phase. A typical beam of light is a bit like a choppy sea – there are lots of different waves that partially cancel each other out. In a laser beam, all the waves are moving together to produce a single big wave train. All of the photons are in the same quantum state. This is why a laser packs much more punch than an ordinary beam of light. The behaviour of bosons also plays a critical role in explaining many other physical phenomena, including superconductivity and superfluidity, as well as the recently discovered Bose-Einstein condensates.

## *The Mighty Atom*

To understand the second category of particles, we must turn to the structure of matter. In 1913, Niels Bohr made one of the greatest breakthroughs in our understanding of the world around us when he constructed a model of an atom in which the electrons orbit the nucleus in a fixed set of energy levels. Bohr used his model to explain the lines in the spectrum of an atom, which had been used to deduce the chemistry of the stars.

When an electron falls from one energy level to a lower energy level, it emits a photon, whose energy is equal to the difference in energy of the two energy levels. As the electron can only exist in a discrete set of energy levels, the photons emitted in this way can only have a certain set of energies, each corresponding to a different colour. Therefore, the spectrum of any material formed from these atoms has its own characteristic set of spectral lines – much like its very own barcode.

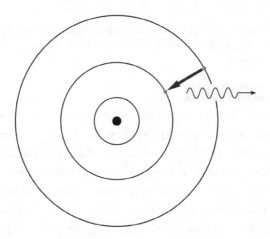

**Figure 75** An electron falls from one energy level in an atom to a lower energy level. The difference in energy is radiated away in the form of a photon.

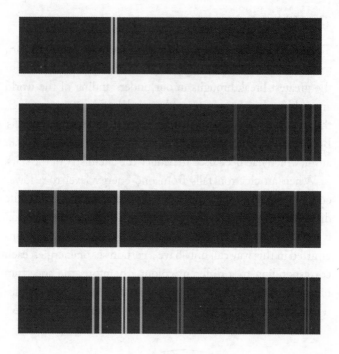

**Figure 76** Each element emits radiation in a characteristic set of energies, corresponding to light of various wavelengths. Four examples are shown in the illustration.

Bohr's model was a great success and won him a Nobel Prize in 1922. However, he felt that the model should be capable of much more. If it really represented the structure of an atom, then it should explain how atoms bond in chemical reactions, and why each atom has its own particular chemical properties. Bohr made some progress along these lines, but eventually had to admit defeat. He passed the problem over to a precocious physics prodigy, Wolfgang Pauli, an Austrian who had made a name for himself by writing a textbook on the new subject of relativity at the age of just 19.

## *The Exclusion Principle*

Wolfgang Pauli became known for his acerbic wit and his harsh criticism of anyone whose thinking he considered sloppy. Rudolf Peierls wrote that a friend showed Pauli the paper of a young physicist, which he suspected was of little value, but he wanted Pauli's opinion. Pauli remarked, sadly, *'Not only is it not right, it's not even wrong!'*

In 1925, Pauli came up with the fix that would enable Bohr's model to explain 'chemistry'. Pauli realised that, in Bohr's original model, we would expect all the electrons in an atom to fall into the lowest energy level of the atom and just sit there. He decided that electrons must have a strange property that prevents this from happening. It has become known as the Pauli Exclusion Principle, and it implies that only one electron is allowed in any particular quantum state.

What this means is that in a hydrogen atom, which contains just one electron, this electron does, indeed, fall down into the lowest energy level. In helium, which contains two electrons, the second electron also falls to the lowest energy level, but it must be spinning in the opposite direction from the first electron. These two electrons have now filled the first energy level. In the next type of atom, lithium, there are three electrons; two go into the lowest energy level (with opposite spins), but the third can only fall as far as the second energy level. In this way, the structure of atoms can be understood, with the electrons filling the energy levels step by step and with no more than one electron occupying each possible state. Pauli realised that it is the outermost electrons – those in the highest partially filled shells, as they are known – that take part in chemical reactions, so he was able to explain the chemical properties of an atom in terms of the number of electrons in the outer reaches of the atom.

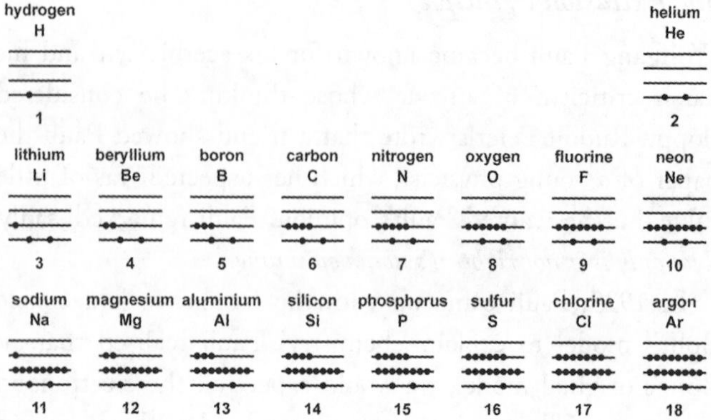

**Figure 77** A schematic representation of the electrons in the first four energy levels of atoms of the first eighteen elements in the Periodic Table. In reality, the energy levels are not equally spaced.

## *Antisocial Particles*

It turns out that electrons are not the only particles that behave in this strange way. A similar situation prevails in the nucleus of an atom, where the neutrons and protons from which the nucleus is formed must each exist in its own distinct quantum state. The energy levels in the nucleus are not arranged in exactly the same way as the electron energy levels outside the nucleus, but the same general principles apply. Neutrons and protons fill up the energy levels step by step.

At an even deeper level, neutrons and protons are each formed of three quarks. Most of the particles that are observed in particle accelerators such as the Large Hadron Collider are formed of quarks. These particles are collectively known as hadrons – hence the name of the Large Hadron

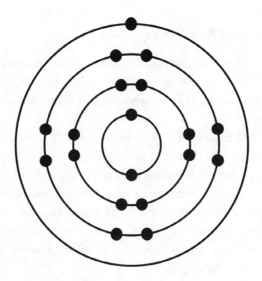

**Figure 78** Schematic diagram of the energy levels in an atom. In the lowest shell, there are two states. The second shell contains eight states with equal energy. The third shell contains eight states with equal energy, and the fourth shell contains eighteen states of equal energy. No two electrons can exist in the same state. The electrons fill the lowest available states. The diagram represents an atom of potassium, which has a single electron in the partially filled fourth shell. It is this electron that is responsible for the chemistry of potassium.

Collider. Again, within all these particles, the quarks obey the exclusion principle, and this determines the structure of hadrons and many of their physical properties.

Particles that obey the exclusion principle are known collectively as *fermions*. These particles include electrons, protons, neutrons, quarks and neutrinos. Each such particle shuns its colleagues. The term 'fermion' is derived from the name of the Italian physicist Enrico Fermi (although 'paulions' might have been more appropriate).

## *The Original Spin Doctor*

What is it, you might ask, that makes these two categories of particle – fermions and bosons – behave in such different ways? The answer is very surprising – it is the rate at which they spin!

In 1940, Pauli took a big step towards a theoretical understanding of this strange state of affairs by proving what is known as the Spin-Statistics Theorem. What Pauli showed was that if special relativity and quantum mechanics are combined into the theoretical framework that we know as quantum field theory, then particles are necessarily divided into two types that behave in very different ways. This is simply due to their spin.

As you might expect, spin is the rate at which a particle rotates – in other words, its intrinsic angular momentum. This is a fundamental property of a particle that cannot change without the particle changing into a different type of particle. Like many quantum properties, spin comes in fixed lumps. Particles can only exist in states where they have multiples of a fundamental unit of spin. The smallest amount of spin that a particle can have (other than no spin) is half a unit of spin.[7]

Pauli's analysis showed that any particles whose spin was a whole number (or integer), i.e. 0, 1, 2 and so on, would love to cluster in the same state as their fellow particles. For instance, the Higgs boson has zero spin, whereas photons and gluons have one unit of spin and the hypothetical graviton has two units. These particles are the bosons.

Pauli also showed that the behaviour of any particle whose spin is a half-integer, i.e. 1/2, 3/2, 5/2 and so on, is quite different. For instance, the spin of an electron, a quark or a neutrino is 1/2. These particles are the fermions.

Whereas bosons are the ultimate copy-cats, liking nothing more than to be in the same state as their neighbours, fermions are the most stubborn and antisocial individuals. They cannot exist in the same state as their colleagues – they obey the exclusion principle. This is fundamental to the organisation of electrons in atoms and it lies at the heart of the subject of chemistry. Also, as we have seen, it plays a similar role in nuclear physics by determining how neutrons and protons are arranged in the nucleus of an atom.

Fermions are the fundamental building blocks of matter. If electrons had no spin (like Higgs bosons) or one unit of spin (like photons), then they would all fall to the lowest energy level in an atom and there would be no chemistry, because it is the electrons in the outer, unfilled shells, that do all the chemical bonding. If electrons were bosons, the universe would be a structureless mush.

Bosons also have an important role in the scheme of things. They are the particles that are exchanged between other particles to produce forces. The first force to be understood in this way was electromagnetism. Atoms are held together by the electromagnetic force. An atom is composed of a positively charged nucleus, surrounded by negatively charged electrons. It is the electromagnetic force between these charged particles that binds the atom together. Electromagnetism also bonds atoms together and is the force behind the whole of chemistry. The quantum theory of the electromagnetic force is called QED. According to this theory, photons are continually being passed back and forth between charged particles, and it is this particle exchange that produces the electromagnetic force.

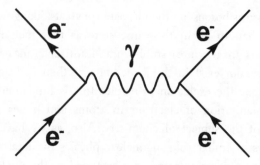

**Figure 79** The interaction between two electrons can be represented by a Feynman diagram. In the above diagram, two electrons approach each other, exchange a photon and then recede from each other again. The exchange of the photon transfers energy and momentum from one electron to the other.

## Yang-Mills Theory

QED has proved to be a phenomenally accurate theory of the electromagnetic force. As such, it is natural that physicists should see it as potentially a great template for building theories for the two nuclear forces – the strong force and the weak force.

Kaluza and Klein conjured electromagnetism out of a curled-up extra fifth dimension. The reason why this is possible is that electromagnetism has a built-in symmetry that is the same as the rotational symmetry of a circle. This symmetry was already present in Maxwell's equations, but it was only with the development of the quantum theory of electromagnetism that the symmetry was understood. It turns out that there is a very natural generalization of QED that describes forces built around bigger symmetry groups.

These theories are called Yang-Mills theories, a name that derives from the Chinese-American physicist Chen-Ning Yang, also known by his westernised name Frank Yang, and his American colleague Robert Mills, who first devised such theories in 1954. These theories have many nice mathematical properties. They contain no arbitrary adjustable parameters; the structure of the theory is completely determined by its symmetry group.

These groups are sometimes referred to as internal symmetries. They represent the symmetries of the quantum fields that exist throughout space, but they are not symmetries of space itself. However, the distinction is not really that clear-cut. It might turn out that what appears to be an internal symmetry can be explained as a geometrical symmetry in a higher dimensional space, as Kaluza-Klein theory suggests. We will see where this idea leads in the next chapter.

Although the original model of Yang and Mills did not fit the facts, it eventually became clear that models of the same kind are exactly what is required to explain both the weak and strong forces. Each of these forces is built around its own symmetry group. This symmetry manifests itself in a number of ways. It implies that instead of involving the exchange of a single particle, such as the photon, these forces are produced by the exchange of a family of particles. It also means that the matter particles that feel the force come in collections that can be transformed one into another by the action of the force.

## *The Standard Model*

The nucleus of an atom is formed of particles known as protons and neutrons, and these particles are bound together by the strong force. If it were not for this incredibly powerful force, then the mutual repulsion of the positively charged protons would blast the nucleus apart in an instant. At an even deeper level, the strong force binds quarks together. We now know that protons and neutrons are formed from two types of quark, known as up quarks and down quarks. A proton is composed of two up quarks and a down quark, whereas a neutron is composed of one up quark and two down quarks. The correct theory of the strong force fell into place in 1973. It is called quantum chromodynamics (QCD).

**Figure 80** Left: A proton is formed of two up quarks and a down quark. Right: A neutron is formed of two down quarks and an up quark.

QCD is a Yang-Mills theory, so it has a similar structure to QED, but with a number of significant differences. QED is built around the simplest possible symmetry for this type of theory – the rotational symmetry of a circle. It accurately describes the electromagnetic force between charged particles and how the force is produced by the exchange of photons. The Yang-Mills idea was to build similar theories around bigger symmetry groups, such as the rotational symmetry group of a sphere. This group can be described by three independent parameters, which correspond to rotations around three perpendicular axes.

Yang-Mills theories such as QCD describe forces produced by the exchange of a collection of particles, not just one particle. Like the photon, these particles are massless bosons. The number of exchange particles is determined by the size of the group. For instance, the Yang-Mills theory built around the symmetry group of the sphere would produce a theory in which there are three exchange particles – one for each of the three parameters that describe the rotations.

QCD is based around a symmetry group that is described by eight parameters. It is called SU(3). This means it describes a force produced by the exchange of a family of eight particles known as gluons, rather than a single photon. Gluons are so named because they provide the 'glue' that sticks quarks together.

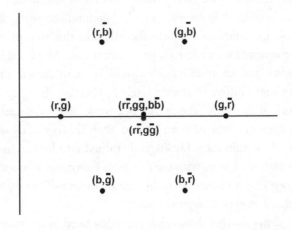

**Figure 81** The gluons that are exchanged to produce the strong force each carry two 'colour' charges. They form a QCD octet. The letters represent the colour charges: r is red, g is green, b is blue. The letters with bars over them are the anti-colours.

In Yang-Mills theories, the matter particles, such as electrons and quarks, can also form collections of particles that are related by the symmetry group. The force sees the members of a multiplet as siblings and it can transform one into another. For instance, in QCD, the quarks form triplets, and this is closely related to the '3' in SU(3). Physicists use the labels 'red', 'green' and 'blue' to distinguish the quarks in a triplet (these labels are quite arbitrary and nothing to do with colour in the usual sense). What this means is that the QCD force can transform a red up quark into a blue up quark, or a green down quark into a red down quark. QCD cannot transform up quarks into down quarks, but there is another force that can perform this magic trick.

This is the weak force. The up quark and the down quark form a weak force doublet. As far as the weak force is concerned, they are twins and, therefore, the weak force is able to transform one into the other. In this way, protons are converted into neutrons and neutrons are converted into protons, and an atomic nucleus may be transformed into a completely different atomic nucleus, thereby changing the nature of the atom. The weak force works like an alchemist, changing one type of atom into another. This is exactly what happens within stars. Hydrogen is turned into helium in the Sun and other stars, with the release of enormous amounts of energy. In even bigger stars, helium is converted into carbon, oxygen and even heavier elements.

It turns out that the weak force is described by a symmetry group that is similar to the symmetry group of a sphere.[8] For this reason, it is produced by the exchange of three particles known as the W-plus, W-minus and Z-nought bosons.

The diagram below shows an example of a weak interaction, in which an up quark is transformed into a down quark. In the same interaction, an electron is transformed into a neutrino.

In the process of understanding the weak force, physicists realised that there is a deep connection between the weak force and electromagnetism. Despite the profound differences

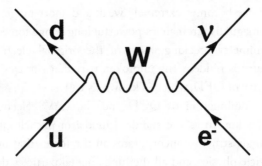

**Figure 82** Weak interaction in which a W boson is exchanged between an up quark (u) and an electron (e⁻). The up quark is thereby transformed into a down quark (d) and the electron is transformed into a neutrino (ν).

between these two forces, it turns out that they are separate parts of a unified electroweak force. Sheldon Glashow, Steven Weinberg and Abdus Salam shared the Nobel Prize for Physics in 1979 for developing the unified electroweak Yang-Mills theory that binds these forces together. It is often known as the GWS theory, after the initials of its three authors. The electroweak Yang-Mills theory is based around a group called SU(2)×U(1).[9]

To understand the electroweak force it was necessary to introduce a new feature into Yang-Mills theories – symmetry breaking. The idea is that some of the symmetry built into the theory is hidden. At very high temperatures, which could mean temperatures of quintillions of degrees, all the symmetry is manifest – but shortly after the Big Bang, as the universe began to cool, some of the symmetry was lost. The most important consequence of this is that the exchange particles gain mass. In the case of the electroweak force, three of the four exchange particles become very heavy, while the fourth, the photon, remains massless. The result is that the weak force becomes extremely weak and short-range, while electromagnetism remains a powerful long-range force. After the symmetry breaking, most of the original electroweak symmetry is hidden. The unbroken part that survives is the symmetry of QED, which is known as U(1).

The combination of QCD and the GWS electroweak theory is known as the standard model of particle physics. This single structure incorporates all the forces that operate in particle physics, and all the fundamental particles that we know of. The matter particles, or fermions, consist of three generations of four particles, as shown in the table below.

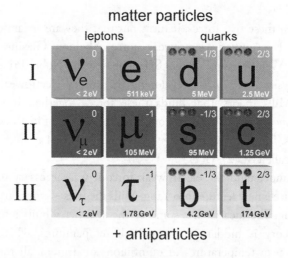

## matter particles

+ antiparticles

**Figure 83** The table of elementary particles in the Standard Model part 1 – the fermions. From left to right: Generation I, the electron neutrino ($\nu_e$), electron (e), down quark (d) and up quark (u); Generation II, the muon neutrino ($\nu_\mu$), muon ($\mu$), strange quark (s) and charm quark (c); and Generation III, the tauon neutrino ($\nu_\tau$), tauon ($\tau$), bottom quark (b) and top quark (t). Each particle's charge is shown at its upper right and its mass at lower right; mass increases downwards in the table.

The exchange particles that produce the forces of the standard model are the photon and the Ws and Z that produce the electroweak force, and the eight gluons that generate the strong force. There is also the Higgs boson, which plays the critical role in the electroweak theory of breaking the symmetry of the electroweak force.[10]

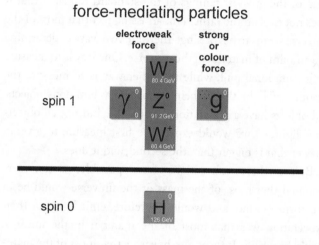

Figure 84 The table of elementary particles in the Standard Model part 2 – the bosons. The force-mediating particles are the photon and the $W^+$, $Z^0$ and $W^-$ particles that mediate the electroweak force, and the octet of gluons that mediate the colour force that produces the strong interaction. The only other boson is shown at the bottom of the table. This is the Higgs (H), which breaks that symmetry of the electroweak force.

We have now reached the forefront of experimental particle physics. So far, the predictions of the standard model are standing up incredibly well in the Large Hadron Collider, and there is no sign yet of any new physics that goes beyond the standard model. However, the standard model does have a number of loose ends. Within a year of it becoming established, theorists were already looking beyond its boundaries to see if they could resolve some of its shortcomings. We will be taking a look at some of these speculative ideas.

## Most of the Universe is Missing!

One of the grossest failings of the standard model is that it does not explain the rather embarrassing fact that most of the universe seems to be missing! There are two ways to determine the amount of material in the universe. One way is to measure its gravitational pull, while the other way is to measure the amount of light that is being emitted by luminous objects. All objects have a gravitational attraction, but not all objects emit light, so we would expect the first measure to give an answer that is bigger than the second, and it does.

Before these calculations were possible, astronomers assumed that most of the mass of the universe would be in the form of stars and would, therefore, emit light, so their expectation was that most of the material in the universe would be visible. It turns out, however, that most of the material in the universe does not emit light. Astronomers call this stuff dark matter, simply because we cannot see it.

The first question is: could the measurements be wrong? After all, it cannot be that easy to measure the properties of galaxies that are millions of light years away. However, astronomers have been working on this problem for many decades, and the measurements are now quite accurate. For instance, the rate of rotation of a spiral galaxy that we view edge-on can be measured from the Doppler shift of the light from its two edges. The starlight from one edge will be red-shifted as the stars move away from us, while the starlight from the other edge will be blue-shifted as it moves towards us. The rate of rotation can then be used to deduce the total gravitational mass of the galaxy. It is clear from these measurements that the rate of rotation of galaxies is so high that they would fly apart if they were solely composed of the visible material. This implies that there must be additional matter holding the galaxies together that is invisible to us. So there is no doubt that the universe contains a lot of material that we cannot see.[11]

The big mystery is: What is it? And this is where everything becomes much more murky, because all the obvious answers – such as dark gas clouds that have not yet formed stars, or burnt-out star remnants such as white dwarfs and neutron stars – cannot be the answer. The Big Bang model of the early universe works very well (I am skipping over the evidence here),[12] but there would be serious problems with it if the universe had formed with much more ordinary matter.

## MACHOs and WIMPs

The possible sources of dark matter fall into two categories, which are referred to as MaCHOs (Massive Compact Halo Objects) and WIMPs (Weakly Interacting Massive Particles). MaCHOs are the burnt-out stars that we have just ruled out, so most physicists believe that the dark matter consists of vast quantities of WIMPs. A WIMP is a stable particle that only interacts very weakly with ordinary matter, which would explain why it forms a separate component of the matter in the universe, and also why it has not already been discovered by particle accelerators or observed in cosmic rays.

Most particles that are created in particle accelerators are unstable, which means that they rapidly transform into other particles. Eventually, the only particles that are left are members of a small collection of stable particles. These include the protons and electrons from which atoms are formed, photons, which are particles of light, and neutrinos. It is fortunate that these particles are stable, because otherwise there would be no atoms and no light. Neutrinos were created in vast quantities in the early universe and are still being created by stars and supernovae. It was once thought that this might explain the origin of dark matter. However, we now know that the mass of a neutrino is too small to account for all the dark matter. Most physicists today believe that the dark matter is probably formed of another unknown type of stable particle that was produced in large quantities in the very early universe. Finding such a particle is one of the main targets of the research at the Large Hadron Collider.

## *Sexy Susy*

The big division in quantum mechanics is between matter particles and force-carrying particles. As we have seen, the particles from which matter is formed, such as quarks and electrons, behave in a very different way from particles such as photons and gluons that produce the forces that bind matter together. The ultimate aim of physicists is to reveal the unifying principles that bind the universe together – the simple laws from which all else follows. In this spirit, it is natural that they should seek a deep connection between these two apparently very different types of particle.

The desire for unification has prompted physicists to devise a new type of symmetry, unlike the others that we have seen. This symmetry is between matter particles and force-carrying particles. It is called *supersymmetry*, a name that is sometimes abbreviated to Susy. It has remarkable and beautiful properties.

If the universe really is supersymmetric, then fermions and bosons must come in pairs. For instance, the electron (which is a fermion) must have a partner that is a boson, and the photon (which is a boson) must have a partner that is a fermion. It would be very neat and tidy if all the known fermions and bosons could be matched up in this way, but unfortunately this doesn't work. As can be seen from the tables above, there is no obvious way to match up the known particles – they have different electric charges, for instance.

It turns out that, if supersymmetry is correct, then all the known fundamental particles must have partners that are yet to be discovered. These hypothetical new particles predicted by supersymmetry have already been named by theorists. The partner of the electron is known as the selectron. In general, the name of the bosonic partner of a fermion is produced by adding the prefix 's' for 'supersymmetry' to the name of the fermion, so that the partner of the neutrino is known as the sneutrino and the partners of the quarks are known as squarks. The supersymmetric partner of the photon is a fermion. Theorists call it the photino. In general, the super-symmetric partner of bosons all end in the suffix 'ino', which gives us Winos, Zinos, gluinos and Higgsinos.

The two particles that form each of the fermion-boson pairs would have equal mass if supersymmetry were a perfect unbroken symmetry. But we know that this cannot be the case because, if it were, the partner particles would have been discovered long ago. This implies that the supersymmetry partners must be much more massive than the known particles. The Large Hadron Collider is searching for signs of these new particles.

The standard model is the best theory of particle physics that we have. So far, every experiment ever performed has produced results that can be explained by the standard model. But, the standard model cannot be the final answer, and physicists are eager for an even better theory. There are many supersymmetric theories whose predictions are under scrutiny. The simplest supersymmetric extension of the standard model is known as the minimal supersymmetric standard model, which gives us the neatly symmetrical acronym MSSM. If supersymmetry is a true symmetry of the universe, then there should be a wonderful harvest of new particles to be reaped. Their discovery could answer one of the biggest mysteries of the cosmos.

## *Shedding Some Light on Dark Matter*

Almost all fundamental particles are extremely unstable, which means that they rapidly decay into other, lighter particles. Matter is formed from the few types of particle that are stable. A very important consequence of supersymmetry is that the lightest supersymmetry partner particle is expected to be completely stable. This particle is usually referred to as the neutralino (because it carries no electric charge). If supersymmetry does play a role in the structure of the universe, then this particle would have been produced in great profusion in the earliest moments of the universe and, because it is completely stable, it will be as abundant now as it always was. This could explain why there seems to be much more matter in the universe than astronomers have been able to observe. Many physicists believe that this particle will turn out to be the wimpy relic particle that explains one of the biggest mysteries of the cosmos. Dark matter could simply be made up of vast quantities of neutralinos. If this is correct, then the LHC may soon make a discovery that is even more important than its discovery of the Higgs boson.

Supersymmetry has grown out of the belief that the laws of the universe must be beautiful. The prediction of a whole host of new particles simply to satisfy our demands for mathematical elegance is incredibly bold. The discovery of supersymmetry would rank as one of the greatest in the history of physics. The closest comparison from the archives is the prediction of antimatter by Paul Dirac. In 1928, Dirac formulated a new type of equation to describe the wave-like behaviour of electrons. His analysis of the equation led to his prediction of a particle with the same mass as an electron, but carrying the opposite charge. Dirac's new particle was discovered by Carl Anderson in 1932, and is known as the positron. This was the first antiparticle to be discovered. It was followed by the antiproton, the antineutron and, indeed, we now know that all fermions have antiparticles and they are readily produced in particle accelerators such as the LHC.

### Grand Unified Theories

Symmetry breaking lies at the heart of the electroweak theory. It has proved to be a great success, and has now been confirmed with the discovery of the Higgs boson. As long ago as 1974, theorists were wondering whether the same trick would work again. Perhaps, when the universe began, there was a single force – then, as the universe cooled, this force might have split in several rounds of symmetry breaking, to give us the forces that we recognise today.

Leaving aside gravity for the moment, there might have been a unified force that would ultimately generate all the particle physics forces. The idea was that, in a first round of symmetry breaking, some of the original unified symmetry would be hidden to produce the two forces that comprise the standard model – the electroweak force and the strong force. This would then be followed by a second round of symmetry breaking due to the Higgs mechanism, resulting in the separate electromagnetic and weak forces, as described by the standard model. Such theories are known as Grand Unified Theories, or GUTs for short. They incorporate all the forces into a single theory with the exception of gravity, which was left for the even more ambitious schemes of the future.

Sheldon Glashow and Howard Giorgi investigated the possible Lie groups to find examples that were big enough to contain the symmetry groups of both the electroweak theory and QCD. The first example that they explored was the SU(5) GUT. The group SU(5) provides a very snug fit for both the SU(3) of QCD and the SU(2)×U(1) of the electroweak theory. The same afternoon, Glashow and Giorgi found another example – the SO(10) GUT. It is also possible to embed the standard model succinctly within the group SO(10).

SU(5) is a 24-parameter group, so the hypothetical unified force would be produced by the exchange of 24 bosons, including the twelve bosons of the standard model.[13] The other twelve exchange bosons would be extremely massive, due to the first round of symmetry breaking. These bosons were named the X and Y bosons. Their mass would be enormous, in the region of a thousand trillion ($10^{15}$) GeV (this should be compared with the mass of the proton, which is a mere 1 GeV). This is almost a trillion times the energies that are being probed in the LHC. It is inconceivable that particle colliders will ever reach the energies needed to investigate Grand Unified Theories. But there is another way in which their predictions can be tested.

## *Are We Gradually Falling Apart?*

In the standard model, electrons can be transformed into neutrinos, and up quarks can be transformed into down quarks, but there is no way to change a quark into an electron or vice versa. The new GUTs devised by Glashow and Giorgi include matter multiplets that contain both quarks and electrons. If this is correct, then the GUT force produced by the exchange of the X and Y bosons would convert quarks into electrons. The huge mass of these exchange particles would make the GUT force incredibly weak, which is good, because otherwise protons and neutrons would be falling apart all around us.

For example, the ultraweak force predicted by grand unified theories would be able to transform an up quark into a positron – the antiparticle of the electron – in processes such as the one depicted below. If the up and down quarks were inside a proton, this is a mechanism by which a proton could spontaneously disintegrate. It offers us a testable prediction of the Grand Unified Theories. Do protons decay?

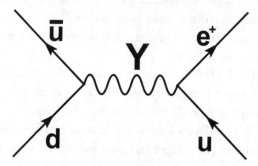

**Figure 85** Hypothetical ultraweak GUT interaction in which a Y boson is exchanged between a down quark (d) and an up quark (u). The down quark is thereby transformed into an anti-up quark and the up quark is transformed into a positron (e⁺). This diagram should be compared to the diagram showing a weak interaction above (Figure 82).

Matter appears to be quite stable, so it is clear that protons certainly hang around for a very long time. The half-life of a proton can be predicted from the mass of the bosons that are exchanged to produce the ultraweak GUT force. Their mass of around $10^{15}$ GeV would give the proton a half-life of around $10^{34}$ years. Proton decay would be a random process, with half the protons in the universe decaying in about a trillion trillion times the current age of the universe. So, even if GUTs are correct, we don't need to worry that we are about to disappear in a flash of radiation any time soon.

This makes detecting proton decay a formidable challenge but, rather than waiting quadrillions upon quadrillions of years for a single proton to decay, it is quicker to fill a tank with a vast quantity of protons and wait for some of them to pop off. For instance, in a tank containing about $10^{34}$ protons, we would expect to see one decay every year or so.

Physicists have built huge underground chambers in which they have been watching out for proton decay. The detectors must be far underground, in order to shield the experiment from background radiation, such as cosmic rays and natural radioactivity. So far, the proton is still hanging on. No evidence for proton decay has emerged.

The GUT unification energy is close to the Planck energy, which suggests that gravity must play a role in the unification. Perhaps gravity holds the key to the unification of all the forces. This possibility has led physicists to look beyond grand unification to even deeper and more outrageous theories.

### What About Gravity?

The 20th century produced two great revolutions in physics. The first was Einstein's relativity. In 1905, Einstein produced a new system of mechanics (special relativity), and ten years later a new theory of gravity (general relativity). The second, and even more profound, revolution was quantum mechanics. The whole of modern physics is understood in terms of these two theories. The realm of subatomic particles and the forces between them are described in terms of quantum mechanics and the standard model. But gravity and the universe as a whole are explained by general relativity.

It is an amazing achievement to be able to explain all that we know of in such a concise way – with just two fundamental theories. Unfortunately, however, the fundamental principles on which the two theories are built do not fit together easily. By the later years of the 20th century, the quest to reconcile their differences had become one of the biggest problems in theoretical physics. Although physicists had successfully discovered quantum theories of all the other forces, the construction of a quantum theory of gravity appeared to be impossible, or at least extremely difficult.

For a while, in the late 1970s, it appeared that supersymmetry might finally offer a navigable route to a quantum theory of gravity. When supersymmetry is incorporated into a theory of gravity, the result is known, quite naturally, as *supergravity*. Particle physicists describe gravity as the force produced by the exchange of massless spin 2 particles, known as gravitons. These particles are the fundamental components of gravitational waves, just as photons are the fundamental components of electromagnetic waves.

As we have seen, supersymmetry relates particles of different spin. Supergravity theories are the ultimate expression of this. They include spin 2 gravitons, spin 3/2 particles known as gravitinos, spin 1 particles like the exchange particles of Yang-Mills theories, spin ½ particles like the matter particles that we are familiar with, and spin 0 particles like the Higgs boson. These theories seem to have all the particle components that are needed to describe the real world. Physicists were especially captivated by the most grandiose of the supergravity theories, which is known as $N = 8$ supergravity. This theory includes eight separate supersymmetries – hence its name. Curiously, it could also be viewed as an eleven-dimensional theory containing just a single supersymmetry. This rather surprising feature of the theory led to the revival of an idea that was over fifty years old: Kaluza-Klein theory.

Kaluza had used an extra dimension to produce a geometrical theory of gravity and electromagnetism. If the fifth dimension was rolled into a tiny circle, the symmetry of this extra dimension would produce a force that could be interpreted as the electromagnetic force by physicists looking at the theory from a four-dimensional viewpoint.

An eleven-dimensional supergravity theory requires an extra seven dimensions. There are many ways in which seven spatial dimensions can be rolled up. What physicists wondered in the late 1970s was: could the extra seven dimensions be rolled up in such a way that they would reproduce the physics of the whole of the standard model by some sort of Kaluza-Klein mechanism? It appeared, for a while, as though this would just about be possible. Perhaps $N = 8$ supergravity would be the basis for a theory of all the forces. In 1979, Stephen Hawking announced that we might be nearing the end of fundamental physics. But it was not to be! Unfortunately, it is not possible to derive the symmetries of the standard model from a supergravity theory.

After decades of searching for a quantum theory of gravity, with despair setting in, the almost miraculous happened. There was a breakthrough by a few investigators, working

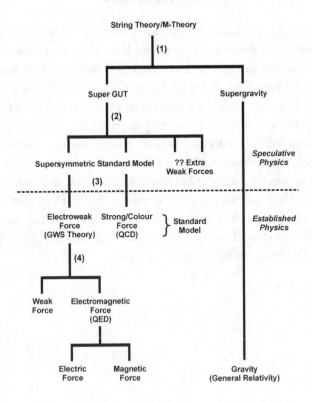

**Figure 86** The ongoing attempts to unify all the forces of nature. The bottom half of the diagram represents established physics. The top half of the diagram depicts further theoretical steps towards total unification. The numbers indicate four major stages of symmetry breaking:

(4) The Higgs mechanism, which breaks the symmetry between the electromagnetic and weak forces.

(3) Supersymmetry breaking.

(2) The breaking of the symmetry of a GUT to the symmetry of the standard model. The extra weak forces indicated here are possible additional forces that are currently unknown, but may be discovered at the LHC.

(1) The breaking of the symmetry of string theory to the symmetry of supergravity, plus a superGUT.

away in an obscure and esoteric theory that was aiming to explain the forces in an atomic nucleus. Much to their initial dismay, the theorists realised that their theory included a force that appeared to act just like gravity. This was not what they were looking for, but it seemed to be a fundamental feature of the theory and there was no way to get rid of it. In a brilliant manoeuvre, they decided to make a virtue out of a necessity and to completely change the focus of their theory. Instead of looking for a theory of the strong force, it now seemed that they had inadvertently stumbled on the Holy Grail – a quantum theory that unified gravity with all the other known forces. This is the theory that we know as string theory. All will be revealed in the next chapter.

Chapter Nine

# THE ENDLESS KNOT

Then they showed him the shield that was of schyre[1] gules[2]
with the pentangle depaint of pure gold hues
he braids it by the baldrick about the hals[3] cast.
That beseemed the segge[4] seemlily fair
And why the pentangle appends to that prince noble
I am intent you to tell, though tarry it me should.
It is a sign that Solomon set somewhile
in betokening of truth by title that it has,
for it is a figure that holds five points,
and each line umbelappes[5] and locks in other,
and aywhere it is endless and the English it call
overall, as I hear, the endless knot.

[1] bright
[2] red
[3] neck
[4] man
[5] overlaps

Sir Gawain and the Green Knight (619-630)

## *Atomic Macrame*

Knots have a long history in art. Intricate knot designs illuminate beautiful Celtic manuscripts such as *The Book of Kells*, created by Irish monks well over 1,000 years ago. Many great Renaissance artists, including Leonardo, Dürer and Raphael, also constructed elaborate knot designs, and contemporary artists, such as John Robinson, have inter-woven knots into their sculptures. Two such sculptures are shown in Plates 9 and 10. Knots also have a long history as magical symbols and talismans. According to the anonymous Gawain-poet of the late 14th century, Sir Gawain sets off on his adventure to meet the Green Knight with a shining gold pentagram knot emblazoned on his bright red shield. That science might make use of knots is not so obvious but, in the 19th century, there was an ingenious attempt to use knots to understand the physics of atoms. This curious idea led to the modern mathematical study of knots.

William Thomson was born in 1824, the son of a Belfast University mathematician. In 1832, his father went to teach mathematics at Glasgow University and, two years later, at the age of ten, William entered the university. He remains the youngest person ever to attend a British university. In 1846, he accepted a professorship at Glasgow University, where he remained for the rest of his life. He was later raised to the peerage as Lord Kelvin, and it is by this name that he is known today. Kelvin held wide-ranging interests in the sciences; as we have seen, he was the inventor of an ingenious mechanical tide calculator. He also made many important contributions to fundamental physics.

In 1867, Kelvin put forward a remarkable proposal that he hoped would explain the properties of the fundamental constituents of matter. Atoms had been debated since the ancient Greek philosophers over two thousand years earlier, and their existence was still not settled. The ancient philosophers had suggested that the structure of matter could be explained if it was composed of indivisible particles – atoms – that move around in otherwise empty space – the void. Other philosophers argued that the notion of voids between atoms was absurd.

By Kelvin's time, most scientists thought that space was filled with a mysterious substance known as the ether. This was the medium through which light waves were believed to travel. If the ether were treated as a fluid filling the whole of space, then any rotation of the ether would have to be around a vortex. Unlike water going down a plug hole or a whirlpool in a river, the vortex in the ether would have to close upon itself to form a loop, as there would be no surface on which it could end, so the vortex would be just like a smoke ring.

Kelvin's ingenious idea was that atoms might be knotted vortices in the ether. He suggested that, if the smoke rings were knotted, this would explain how substances could be formed from different types of atom. Each type of atom would be a different knot in the ether. So that, for instance, a hydrogen atom might be a trefoil knot, while an oxygen atom might be a figure of eight knot. As well as fulfilling the needs of 19th century physics, this would counter the arguments of the philosophers, ancient and modern, concerning the absurdity of voids between the atoms. In a sense, Kelvin turned this objection of the philosophers on its head. Rather than matter being composed of solid atomic particles dispersed in a void, in Kelvin's theory, the only voids are along the cores of the knotted atomic vortices which are dispersed in the ether.

Kelvin noted several ways in which his knot hypothesis might explain the nature of atoms. The wide range of possible knots might account for the variety of atoms. The impossibility, at least in Kelvin's time, of the transmutation of the elements could be explained by the fact that two different knots could not be deformed into each other by any amount of stretching or twisting without cutting the knot. Even the stability of matter in general could be explained by the impossibility of shrinking a knot away to nothing. The fact that the physical properties of atoms take discrete values, rather than a continuous range of values, would also follow from the discrete nature of knots. From a modern perspective, it might not appear that this fact needs an explanation, but it was suggested by some ancient Greek atomists that there should exist an infinite variety of atoms whose properties, such as mass, would be described by continuous parameters.

In many ways, Kelvin's conception of the fundamental structure of matter had a similar flavour to string theory, the ambitious programme that is engaging many of today's leading theorists, which aims to explain the whole of physics within a single theory. The part of Kelvin's programme which he considered to be of most significance was his attempt to explain atomic spectra in terms of the vibrations of the vortex loops. Kelvin hoped that it would be possible to demonstrate that the light emitted by a particular substance was related to the way that its atomic knots would vibrate. Of course, this turned out to be impossible because, although Kelvin's idea might appear very attractive, we now know that it is completely wrong.

## The Gordian Knot

Kelvin and his collaborator Peter Tait set out to assign a distinct knot to each element and to thereby explain the structure of the Periodic Table. The first step was to determine which knots it is possible to tie. This apparently simple question turned out to be a very difficult problem, which has led to the development of knot theory as a branch of mathematics. Following Kelvin and Tait, mathematicians think of knots as closed loops with no loose ends, so they cannot be untied. Two knots are different if no amount of stretching and manipulation, without cutting the loops, will transform one knot into the other.[1]

The puzzles that lie at the heart of knot theory are to determine whether two knots are equivalent, and to classify all possible knots. This has proved to be very tricky, even though knots are fairly easy to visualise and can readily be made out of pieces of string. To distinguish different knots mathematicians look for properties that differ from knot to knot. These must be characteristics that remain unaltered, or invariant, under any manipulation such as stretching which does not sever the knot. The simplest of these knot invariants, as they are called, is the crossing number. A knot may be laid out on a flat piece of paper, so that at no point do three strands cross over each other. If the diagram is constructed so that the number of times the loop crosses over itself is a minimum, then this number is the crossing number. The unknot, which is just a plain unknotted loop, has a crossing number of zero.

The trefoil knot can be laid out so that it has three crossings. The knot may be manipulated to increase the number of crossings, but no amount of pulling and pushing will decrease the number of crossings. The trefoil knot therefore has crossing number three. The figure of eight knot has crossing number four. This shows that the trefoil knot and the figure of eight knot must be different knots, as we would expect.

By itself, crossing number is insufficient to completely distinguish all but the simplest of knots. There is just one knot with crossing number three and one knot with crossing number four, but there are two with crossing number five, three with crossing number six, seven with crossing number seven, twenty-one with crossing number eight and from there on, the number of different knots increases rapidly. To mathematically distinguish between knots with the same crossing number requires more sophisticated methods. All of the prime knots with crossing number up to nine are shown in the figure below. This figure also shows all links with crossing number up to eight. A link is a knot formed from more than one separate loop of string.

Knot theory has drawn the attention of physicists again in recent times. Vaughan Jones, who is a mathematician from New Zealand, and the American, Ed Witten, received the Fields medal in 1990. This is the highest tribute in mathematics and is generally regarded as the equivalent of a Nobel prize in the sciences. The award was in recognition of their advances in knot theory and its relationship to physics. Witten is one of the world's leading string theorists and he is one of the stars of this chapter. Knot theory is now recognised as an important branch of topology, a subject that has become closely entwined with string theory. We will take a look at the broader subject of topology later.

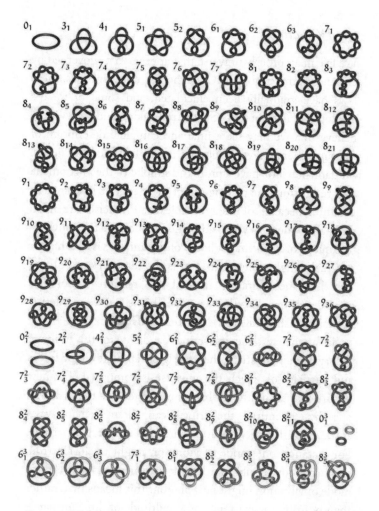

**Figure 87** Tabulation of knots with crossing number up to nine and links with crossing number up to eight.

## *Good Vibrations!*

We live in an orderly universe that appears to be governed by elegant geometrical laws. Over the last four centuries, these laws have gradually been elucidated, and some of today's leading theorists, notably Stephen Hawking and Ed Witten, believe that we may see a final and complete description of the fundamental laws of physics in our lifetimes. While the fundamental laws have a profound simplicity, the phenomena that result from the playing out of these concise laws are also beautiful because of their complexity. Physicists are filled with awe when they consider the wonders of the universe. The quest for an ultimate theory of the universe is a search for spiritual enlightenment. Its aim is the discovery of nothing less than the operating manual of Creation – the rules governing how everything works. This is not a new desire. It is what inspired Kepler, Newton and Einstein.

String theory is the first serious candidate for this ultimate theory. The aim of string theory is to encapsulate all the forces and particles of which the universe is composed. The new feature that string theory brings to the table is the idea that one physical entity – the string – can vibrate in many ways, and each different vibration represents a different particle. For instance, one mode of vibration might be an electron, another mode of vibration might be a neutrino and a third mode of vibration might be a photon. This means that, rather than positing the existence of a multitude of different particles, there is just one fundamental type of object – the string.

This apparently simple idea has very deep consequences. String theory has turned out be far richer and more surprising than anyone could have imagined. Physicists and mathematicians have been studying its implications for several decades, and the full meaning of the theory remains a mystery. Many weird and wonderful ideas have grown out of this research, but the jury is still out about whether it has any connection to the real world. Experimental support is still lacking, so it remains a purely speculative search for the ultimate theory that explains all the forces of nature. So what is string theory all about and why is it so important?

Throughout the 1950s and 1960s, new particles were popping up in particle accelerators at an alarming rate. Theorists took up the challenge of working out how all these discoveries fit into the grand scheme of things. Among the accumulating data, there were collections of particles with similar properties, but with different spin. Significantly, the higher the spin of the particle, the greater its mass. One intriguing explanation was that all these particles were produced by a single object that was spinning at different rates, and the faster that it was spinning, the greater the mass.[2]

Hitherto, particles had always been considered as point-like entities. Now, it was proposed that perhaps they were actually one-dimensional – like a short piece of string. We can imagine intuitively that the faster the string spins, the higher its energy – and, because of the equivalence of energy and mass, the higher the mass of any particle that it might represent. Just like a violin string or a guitar string, this elementary string would also be able to vibrate in various ways, and each mode of vibration would correspond to a different type of particle. If the new particles that were being discovered could be matched to the string vibration modes, then this would represent a great breakthrough and a new unifying principle. Instead of large numbers of completely independent particles, they would all be produced by the vibrations of a single fundamental entity. The lowest-mass particle would be the fundamental mode of vibration of the string. The harmonics would give us more massive particles, and the higher the harmonic, the greater the mass of the particle.

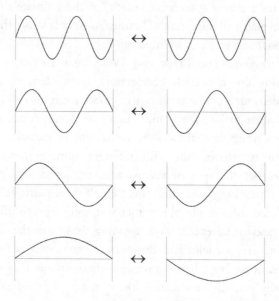

**Figure 88** Modes of vibration of a string. Each of the four pairs of diagrams shows two momentary snapshots of a vibration, at opposite points in the cycle. The full vibration is an oscillation between these two positions. The bottom pair of diagrams shows the fundamental mode of vibration, also called the first harmonic. Above it are the second, third and fourth harmonics.

This idea seemed to fit some of the data quite well, but it would soon be overshadowed by the spectacular success of a more conventional theory that would explain the new particles. This theory is quantum chromodynamics, or QCD. QCD is now recognised as the correct theory of the strong force. It has passed every test to which it has been subjected in particle accelerator experiments. According to QCD, all the particles that feel the strong force are composed of combinations of quarks and anti-quarks that are held together by the exchange of gluons. Crucially, the gluons also feel the strong force, and this makes the force quite different to electromagnetism.

Photons are not electrically charged so, although they are exchanged to produce the electromagnetic force, they do not feel the force themselves. This means that the electromagnetic force falls away gradually with distance. By contrast, the mutual interaction of gluons means that the gluons that are exchanged between two quarks are squeezed into a thin tube between the quarks, with the result that the strength of the force actually increases with distance. We now know that the particles that physicists classify as 'mesons', which originally meant 'middle weight particles', are formed of a quark and an antiquark, bound together by the exchange of gluons. We have a fundamental understanding of how the strong force operates at the level of particle interactions, and we can now see how, in certain circumstances, it can mimic a string. The quark and the antiquark that are whirling around each other to form a meson are held together by a tube of gluons but, from a distance, they look like charges at the end of a string.

## How Long is a Piece of String?

Physicists had struggled to match some of the features of the string models to the physics of the strong force. In addition to the mini-violin strings known as 'open' strings, it was also possible to consider vibrating loops, known as 'closed' strings. In fact, the theory was only consistent if closed strings were included as well as open strings, because strings can only interact at their ends. In this way, two strings can join to become one. But the two string ends that are about to interact cannot know whether they belong to different strings or not, which means the possibility must exist for the two ends of an open string to join to form a closed string. This simple fact would lead to a complete re-evaluation of string theory.

The fundamental mode of vibration of a closed string looks identical to a massless spin 2 particle. This particle is impossible to reconcile with the physics of the strong force. Indeed, it is identical to the graviton, a particle whose exchange would produce the force of gravity in a quantum theory of gravity. Particle physicists had struggled for decades to find a consistent theory of quantum gravity; but string theorists now had quantum gravity thrust upon them and they could not get rid of it.

By the middle years of the 1970s, the stringy approach to the strong force had been abandoned by all except its most ardent supporters, but a small band of enthusiasts remained enchanted by the remarkable properties of the theory. They held a passionate belief that strings were so astonishing that they must play a role in the architecture of the universe. Two of those who kept the faith were an American theorist called John Schwarz and his French colleague, Joël Scherk. In 1974, they realised that it might be possible to turn string theory on its head and make a virtue out of one of its vices. They decided that, instead of trying to adapt string theory, perhaps they should accept what the theory was telling them and see where it would lead. If it was impossible to get rid of the closed strings with their graviton-like vibrations, then maybe string theorists should accept that their theory was not applicable to the physics of the strong force, but that it might play a much more fundamental role in nature. It might be more natural to consider string theory as a theory of gravity.

If string theory were to be resurrected as a much more fundamental theory, then this would require a complete reassessment of the size of the strings. When modelling the strong force, it was assumed that strings must be around the size of a meson or a proton. This meant that the length of the string would be about $10^{-15}$ metres, which is around a tenth of the size of an atomic nucleus or one hundred thousandth of the size of an atom. This would imply that string vibrations would have an energy equivalent to the masses of the mesons and other particles observed in accelerator experiments.

Scherk and Schwarz offered a brave reappraisal of the role of strings in physics – one that would imply a dramatic rescaling of the dimensions of string physics. If strings were to explain gravity, then their size must correspond to the length scale on which quantum effects become important in gravity. As we saw in an earlier chapter, this distance is known as the Planck length, and it is a minuscule $10^{-35}$ metres. The energy required to excite such a string would be correspondingly much higher than in the original incarnation of strings. The harmonics of the string would produce particles with a mass in the region of the Planck mass, which is $10^{19}$ GeV. This is around a million billion times the energy released by the proton collisions in the Large Hadron Collider, and it is an almost inconceivable energy for a single particle to carry. Which means that we should not expect any strings to be excited into their higher harmonic vibrational states, except in the most extreme circumstances, such as the Big Bang or at the heart of a black hole. The excited states play an important role in the theory. They must be retained if the theory is to make sense, but they are very much in the background and we should not expect to see them in normal circumstances. If string theory is correct, then the whole of our everyday physics is due to the lowest modes of vibration of the strings.

## *The Magic Circle*

String theory naturally incorporates gravity. More than that, it proved impossible to construct any type of string theory without gravity. Gravity was an inescapable feature of the string. So as long as the quantum version of the theory worked in a consistent way, then that long-sought elusive beast – a quantum theory of gravity – might almost be in the bag. This is where things became even more interesting. Reconciling gravity and quantum mechanics is almost, but not quite, impossible. For this reason, most string theories just do not work, as we will soon see.

What makes string theory truly remarkable is that it does not just include gravity. The lowest mode of vibration of an open string is a massless spin 1 particle. This is a particle that we would recognise as a photon. We can make the string even more alluring by attaching charges to the ends of the string. Essentially, these charges are just like the quark and antiquark within a meson. If we do this then, instead of the lowest mode describing a single spin 1 particle, there will be a number of massless spin 1 particles, corresponding to the different charge combinations of the string. These are particles that we would recognise as gluons.

String theory seems to automatically incorporate the symmetries in just the right way to make everything fit. Just as the existence of graviton-like vibrations implies that the theory incorporates the spacetime symmetries of general relativity, so the existence of gluon-like vibrations implies that the symmetries of Yang-Mills forces like QCD have been correctly included in the theory. Something very subtle seems to be going on behind the scenes. The new interpretation of strings offered the possibility of a total unification of all the forces and particles within a single theory. This was all great news for the few physicists who took an interest in this esoteric and highly speculative branch of fundamental physics. But don't break open the champagne just yet! There were other features of string theory that were not so appealing.

## Klingons on the Starboard Bow

> If we fire an inverse tachyon beam into the anomaly, quantum decoherence should re-stabilize the chroniton field.
>
> *Star Trek*

String theory looked promising; any prospect of a quantum theory of gravity was worth a thorough investigation. However, string theory had some serious drawbacks that cast doubt on its role as a unified theory. First, although the fundamental string vibrations could describe force-carrying particles that look like photons, gluons and gravitons, there were no vibrations that could be interpreted as matter particles, such as electrons, quarks and neutrinos. In particle physics language, force-exchange particles are known as bosons and matter particles are known as fermions. The string vibrations could explain bosons, but not fermions, and so the original version of string theory is called the *bosonic string*.

To describe the fundamental forces of nature, it is necessary to construct quantum theories that satisfy the principles of relativity. After all, the theory must work when particles are travelling at or near to the speed of light. But, quantum mechanics and relativity do not bind together easily, so finding any such theories that are mathematically consistent is a tall order, and this is why a quantum theory of gravity is so elusive. Now, although string theory seemed to provide a route to a quantum theory of gravity, it was soon realised that the theory only works in 26-dimensional spacetime. This was slightly embarrassing, as the first prediction of string theory appeared to be that the universe should have 25 spatial dimensions, rather than the three that we are aware of.

This might sound bad, but there was another problem that was even worse. The mass of the lightest particle represented by the string was negative. Such a particle is known as a tachyon (from the Greek *tachys* meaning fast), because it would appear that it must always travel faster than the speed of light. These particles are well known to fans of *Star Trek* (if not to particle physicists). Unfortunately, rather than allowing faster-than-light signalling, or enabling your starship to exceed Warp Factor 1, the presence of tachyons in the theory is interpreted to mean that the theory is inconsistent – or at least that it is not a suitable model for the real universe. These features seemed to imply that string theory was fatally flawed. However, the subject was still young and vibrant, and it was hoped that further research would iron out the wrinkles.

## Superstrings

> Nature uses only the longest threads to weave her patterns, so each small piece of her fabric reveals the organisation of the entire tapestry.
>
> R. P. Feynman, *The Character of Physical Law.*

String theorists are very imaginative and determined people, and progress was swift. Their theory was reborn in a new guise that incorporated supersymmetry (this was how supersymmetry was originally discovered). As described in the previous chapter, supersymmetric theories are built around a partnership between matter particles and force carriers so that, for every force-carrying particle, there is a matter particle and vice versa. The new supersymmetric string theory – or *superstring theory*, as it is known – therefore contains both fermions and bosons. There are no negative energy states in supersymmetric theories so, as a bonus, supersymmetry automatically did away with any nasty tachyonic particles, and this potentially disastrous feature of the original string theory was resolved.

Superstring theory now had reasonable prospects of being moulded into the first serious contender for the title of Theory of Everything – that is, a theory that would explain all forces and particles – effectively, a theory that would wrap up fundamental physics and provide us with answers to all our deepest questions, such as how the universe began and why it is like it is.

What about the embarrassing number of extra dimensions? Since Einstein, we have known that gravity is all about matter warping space and, as string theory incorporates gravity, it should be able to tell us something about the shape of space. This is, indeed, the case. Superstring theory is only viable in a universe consisting of nine space dimensions in addition to the time dimension! This is an improvement on the bosonic string, but the problem has not exactly been cured in superstring theory. Maybe this isn't so great after all!

If the answer had turned out to be that the one viable theory demanded three space dimensions, then theorists would have been jumping for joy. They might have claimed that an age-old mystery had been solved. But nine dimensions of space? If such a restriction on a theory had occurred in any other branch of physics, then the theory would have been discarded as just another pretty, but incorrect, theory of physics. But string theorists are aiming for the ultimate theory, and such a theory must be able to account for the fundamental nature of space and time – so maybe we should just take it on the chin and see where it leads us. Perhaps we can turn the extra six dimensions to our advantage. After all, the four dimensions of spacetime are well accounted for by gravitation. Maybe the other six dimensions play a role in the dynamics of the other forces and the properties of the particles that feel these forces.

There were still doubts about whether superstring theory would work as a quantum theory. Essentially, would all the wonderful symmetry encapsulated within the theory survive in the quantum version of the theory?

## *The Superstring Revolution*

In 1984, John Schwarz and the British theorist Mike Green triggered the first superstring revolution by proving that the symmetries of superstring theory do, indeed, survive in the quantum version of the theory, as they must if the theory is to make sense as a potential ultimate theory. A major hurdle had been crossed in the progress of the theory and suddenly everyone was interested. In the process Green and Schwarz had shown that the possible Yang-Mills symmetries in the ten-dimensional superstring theory were very limited. There were just two alternatives described by the Lie groups SO(32) and $E_8 \times E_8$.

This was a remarkable result; particle physicists can select whatever symmetry group they like when forming a theory. Of course, the aim is to match the symmetry groups to those that describe the real world. But if the symmetries of the standard model prove to be part of some larger GUT symmetry group, there is nothing to prevent physicists from choosing a more appropriate symmetry group. String theory is very different: there are just two choices. If neither of these options describes the real world, then string theory must be ruled out. This got physicists very excited. If we believe in an ultimate theory of the universe that explains the whole of physics, then the fundamental symmetry at the heart of the theory must be very special. It should, in some sense, be pre-determined and not arbitrary.

The two viable groups are closely related. (SO(32) is the group of rotations in 32 dimensions; it is an internal symmetry of the theory, so these are not 32 dimensions of real physical space.) Both symmetry groups are huge by comparison with the standard model. They would produce theories of forces that are generated by the exchange of 496 gluons (as these theories are supersymmetric, they would also include 496 matter particles). Compare this to the standard model, which requires the exchange of just 12 bosonic particles: one – the photon – to produce electromagnetism; three – the $W^+$, $W^-$ and $Z^0$ – to produce the weak force; and eight gluons to produce the strong or colour force.

### E is for Ecstasy

It was the $E_8 \times E_8$ symmetry that really attracted attention ($E_8 \times E_8$ simply means two independent copies of the group $E_8$). The following diversion will give some idea of what is special about $E_8$.

The game of classification is a great pastime for all geometers. We have already taken a quick look at the efforts of knot theorists to classify knots. The aim is to collect a complete set of objects with a particular property. For instance, the Platonic solids are polyhedra whose faces are all of one type of regular polygon, with the same number of polygons meeting at each vertex. The geometers of Ancient Greece proved that there are only five such polyhedra. This simple fact fired Kepler's lifelong search for the laws of astronomy. What if the restriction to a single type of polygon is lifted? Then we have a new set of polyhedra known as the semi-regular polyhedra, whose faces are polygons of more than one type. The full set of these polyhedra was also known in ancient times.

For example, the triangular prism has two equilateral triangle faces with three square faces between them. We can form a type of prism by placing a sequence of square faces between any pair of identical regular polygons, so the triangular prism is the first member of an infinite family of prisms. Each member of the series is a semi-regular polyhedron.

---

**Puzzle 11**

If a triangular prism has three square faces, a pentagonal prism has five square faces and a hexagonal prism has six square faces, how many square faces does a square prism have?

---

There is a second family known as the antiprisms, in which a pair of identical polygons is separated by a sequence of equilateral triangles. Each member of the infinite series of antiprisms is also a semi-regular polyhedron.

These two families do not exhaust the list of semi-regular polyhedra. For instance, there is the truncated cube, which can be constructed by cutting the corners from a cube.

---

**Puzzle 12**

If a square antiprism has eight triangular faces, a pentagonal antiprism has ten triangular faces and a hexagonal antiprism has twelve triangular faces, how many triangular faces does a triangular antiprism have?

---

The truncated cube has eight triangular faces and six octagonal faces. Altogether, there are thirteen semi-regular polyhedra that do not belong to either of the two families. These polyhedra were first listed by Archimedes and, for this reason, they are known as the Archimedean polyhedra.

The classification of the semi-regular polyhedra is quite typical. Geometers often find that there are one or more infinite families, plus a fairly small number of exceptional cases.[3] Each member of a family can be constructed using a general method that will work in every case. By contrast, construction of the exceptional cases will only work in a few special cases or it may even be unique. This makes the existence of the exceptional examples more surprising and, for this reason, they attract much more attention from mathematicians.

---

**Answer to Puzzle 11**

The square prism is identical to a cube. It has six square faces.

---

**Answer to Puzzle 12**

The triangular antiprism is identical to the octahedron. It has eight triangular faces.

---

The answers to these two puzzles show some simple geometrical quirks or coincidences among the first few members of these infinite series. Similar mathematical quirks play a role in the existence of the exceptional geometrical objects.

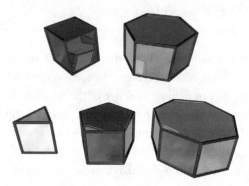

**Figure 89** The first five members of the family of regular prisms. Top row: square prism (or cube), hexagonal prism. Bottom row: triangular prism, pentagonal prism, heptagonal prism.

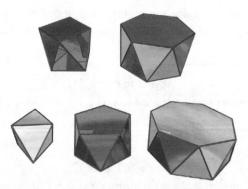

**Figure 90** The first five members of the family of regular antiprisms. Top row: square antiprism, hexagonal antiprism. Bottom row: triangular antiprism (or octahedron), pentagonal antiprism, heptagonal antiprism.

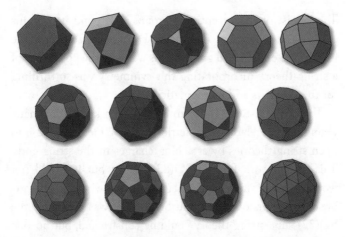

**Figure 91** The Archimedean Polyhedra – these are the 13 exceptional semi-regular polyhedra that do not belong to either of the families. From left to right. Top Row: truncated tetrahedron, cuboctahedron, truncated cube, truncated octahedron, rhombicuboctahedron.
Middle Row: truncated cuboctahedron, snub cube, icosidodecahedron, truncated dodecahedron.
Bottom Row: truncated icosahedron, rhombicosidodecahedron, truncated icosidodecahedron, snub dodecahedron.

Just like Kepler, modern unifiers are attempting to tune in to the fundamental harmonies of the universe and ask whether it is constructed from a beautiful geometrical master plan – and the evidence suggests that it might be. If this is true, then what are the special geometries on which its architecture is based? The Lie groups that sit at the heart of our modern understanding of the forces of nature were classified by the French mathematician Elie Cartan in 1894, long before their application to the forces of nature was dreamt of. He proved that there are four infinite families of Lie groups (SO(32) belongs to one of these families). There are also five exceptional Lie groups that do not belong to one of the families.

The largest of the exceptional groups is $E_8$, and it contains each of the other four. This makes $E_8$ rather special; it is the king of the exceptional groups. This was why the possibility of a string theory incorporating this symmetry was so thrilling for the theorists and mathematicians.

There was just one problem. It had been known for many years that Yang-Mills symmetries could be incorporated into open string theories by attaching charges to the string ends. This would work for the $SO(32)$ theory, but it would not work for any of the exceptional groups. Following the groundbreaking results of Green and Schwarz, it was clear how the $SO(32)$ superstring theory could be constructed, but no-one knew how to construct a superstring theory that incorporated the $E_8 \times E_8$ symmetry. Surely there had to be a way! The possibility of such a theory was just too good not to be true.

## The Harvard String Quartet

In 1985, the missing string theory was revealed in a remarkable construction devised by David Gross, Jeffrey Harvey, Emil Martinec and Ryan Rohm, otherwise known as the Harvard String Quartet. They combined features of the bosonic string with features of the superstring to construct what they called the *heterotic string*. The heterotic string is a supersymmetric ten-dimensional theory of closed strings that incorporates either the $SO(32)$ or $E_8 \times E_8$ symmetries. These symmetries are not due to charges at the string ends (the heterotic string theories do not include any open strings, so there are no string ends); the charges are distributed around the closed strings.

The existence of the $E_8 \times E_8$ heterotic string raised the excitement over string theory to fever pitch. Not only is $E_8$ a unique esoteric group, but it is also a great starting point for the enormous leap down to the familiar physics of the standard model. It simultaneously captures both the mathematically sophisticated essence of string theory and the hope of finding a link to established physics. The two $E_8$ components are completely separate. The whole of the standard model could be incorporated into one of the $E_8$ components, so what about the other $E_8$? It was highly speculative, but it might mean that matter is divided into two sectors that only interact with each other gravitationally. If all ordinary matter is formed of particles that interact due to the standard model forces that originate with one $E_8$, then perhaps there is a whole world of other particles that interact together with forces originating in the other $E_8$. This would be a 'hidden sector' that we would only be aware of through its gravitational effect on ordinary matter. Maybe, in this way, the $E_8 \times E_8$ heterotic string could provide a natural answer to the existence of dark matter.

An $E_8$ symmetry group would mean that there are eight different charges carried by fundamental particles. These particles would come in sets of 248, with each particle carrying its own combination of the eight charges. The full set of particles could be plotted as the vertices of a geometrical structure in eight-dimensional space.[4] As this is more than the number of dimensions available to us, the edges and vertices of this structure have been projected down to two dimensions to produce the illustration shown as Plate 11. This illustration should be compared with the much simpler octet of particles shown in Figure 81, which is the equivalent structure for the QCD symmetry group.

With the discovery of the $E_8 \times E_8$ heterotic string, it appeared as though a viable Theory of Everything might have been discovered. The theory seemed to represent just about the only way in which a quantum theory of both gravity and

Yang-Mills forces could be constructed that would include the standard model forces and matter particles. Theorists could now argue that all that remained to be done was to find the connections between this theory and the standard model; it was simply a matter of proving that the low energy limit of string theory was precisely the forces and particles encapsulated within the standard model.

There is a huge gulf between the natural energy scale of strings, which is the Planck energy, and the energies that can be attained at the LHC. The LHC is designed to produce proton collisions at energies of 14 TeV, i.e. around $10^4$ GeV – way below the energies where gravity is expected to play a role in particle collisions. Nevertheless, string theorists are bold enough to attempt to leap this grand canyon in energy.

## *The Shape of Space*

If string theory is to be a useful description of the universe, it is necessary to make contact with the real world of established physics. The most startling feature of string theory is that it only works in a universe with nine spatial dimensions and one time dimension. This would seem to be six spatial dimensions too many to fit the world that we inhabit. However, we shouldn't be too hasty. As string theory incorporates Einstein's general relativity, it is responsible for determining the geometrical structure of spacetime. Somehow, the collective behaviour of the string field might mould the background spacetime through which the strings move.

It is possible that not all dimensions are created equal. String theorists assume that the extra six dimensions must be very small – so small that we are completely unaware of their spatial extension. It is usually assumed that they are comparable in size to the Planck length, which would make them far too small to probe in any conceivable experiment. However, this does not mean that these six dimensions do not matter and can just be forgotten. Far from it, string theorists expect that the way in which these dimensions are wrapped up is crucially important for the properties of our universe. The structure into which the six tiny dimensions are wrapped is expected to determine the properties of the non-gravitational forces and the fundamental particles that are observed in particle accelerators.

So, how can dimensions curl up, such that we are unaware of them? According to string theorists, we have three macroscopic spatial dimensions that have been expanding since the Big Bang, but there are also six tiny spatial dimensions that have not expanded.[5] We are not aware of these additional hidden dimensions, as they are tiny even when compared to the size of an atomic nucleus. String theorists refer to these hidden dimensions as *compactified*.[6]

Compactification of hidden dimensions is similar to Kaluza's idea from 1919. In the original Kaluza-Klein theory, there was a hidden circular dimension which gave rise to the electromagnetic force. In general, Kaluza-Klein theories use the symmetries of hidden dimensions to explain the non-gravitational forces of our universe. The role of the hidden dimensions in string theory is slightly different. Our current understanding of particle physics is encapsulated by the standard model. String theory is a ten-dimensional theory with far more symmetry than is required to explain the physics of the standard model. One of the requirements of realistic string compactification schemes, as they are known, is that most of the symmetry must be broken in order to begin a conversation with the well-established physics of the real world.

There are an enormous number of ways to curl up the six extra dimensions of string theory. One of the tasks faced by string theorists is to determine the shape of these hidden dimensions. As we have said, the shape of these dimensions determines the properties of physics in the macroscopic universe. This is because the strings can wrap themselves around the hidden dimensions, and this will affect the energy of the strings and the symmetry between different string states. The strategy that theorists have adopted is to explore the possible geometries of the hidden dimensions in order to search for a structure that would produce physics resembling established physics.

If there were just a single hidden dimension, the possibilities would be very limited. The hidden dimension could only form a line segment or a circle. With two hidden dimensions, there would be many more options. One interesting possibility is that the two hidden dimensions would form a torus. This is the name that mathematicians give to objects that are shaped like a tyre. The torus has been used as a toy model to study compactifications, but it cannot reproduce the physics of the real world. Plate 12 shows a collection of beads wrapped around a torus to form a torus knot.

## *Making Contact with the Real World*

> *Real World* – A well-known piece of international cinema, of little artistic value, but enormous popular appeal.
>
> Thomas Banks, *Modern Quantum Field Theory: A Concise Introduction* (Cambridge University Press, 2008), p. 63 footnote 3.

Einstein showed us that gravity determines the shape of space and time. String theorists believe that gravity also moulds the shape of hidden dimensions, and that these extra dimensions thereby control the form taken by the other forces. Potentially, this represents a complete geometrisation of fundamental physics. It could be seen as the culmination of Einstein's search for a unified field theory.

We can now take a closer look at the six hidden dimensions to see what their structure implies for the real-world physics currently being explored at the LHC. Is it possible that the extra dimensions might curl up in just the right way to explain the physics of the standard model? If there is a unique way to curl up these dimensions that leads to the correct physics, then maybe we have cracked it and string theory really is the ultimate theory that physicists are seeking.

Most theorists think that supersymmetry is a fundamental component of any viable unified theory of particle physics. For this reason, their first requirement for a good compactification scheme is that it must produce a real-world theory that exhibits supersymmetry. As we have seen, supersymmetry is a symmetry between matter particles and force-carrying particles. It implies that matter particles and force-carrying particles must come in pairs – for every matter particle there is a partner force-carrying particle, and vice versa. Strictly speaking, supersymmetry is not an essential feature of string compactification, as it is yet to be observed in collider experiments. Nonetheless, supersymmetry has many very elegant properties that are useful for tying up some of the loose ends of the standard model, so most theorists expect that it will be found in particle colliders in the near future. String theory in ten dimensions is necessarily supersymmetric, so this is a good start. But, according to string theorists, the survival of supersymmetry in the particle physics of the familiar four-dimensional world of space and time where we live is determined by the structure of the hidden dimensions.

The simplest compactification schemes, such as those on a torus, produce too much supersymmetry in particle physics. In other schemes, supersymmetry would be lost completely. But there is a type of six-dimensional manifold or hypersurface that will produce just the right amount of supersymmetry in particle physics. In 1976, the Chinese mathematician Shing-Tung Yau solved a puzzle that had been posed by the Italian mathematician Eugenio Calabi.[7] This was great timing because, just a few years later, the solutions would turn out to be exactly what string theorists were looking for. The special Goldilocks-like hypersurfaces are the ones that were first explored by Calabi and Yau. They are known to mathematicians as Calabi-Yau manifolds. If we insist, and most theorists do, that we want our particle physics to be supersymmetric, then the six compactified dimensions must form a Calabi-Yau manifold.[8] One of the first such manifolds to be investigated is known as the quintic hypersurface. It is shown in Plate 13.

Where does this leave us with regard to the other features that we would like from a successful compactification scheme? If string theory is to be the ultimate theory, then it must account for all the forces and particles described by the standard model. The standard model combines the GWS theory of the electroweak force and QCD – the theory of the strong force. Together, these two forces are symmetrical under the group $SU(3) \times SU(2) \times U(1)$. These symmetries fit neatly within the grand unified groups $SU(5)$ or $SO(10)$, which fit within one of the $E_8$s of the $E_8 \times E_8$ heterotic string. Compactification on a Calabi-Yau hypersurface breaks much of the $E_8$ symmetry. There are string compactification schemes that come very close to producing the standard model symmetry group. But most such schemes also include other forces in addition to the electroweak and strong forces. Physicists at the LHC are on the lookout for any signs that such extra forces exist.

String theory must also explain the collection of matter particles that the forces act upon. There are twelve known matter particles and they fall naturally into three generations, each of four particles, as shown in the table in the previous chapter. The first generation consists of the four lightest particles: the electron; the electron neutrino and the up and down quarks. The second and third generations are heavier replicas of these particles. So, for instance, the electron has two relatives that carry the same charges and therefore interact in the same way, but are much heavier. These are the muon, which is just over 200 times the mass of the electron and the tauon, which is close to 3,500 times the mass of the electron.

Physicists do not yet have any explanation for this apparent replication of the matter particles, but, if string theory is to be the correct ultimate theory, then it should be able to provide the answer. As we will see below, the hidden dimensions of string theory offer a possible explanation, and it gives a nice insight into how string theorists use geometry to explain physics. To set the scene, we need to take a brief excursion into the weird world of rubber geometry, known to mathematicians as topology.

---

**Puzzle 13**

Count the numbers of faces, edges and vertices (otherwise known as corners) of a cube, and call these numbers F, E and V respectively. What is the value of $Q = F - E + V$?

Count the numbers of faces, edges and vertices of a tetrahedron. What is the value of $Q = F - E + V$ for the tetrahedron?

---

## The Topology of the Universe

Topologists concern themselves with the most fundamental structural features of geometrical objects. These are the features that are unchanged by any amount of stretching and warping. In topology, distance does not matter. If two objects can be morphed into each other without any tearing, they are considered to be identical. A cup is topologically equivalent to a doughnut, for instance, which is why the tea-break can be so confusing in the maths department.

It is one thing to declare that we are not interested in any distance relationships, but quite another to do anything useful with it. This idea only has value if there exist quantities that remain unchanged under such distortions. Mathematicians know them as topological invariants. These numbers encode the fundamental structure of an object. It is the essence of an object that will not change, no matter how much it is pulled, twisted and distorted, as long as it is not cut or torn. We have already seen an example of a topological invariant earlier in this chapter – the crossing number of a knot.

---

**Answer to Puzzle 13**

A cube has six faces, twelve edges and eight vertices, so $Q = 6 - 12 + 8 = 2$. A tetrahedron has four faces, six edges and four vertices, so $Q = 4 - 6 + 4 = 2$.

---

Although polyhedra have different numbers of faces, edges and vertices, there is a combination of these three numbers that is the same for all polyhedra (or at least the ones that we are most familiar with). The combination $F - E + V$ is known as the Euler number of a polyhedron. It is always equal to the number 2. Try another example – the icosahedron: 20 faces, 30 edges, 12 vertices.

Although it is named after the 18th century Swiss mathematician Leonard Euler, this simple property of polyhedra was certainly known to René Descartes at least a century before Euler's time. It is actually a topological invariant. If we imagine inflating a rubber polyhedron until all its edges are smoothed out and it morphs into a smooth surface, then it so happens that the Euler number is only equal to 2 if the polyhedron is topologically equivalent to a sphere.[9] What happens if we make a polyhedron with a hole in it?

---

**Puzzle 14**

How many faces, edges and vertices does the polyhedron have in the figure below? What is its Euler number?

---

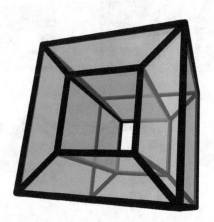

**Figure 92** A polyhedron that is topologically equivalent to a torus.

**Answer to Puzzle 14**

The polyhedron shown in the figure has sixteen faces, thirty-two edges and sixteen vertices. Its Euler number is $Q = 16 - 32 - 16 = 0$.

The Euler number of the polyhedron in the figure above is zero! If the polyhedron were inflated, it would not turn into a sphere – it would become a torus. In other words, the polyhedron is topologically equivalent to a torus. It is natural to extend the idea of the Euler number to smooth surfaces, such as spheres and tori. This means that the Euler number of a sphere is 2 and the Euler number of a torus is 0. In general, each handle[10] that is added to a surface decreases the Euler number of the surface by 2.[11]

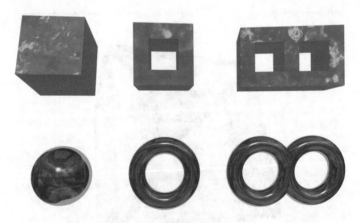

**Figure 93** Above: Three polyhedra. Below: The surfaces that are their topological equivalents. From left to right: Sphere (Euler number 2), Torus (Euler number 0), Double Torus (Euler number −2).

The Euler number can be defined in a similar way in higher dimensions. The relationship between the Euler number and the holes is quite similar, even though there are many more strange and exotic ways for a surface to curl up in higher dimensions.

String theory's hidden dimensions might explain why physicists see several generations of fundamental matter particles in their accelerator experiments. When strings twist around the holes in the six-dimensional hypersurface, it affects the string vibrations and the particles that they correspond to. It is rather surprising, but the number of generations of matter particles that we see in the standard model could be determined by the topology of the compactified space. It turns out that the Euler number of the hypersurface would be equal to twice the number of generations. The Euler number of the quintic hypersurface shown in Plate 13 is 200, which means that it cannot be the correct shape of the hidden dimensions, as it would produce a total of 100 generations of matter particles (which is 97 generations too many).

The quintic hypersurface can be used as the starting point for a more promising hypersurface. It has two separate five-fold symmetries. Some of this symmetry can be discerned in the illustration. By using these symmetries to fold up and 'glue' the hypersurface, it is possible to create a new Calabi-Yau hypersurface, with fewer holes and an Euler number that is correspondingly reduced to $Q = 200/(5 \times 5) = 200/25 = 8$. Compactification on this hypersurface would produce physics with just four generations of matter particles. This is still too many as we know that, in the real world, there are three generations and no more, but it is encouragingly close. Several Calabi-Yau hypersurfaces have now been discovered with an Euler number equal to six that would produce the three generations that we see.

## *Green, Schwarz and Witten*

The rate of development of string theory in the middle years of the 1980s was such that the end of fundamental physics seemed to be in sight. Many theorists believed that there were just a few loose ends to tie up before string theory could be proclaimed as the ultimate theory of physics. Green and Schwarz teamed up with Ed Witten to write the definitive book about superstring theory. Ed Witten is based at the Institute of Advanced Study in Princeton, where Einstein spent his later years. Witten has an incredible intuition for maths and physics. He has attracted some of the world's leading theorists to work with him, but his insights are so out of the ordinary that his PhD students have been known to refer to him affectionately as 'The Martian'.

In January, 1987, the world's oldest publishing house, Cambridge University Press, published Green, Schwarz and Witten's two-volume *Superstring Theory*. The work was timed to coincide with the 300th anniversary of the publication of Newton's *Principia* by the same publisher, the implication being that the monumental new work might prove to be as important as its great predecessor. Stephen Hawking retired in 2009 and Mike Green was appointed the new Lucasian Professor of Mathematics in Cambridge and now holds the post once held by Isaac Newton.

The elation of the 1980s eventually dissipated, with the realisation that the path to low energy physics was not going to be an easy one. There were just too many possibilities. By the 1990s, string theory appeared to be stagnating. However, just as string theory was beginning to lose its impetus, a new wave of bewildering ideas gave it a further stimulus.

## *From Membranes to Pea Brains*

Having taken the great leap from point particles to one-dimensional strings, one question that comes to mind is, why stop at one dimension? In other words, what about vibrating two-dimensional membranes or three-dimensional blobs? And if the theory demands nine spatial dimensions, what about entities with four, five, six or more dimensions? Is there something special about one-dimensional objects?

It turns out that one-dimensional strings do have special mathematical properties, but that the structure of string theory is even more complex than originally believed. If strings can determine the geometry of space in its entirety, then it is only natural that there should be string field excitations corresponding to objects with spatial extensions of any number of dimensions from zero (i.e. point particles) up to nine dimensions. The two-dimensional objects are known as membranes. They would look like a vibrating drum or a hollow sphere. In general, these objects are known as p-branes, which is a light-hearted contraction of 'p-dimensional membrane'. In other words, 'p' refers to the number of spatial dimensions that the object occupies – so that, for instance, a membrane might also be known as a 2-brane.

P-branes are collective modes of the string field, which makes a 1-brane analogous to a vortex line in a fluid. Thus, the theory includes the fundamental strings that we started with, as well as these new vortex strings, plus all their higher dimensional equivalents. You might think that this complicates matters somewhat, and you would be right. We started with vibrating strings and now we have an embarrassment of riches – an entire zoo full of vibrating p-branes. There was another side to the second string revolution – the discovery of string dualities.

## *String Dualities*

String theory is the first plausible answer to the unifier's dream of an ultimate theory. We might expect such a theory to be unique, taking the view that the universe must be as it is because there is only one way to make a universe, and this is it. However, string theory is not quite the unique theory that we might have hoped for. Several different variants have already been mentioned. There are five different superstring theories, which is rather puzzling. Theorists realised, during the 1990s, that there are subtle connections between the different types of superstring that are known as dualities.

Duality is the term used by mathematicians to express a reciprocal relationship. Polyhedra exhibit a geometrical duality that we will take a look at before returning to strings. The midpoints of the faces of a regular polyhedron are the vertices of a second regular polyhedron. For example, the midpoints of the faces of a cube are the vertices of an octahedron. By connecting these points to their nearest neighbours, we can find the edges of the octahedron and, thereby, inscribe the octahedron in the cube. Similarly, the midpoints of the faces of the octahedron are the vertices of a cube, so we can also inscribe a cube within the octahedron. The cube and the octahedron are dual to each other.[12] Performing the duality operation twice returns us to our starting point.[13]

---

**Puzzle 14**

The tetrahedron has four triangular faces. It has six edges and four vertices. What polyhedron is dual to the tetrahedron?

---

The icosahedron and the dodecahedron are another pair of dual polyhedra. In general, a duality operation converts one object into a second and simultaneously converts the second object into the first, so that if the duality transformation is applied a second time, we are back where we started from.

In addition to the two heterotic string theories, there are three other superstring theories that are classified as the type I, type IIA and type IIB theories. All five theories are ten-dimensional theories. Although they appear quite different, they are related by dualities. The first of the string dualities is a transformation of length scales. Short distances in one string theory correspond to long distances in another. This is called T-duality. If the Planck length is the natural scale for string

**Figure 94** Dual polyhedra. Left: Tetrahedron with a second tetrahedron inscribed. The tetrahedron is self-dual. Centre: Cube with inscribed octahedron. The cube and octahedron are dual polyhedra. Right: Dodecahedron with inscribed icosahedron. The dodecahedron and icosahedron are dual polyhedra.

---

**Answer to Puzzle 14**

As can be seen from the figure above, the midpoints of the faces of a tetrahedron are the vertices of a second tetrahedron, so the tetrahedron is dual to itself. Mathematicians describe it as being 'self-dual'.

---

theory, then when we examine one string theory at distances greater than the Planck length, the theory looks exactly like another theory at distances smaller than the Planck length.

This might mean that there is a natural cut-off in string theory. Physics below the Planck scale is rather ill-defined; space might appear like a random foam. But perhaps we do not need to worry about this because, as soon as space seems to be getting too choppy, we can transform to the dual string theory, where we are working at longer distance scales. T-duality relates the two heterotic theories, which means that the SO(32) theory at short distances is exactly the same as the $E_8 \times E_8$ theory at long distances, and vice versa. T-duality relates the type IIA and type IIB theories in exactly the same way.

The second string duality is known as S-duality. It is a transformation in the strength with which the force is transmitted. It is very difficult to perform calculations with strong forces.[14] However, one string theory in the regime where the force is strong is equivalent to a second string theory where the force is weak. Like T-duality, it seems that, just as we are about to lose our understanding of the theory, we can switch to the dual theory, where our life becomes a lot easier.

S-duality relates the type I theory to the SO(32) heterotic theory, and the type IIB theory is self-dual under S-duality. The effect of increasing the strength of the interaction in the type IIA and $E_8 \times E_8$ theories is much stranger. In these two cases, as the strength of the force increases, the theories seem to grow an extra dimension and turn into a new 11-dimensional theory. The low energy particle content of this theory corresponds to that of the theory known as 11-dimensional supergravity, mentioned in the previous chapter.[15] With the discovery of these dualities, it became clear that the different string theories are very closely related.

## *Witten's Miracle Theory*

> 'They were learning to draw,' the Dormouse went on,
> yawning and rubbing its eyes, for it was getting very sleepy;
> 'and they drew all manner of things – everything that begins
> with an M.'
> 'Why with an M?' said Alice.
> 'Why not?' said the March Hare.
>
> Lewis Carroll, *Alice's Adventures in Wonderland*.

It was the arch-unifier himself, Ed Witten, who took the bold step of drawing all the threads together. In 1997, Witten spun a web of dualities and declared that, rather than considering these to be relationships between different string theories, in reality there could be just one theory, and the relationships were symmetries of that one overarching theory. Witten admitted that the fundamental principles of this theory were still unknown, but he felt that he had found the clues that would eventually lead to it. He named this miraculous and still mysterious theory 'M-Theory'. It is a theory from another planet.

String theory is a cruel mistress. She gives with one hand and takes away with the other. She tantalises us by promising everything, but never quite seems to reveal all. Even after around 35 years of development, the subject remains immature and full of surprises. Just like the works of Kepler, string theory probably contains a kernel of truth within a grand labyrinth of divine harmonies. It is an incredibly complicated collection of mathematical ideas and, increasingly, it has become a sophisticated branch of pure mathematics rather than a theory of physics.[16]

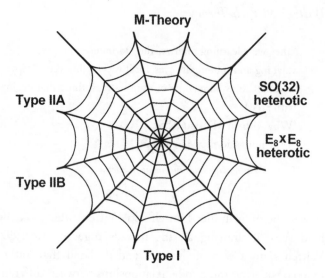

**M-Theory**

**Type IIA**

**SO(32) heterotic**

**E₈ × E₈ heterotic**

**Type IIB**

**Type I**

**Figure 95** The five string theories are tied together by a web of dualities. This suggests that they are all parts of a single all-embracing theory known as M-Theory.

Many physicists have been seduced, and it is very difficult to resist the allure of such an enchanting beauty. String theory is like the most beautiful and tantalising seductress tempting us with her charms, but her true nature remains a secret.

### *The Lie of the Land*

'What if the hokey cokey *really* is what it is all about?'

The six-dimensional Calabi-Yau hypersurfaces have not yet been classified, so no-one knows how many such hypersurfaces there are. There might be an infinite number. Furthermore, string theorists have no idea how nature might choose between the myriad possibilities. Although there are Calabi-Yau hypersurfaces that would produce the correct number of generations of particles, what makes these hypersurfaces more suitable for the creation of a universe than any of the other options? No-one knows. There is a whole landscape of possibilities. In fact, the question of explaining how string theory might choose is known as the landscape problem. It has cast doubt on whether theorists will ever be able to match the predictions of string theory to physics that can be tested in the laboratory.

Even so, it is, perhaps, a bit early to despair completely. There are some generic predictions of string theory that might turn up at the Large Hadron Collider. Supersymmetry could exist without string theory, but its discovery at the LHC would encourage theorists to believe that they are right to seek even greater symmetries in the structure of the laws of nature and, as supersymmetry fits so naturally within string theory, any sign of supersymmetry would be seen as a vindication of their efforts.

Most compactification schemes lead to extra forces beyond those of the standard model. Physicists at the LHC are on the look out for new bosonic particles that would mediate these forces. Again, it is possible that forces other than the electroweak and strong forces are at play in particle physics without the existence of string theory, but their discovery would be hailed as support for the ideas of string theorists.

We will now travel from these incredible speculations about the innermost heart of matter and the structure of space on the shortest conceivable length scales, to the latest advances in our understanding of space on the longest scales. We will visit the most powerful objects in the universe and travel back to the origin of the universe and the earliest moments in time.

## Chapter Ten

# ACROSS THE UNIVERSE

Sounds of laughter, shades of life
Are ringing through my opened ears
Inciting and inviting me.
Limitless undying love, which
Shines around me like a million suns,
It calls me on and on across the universe.

John Lennon and Paul McCartney, *Across the Universe*

A passing glance at the night sky might give the impression that the stars are scattered at random. However, this is not the case; the sky has its own geography. The planets are confined to a narrow ring near the ecliptic. The Milky Way defines another band across the night sky and, within this luminous arc, many of the gems of the night sky reside; there are open clusters, ghostly nebulae and dense star fields. This is also where the occasional outbursts of recurrent novae tend to be found. The Milky Way is the plane of our galaxy projected onto the night sky.

It is a hundred years since Einstein produced his extraordinary theory that describes gravity as curved spacetime. The world may look rather different to how it appeared a century ago, but the universe has changed out of all recognition. When Einstein completed his masterpiece in 1915, astronomers imagined that our Sun was one of countless stars in an island universe formed of the Milky Way. Other misty patches in the night sky, such as the Great Nebula of Andromeda, were believed to be gaseous regions within our own galaxy. The distance to these faint clouds was unknown.

The trillion or so stars that form our galaxy lie in a disc with several spiral arms. It is around 100,000 light years across, and we live within the disc about 26,000 light years from its centre. We now know that our galaxy is one of many. There are around 100 billion galaxies in the observable universe. The Andromeda galaxy is our closest galactic neighbour, apart from a few dwarf galaxies. It is just over two million light years distant and is believed to be similar in size and shape to our own galaxy.

In the 1920s, Edwin Hubble discovered that the characteristic lines in the spectrum of light from distant galaxies are shifted to the red end of the spectrum. This red shift indicates that the galaxies are racing away from us at an incredible rate. Hubble showed that the more remote the galaxy, the faster it is receding from us, which means that the entire universe is expanding. The red shift of spectral lines enabled astronomers to map out a vastly greater universe. Almost overnight, Hubble had dramatically enlarged the size of the universe.

**Figure 96** The Andromeda galaxy, which is thought to look similar to our own Milky Way galaxy. (© HST, NASA.)

## To the Ends of the Universe

Galileo first pointed a telescope at the night sky in the year 1609, just 400 years and a mere five lifetimes ago. There have been great advances in the equipment used by astronomers in the last four centuries and, in recent decades, the rate of improvement has been astonishing. Astronomers can now scan the heavens at all wavelengths, from radio waves to gamma rays, and with a much greater resolution than previous generations.

In the early years of radio astronomy, it was difficult to locate the exact position of the objects whose radio emissions were being detected. In 1963, an ingenious technique was used to pin down the position of one radio source catalogued as 3C 273, by timing the exact moment when it passed behind the Moon. The astronomer Maarten Schmidt used the precise location from this occultation to track down the object with what was then the world's largest optical telescope at the Hale observatory on Mount Palomar in California.[1] He recorded the object's optical spectrum, which would reveal the chemical elements that it contained. However, the spectral lines did not match any known elements – they were completely mysterious.

Eventually, Schmidt realised that the lines were the usual lines produced by elements such as hydrogen and helium, but they had undergone an enormous shift. The wavelength of each line was 16 percent greater than those measured in the laboratory. This huge red shift would imply that the distance to 3C 273 is an incredible two billion light years, making it the most luminous object ever discovered.

3C 273 was the first example of a new class of astronomical objects that appeared point-like, just as stars do, but with enormous red shifts. These objects were named *quasars* (quasi-stellar objects). If they really were located at the vast distances that their red shifts implied, then their energy output had to be gargantuan. Even some of the most daring astrophysicists of the day, such as Fred Hoyle, questioned the interpretation of the red shift-distance relationship in these cases, as the consequences appeared to be so outlandish.

The controversy persisted throughout the 1960s. It was not until the advent of much better telescopes, such as the Hubble Space Telescope in the 1990s, that astronomers could identify the galaxies that surround the quasars, proving that they really are located in the core regions of galaxies lying at immense distances. We now know that quasars are the sites of incredibly violent activity at the centres of extremely faint and distant galaxies. Quasars fluctuate in brightness over very short periods of times – as short as a few hours – which means that the central powerhouse of a quasar must be very small indeed – just a few light hours across. They are the most extreme examples of what have become known as active galactic nuclei.

There are much closer active galactic nuclei that offer clues to the nature of the beasts that lie within their core. Some of these objects appear to be the source of immense jets of material spewing into intergalactic space. Cygnus A is one of the most powerful radio sources in the sky. It lies at a distance of 600 million light years, which is a huge distance, but it is still much closer than the quasars. The radio waves that it emits originate in two enormous lobes of plasma that are being created as two oppositely directed jets plough into intergalactic space, as shown in the figure below. The jets are emanating from the centre of a galaxy which is not visible in the image. The object that is producing the jets must be incredibly stable, as the jets have been fired in the same straight lines for millions of years.

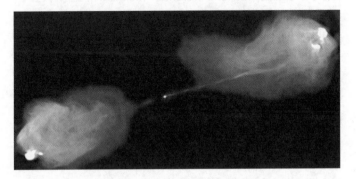

**Figure 97** The hyperluminous radio galaxy Cygnus A, showing intense jets and lobes that are thought to be issuing from a supermassive black hole. (© NRAO/AUI. Investigators: R. Perley, C. Carilli & J. Dreher.)

## *The Ultimate Power Source*

Quasars are the brightest objects in the universe with, perhaps, a trillion times the energy output of the Sun. This is equivalent to transforming several stars' worth of material into pure energy every year in accordance with Einstein's famous relationship between mass and energy. And all this from an object that appears to be about the size of the solar system. So what can possibly be powering these colossal beacons from the edge of the universe?

The sheer scale of the energy generated by quasars rules out most possible energy sources. Einstein showed that mass is just another form of energy, and that even a small amount of mass is equivalent to a huge amount of energy. In any process in which energy is released, an equivalent amount of mass must be lost. In the processes we are most familiar with, such as chemical reactions, this mass loss is tiny. For instance, the explosive power of TNT is well known. When TNT ignites, a large amount of energy is released. But, this corresponds to the loss of a mere five millionths of a percent of the mass of the TNT.

Only in nuclear reactions does the mass loss become measurable. Nuclear power stations generate energy by the fission of uranium nuclei. Each such fission converts about 0.1 percent of the mass locked up in the nucleus into energy. Stars are also lit up by nuclear processes. This time, heavier nuclei are built up from light nuclei. Stars such as the Sun generate energy by nuclear fusion, in which hydrogen is converted into helium. In this way, about 0.7 percent of the mass is converted into energy. The energy released by nuclear fusion is therefore much greater than that of nuclear fission. Hopefully, in the not too distant future, this might be how our electricity is generated.[2] It is perhaps rather surprising, but even nuclear processes pale into insignificance compared with the energy generated by extreme gravitational processes, which is why the collapse of a star in its death throes can produce a supernova that outshines an entire galaxy containing hundreds of billions of stars.

The most extreme gravitational environment is that surrounding a black hole. The British astrophysicist Donald Lynden-Bell saw this as a solution to the enigma posed by quasars and other active galactic nuclei. In 1969, he suggested that the tremendous energy output of a quasar could only be explained by stars or gas clouds falling into a rapidly spinning black hole situated at the heart of a galaxy. There is no other known object that could conceivably produce such a vast output of energy from such a small region of space. When material falls into a black hole, it is possible for a large proportion of its mass to be released as energy before its final plummet over the event horizon. The exact amount of energy emitted in this way depends on how fast the black hole is spinning, and on the trajectory followed by the material as it is stretched and crushed in the intense gravitational field of the black hole. The faster a black hole spins, the closer any debris can approach before ultimately entering the abyss – and the closer this final approach, the greater the amount of energy released. We can expect that black holes will be spinning extremely fast,[3] and observational evidence to back this up is beginning to accumulate. In the most extreme case of a rapidly spinning black hole, up to a staggering 42 percent of the mass of the debris falling in may be released as energy before the debris disappears over the event horizon.

If quasars shine for millions, or even hundreds of millions of years, as seems to be the case from a statistical analysis of their population in the distant universe, then the accumulated mass of each of these black holes would be huge. Lynden-Bell proposed that a quasar must be the central region of a distant galaxy where a supermassive black hole with a mass of perhaps 100 million suns is shredding and devouring the stars and gas clouds in its neighbourhood.[4] This black hole would be surrounded by a vast accretion disc, where shredded stars race around in a cosmic Catherine wheel of epic proportions.

The real fireworks are at the centre of the disc, where two intense jets of material are blasted outwards from the poles of the supermassive black hole. This material is accelerated almost to light speed by the intense magnetic fields in the accretion disc, which forms a cosmic particle accelerator. The black hole would spin like a supermassive gyroscope, whose spin axis would remain stable for millions of years, which explains the straightness of the jets in the Cygnus A system shown above. The geometry of the jets from active galactic nuclei is now being studied. There are some examples where the jets show a distinctive kink, and this is interpreted as the realignment of the supermassive black hole spin axis, due to a merger with a second supermassive black hole.

Quasars are the most distant objects that we know of, and they were much more common in the early universe. Lynden-Bell suggested that if his proposal was correct, there should still be supermassive black holes in the nearby galaxies of today. Having gorged themselves for billions of years on the material in their vicinity, these monsters might now be napping quietly in their lair, but it should still be possible to spot the obvious signs of these mighty beasts. It seems likely that all galaxies, including our own Milky Way, go through a quasar phase in their early history, before settling into a quieter existence when their central black hole has consumed all the material in its immediate neighbourhood.

The evidence for supermassive black holes at the heart of active galactic nuclei has strengthened enormously in recent years. A relatively close active galaxy is the nearby supergiant elliptical galaxy M87, which lies at the heart of the Virgo cluster of galaxies, 53.5 million light years away. The galaxy shows a prominent jet that projects five thousand light years from the core of the galaxy; the jet from the opposite pole cannot be seen from Earth. The material spewed outward by the jets over vast aeons of time has formed lobes that now stretch 250,000 light years into intergalactic space. It has been estimated that the centre of M87 is home to a super-massive black hole with a mass of at least three billion suns,[5] which would make the event horizon of this gaping abyss comparable in size to the entire solar system.

We are now sure that Lynden-Bell is correct. What we see as a quasar or other active galactic nucleus is the high-energy environment at the centre of a distant galaxy, where a super-massive black hole is gorging itself on the surrounding stars and gas clouds. To finally clinch the case for supermassive black holes, we should study the evidence for one that is much closer to home.

So, is there really a supermassive black hole at the centre of our own galaxy?

### Flying Teapot

Have a cup of tea, have another one, have a cup of tea
High in the sky, what do you see?
Come down to Earth, a cup of tea
Flying saucer, flying teacup
From outer space, Flying Teapot.

Daevid Allen, *Flying Teapot*

The figure below shows a beautiful region of the night sky in the constellation Sagittarius. Part of the constellation forms an asterism known to amateur astronomers as the 'teapot'. The steam from the spout of the flying teapot is formed of the many nebulae and gas clouds in the direction towards the centre of the galaxy. The exact centre of the galaxy is indicated by a cross in the figure, just near the spout. The name that radio astronomers have given to this region is Sgr A*. This abbreviation means the most powerful source of radio signals in the constellation of Sagittarius, and the star * is added to emphasise the special nature of this object. In our galaxy, this is where the action is. Our immediate cosmic neighbourhood is incredibly quiet. The Sun is surrounded by oceans of space, and it is over four light years to the nearest star. By contrast,

**Figure 98** The night sky in the direction towards the centre of the galaxy, including the 'teapot' asterism in the constellation of Sagittarius.

within one light year of the centre of the galaxy there are, perhaps, a million stars. These include many burnt-out stellar remnants such as neutron stars and black holes, as well as many luminous blue supergiants.

The galactic centre is shrouded in hot gas, which blocks the visible light emitted from the stars in this region of the galaxy. But, infra-red radiation is much better at penetrating the murk. The German astronomer Reinhard Genzel is an expert in infra-red astronomy and has pioneered the study of this region of the night sky. In the early 1990s, Genzel used the European Southern Observatory's 3.5-metre New Technology Telescope in Chile to study the innermost heart of the galaxy. These observations show that the stars at the centre of the galaxy are moving much faster than any of the others in the galaxy. The closer in that we peer, the faster the stars seem to be travelling. If the distribution of matter in the galaxy were uniform, we would expect the stars near the centre to be travelling much more slowly.[6] The observations suggest that there is a very high concentration of mass right at the centre. Furthermore, the location of the point right at the centre appears to be fixed, while all else whirls frantically around it.

Genzel's observations have been followed up by the American astronomer Andrea Ghez and her team, with the world's largest telescopes – the two ten-metre Keck telescopes in Hawaii. Ghez has pioneered the use of state-of-the-art techniques such as adaptive optics to produce ultra-high-resolution images. Adaptive optics improves the resolution of the images from the Keck telescopes by a factor of about twenty.

The stars right at the centre are moving so quickly that, over the course of just a few years, it has been possible to plot out significant segments of their orbital paths. The closest neighbours to Sgr A* are racing around at up to five million kilometres per hour.[7] As well as tracking their motion across the sky, it is possible to measure their velocity towards or away from us by using the Doppler shift of their light. This has enabled Ghez and her team to calculate accurate trajectories of these stars in three dimensions. By imaging these stars every few months since 1995, they have calculated the orbits of a dozen or so of the stars closest to the centre of the galaxy. Their remarkable results are plotted in the illustration shown as Plate 14.

One such star, designated SO-2, has now been monitored over the course of an entire orbit.[8] This star completes its highly eccentric orbit around the beast at the centre of the galaxy once every fifteen and a half years or so. It will be watched eagerly as it returns for another close encounter with the central black hole in 2018.[9] Ghez has now found a star known as SO-102, with an even smaller 11.5-year orbit.[10]

The speed at which SO-2 and these other stars are moving is determined by the mass of the object that they are orbiting. This relationship is encapsulated in Kepler's Third Law, which can be used to calculate the mass of the object at the centre of the galaxy. It turns out that the stars are racing around an object with a mass that is about four million times that of the Sun, and this object is smaller than the Earth's orbit around the Sun. The only possible conclusion is that it is a super-massive black hole. The Schwarzschild radius of a black hole of this mass is around 12 million kilometres. By comparison, the radius of the Sun is 700,000 kilometres. So the black hole's event horizon is about twenty times the diameter of the Sun.

The ultimate challenge is to image the event horizon of the black hole, but this will require another step up in the resolving power of the world's best astronomical instruments. Shep Doeleman of MIT (Massachusetts Institute of Technology) is leading an incredibly ambitious international effort to assemble the *Event Horizon Telescope* (EHT) in order to achieve this. Success will require at least 5,000 times the resolving power of the Hubble Space Telescope.[11] The EHT will be an Earth-sized instrument operating in the far infra-red/microwave region of the spectrum. It will combine the data collected by a network of radio telescopes around the world to produce images with an unparalleled resolution. Writing in 2009, Doeleman claimed that it is 'almost certain that direct imaging of black holes can be achieved within the next decade'.[12]

## *The Big Bang*

We have known since 1929 that distant galaxies are receding from us and that the more distant the galaxy, the faster it is racing away. Running the universe backwards, this means that the galaxies must have been much closer together in the past. It would appear that the universe and everything in it was compressed into a point in the distant past, and that it has been expanding from this point ever since.

The beginning of the universe has a catchy name – the Big Bang – but it was christened by an ardent critic of the theory, the astrophysicist Fred Hoyle. It is a great name, which is why it has stuck, but it is also rather misleading. The Big Bang is often represented as an explosion within the universe, and this is definitely *not* correct. It suggests that the universe is a pre-existing container that held a cosmic egg from which the material that forms the stars and galaxies burst forth. This leads to the misconception that the Big Bang happened at a particular place. In fact, if the Big Bang happened anywhere, it happened everywhere at once. Every point in space is equally close to the Big Bang. We now know that the time since the Big Bang is 13.8 billion years. The idea is that the universe in its entirety – space, time and matter – began at the Big Bang.

It helps to consider the analogy of a balloon that is being blown up. The main difference is that the surface of a balloon is two-dimensional, whereas space is three-dimensional. As the balloon expands, every point on its surface moves away from every other point and, the further apart two points are, the faster they recede from each other – just like the galaxies in the real universe. We can run the expansion backwards, until every point on the balloon coalesces into a single point, which represents the origin of this rubbery universe. From this perspective, we can see that every point on the balloon universe is equally distant from its origin and, in fact, that the balloon Big Bang happened everywhere simultaneously.

**Figure 99** Balloon model of the expanding universe.

## *Did the Big Bang Really Happen?*

There is remarkably good evidence for the Big Bang. First, as Hubble discovered, the universe is expanding. It is also worth noting that the universe does not appear to contain any objects, such as stars, that are older than 13.8 billion years. This is a very important and, perhaps, overlooked, consistency check on the Big Bang theory.

But there is also very good independent observational evidence. The universe would have been much hotter and denser in the past. For the first couple of minutes, it would have been a nuclear furnace in which fusion reactions would have created deuterium (heavy hydrogen), helium and traces of other very light elements. These conditions would not have persisted for long enough for any heavier atoms to be produced; all of the heavier elements were generated much later in stars and supernova explosions. It is possible to measure the amounts of deuterium and helium and other elements in the universe, and the observations closely match the amounts expected from modelling the Big Bang.

## *Listening to the Noisy Soup!*

Arno Penzias and Robert Wilson, two engineers working for Bell Labs, discovered the most compelling evidence for the Big Bang in 1964 when they were building a very sensitive new antenna in New Jersey. Their equipment was plagued with background noise, which they initially assumed to be due to a fault in their equipment. They tried everything to eradicate the noise. Eventually, the explanation was provided by the Princeton astrophysicists Robert H. Dicke, Jim Peebles, and David Wilkinson, who were preparing to search for microwaves from the early universe. What Penzias and Wilson had discovered was the cosmic microwave background, whose existence had been predicted as early as 1946 by the Russian physicist George Gamow.

So where do all these microwaves come from? After the era of nuclear synthesis, the expanding universe consisted of a plasma soup of charged particles, composed largely of hydrogen and helium nuclei and free electrons. This soup would have been awash with photons – the fundamental particles from which light is formed (any other particles in the soup, such as neutrinos, would have gone on their merry way by this time and ceased to interact with the matter). The photons would have bounced around, continually scattering off the nuclei and electrons.

After around 380,000 years of expansion, the matter would have cooled to about 3,000 degrees. It was now cool enough for hydrogen atoms to form. Prior to this, any electron that combined with a proton to form an atom would immediately have been kicked out of the atom by a passing photon. Once the temperature had cooled below this, all the matter would have condensed into atoms, and the photons would no longer have been able to interact with the matter. Just as hydrogen gas is transparent, so now the universe was transparent. It was still bathed in radiation, and the photons forming this radiation had the energy and wavelengths corresponding to that emitted by matter at 3,000 degrees. However, the photons no longer had enough energy to disrupt any atoms and there were no other charged particles available for the photons to interact with, so the energy spectrum of the radiation was frozen in at this temperature.

The photons continued to race across the universe for billions of years, and the universe continued to expand beneath their feet. These are the photons producing the noise that Penzias and Wilson could not escape. Each photon last interacted with an electron or some other charged particle 13.8 billion years ago, just after the Big Bang – and, since then, the universe has expanded in size by just over 1,000 times, so the wavelength of the photons has been stretched by a factor of over 1,000. What set out a vast distance away as a photon of visible light is now detected as a photon with a wavelength in the microwave range. This stretching means that the microwave background is now identical to the electromagnetic radiation that would be emitted by an object with a temperature of just 2.7 degrees above absolute zero – less than one thousandth of its original temperature.

## *Mapping the Early Universe*

In 1989, NASA launched the probe COBE (Cosmic Background Explorer) in order to produce a detailed map of the cosmic microwave background. COBE was followed up by WMAP (Wilkinson Microwave Anisotropy Probe), which was launched in 2001. WMAP greatly increased the resolution in the measurements of the temperature variations in the microwave background and pinned down the age of the universe to 13.78 billion years. The microwave background has an almost perfectly constant temperature of 2.726 K right across the whole sky. The map produced by WMAP is shown in the figure below. It covers the entire sky, showing regions that are very slightly cooler or very slightly warmer than average. The dark areas are 0.00002 degrees warmer and the pale areas are 0.00002 degrees cooler than average.

These very slight temperature variations correspond to very slight variations in the density of the universe just 380,000 years after the Big Bang. The denser regions are the seeds that would grow into clusters of galaxies as the universe evolved.

**Figure 100** Map of the temperature variations in the cosmic microwave background as observed by the Wilkinson Microwave Anisotropy Probe. (© NASA / WMAP Science Team.)

In 2008, the European Space Agency launched the Planck probe, whose mission includes teasing out more information from the microwave background and refining the map produced by WMAP even further.

### The Flat Universe Society

The evidence for the Big Bang all stacks up. But, the Big Bang model still throws up a few tricky posers.

If the universe is expanding like a balloon, then we would expect it to appear curved, like the surface of our balloon, but the universe seems to be flat.[13] Should we all join the Flat Universe Society? Perhaps not. We are familiar with the fact that, when we survey our surroundings on Earth, the Earth looks flat in our vicinity, even though we know that the Earth is spherical. This suggests that the universe must be very much larger than the region we can see.

When we look out into the heavens, we are seeing light that set out on its way towards us long ago. However, we can only peer out 13.8 billion light years in each direction. The light from any objects that are further away than this could not have reached us since the origin of the universe. This entire expanse of space looks flat, but it seems that when we gaze into the furthest depths of space, we are seeing just a small portion of the cosmos. There is every reason to assume that space continues onwards well beyond the horizon.

## *Who's Been Heating My Porridge?*

There is an even more perplexing issue. Imagine heating a bowl of porridge in a microwave oven. There may be lumps in the porridge and it may not be heated evenly but, if we leave it for a couple of minutes, the heat will spread throughout the porridge until it is all at the same temperature.

Like our porridge, the universe is remarkably uniform from horizon to horizon. The cosmic microwave background is the same temperature throughout the sky. But the light that is arriving from one direction has travelled 13.8 billion light years to reach us and the light from the opposite direction has also travelled 13.8 billion light years. These two regions are almost 28 billion light years apart. Since the beginning of the universe, insufficient time has elapsed for any radiation or other information to communicate between these two regions of the universe, yet they appear to have the same temperature. Unlike our porridge, there should not have been enough time since the dawn of creation for the universe to achieve a uniform temperature.

This might sound like a minor philosophical conundrum. It is not the sort of problem that would keep most people awake at night. But, cosmologists are light sleepers. Just like in the story of *The Princess and the Pea*, any lumpy piece of universe under the mattress will keep a cosmologist awake all night.

## *The Grand Vizier's Garden Party*

> Her words, when they had ceased, were greeted by
> A sparkling of scintillas in the spheres,
> As showers of sparks from molten metal fly.
>
> Tracing each fiery circle that was theirs,
> They numbered myriads more than the entire
> Progressive doubling of the chess-board squares.
>
> Dante Alighieri, *Paradise* XXVIII (88–93)[14]

In 1981, an American cosmologist Alan Guth proposed a solution to these issues. He suggested that during the very, *very* early epoch immediately after the Big Bang, just for the tiniest fraction of a second, the universe inflated exponentially. In the most minuscule moment, the universe was enlarged from being an infinitesimal speck to perhaps the size of a pea. It then continued to expand at a much more leisurely constant rate until reaching the size that we observe today.

This reminds me of a famous story about the origin of the game of chess, as told by the 13th century Kurdish writer Ibn Khallikan.[15] According to the tale, chess was invented by the Grand Vizier Sissa ben Dahir, who offered it to his lord, the king of India. The king was so pleased with the game that he asked Sissa to name his reward. Sissa's reply was that the king could repay him by placing a grain of wheat on the first square of the chessboard, two grains of wheat on the second square, four on the next and, on each subsequent square, double the previous one. The king readily agreed to this modest-sounding request. Only later would he realise that he had given away wheat worth much more than his entire kingdom.

This story illustrates the deceptive power of exponential growth. We can quickly work out how many grains there are on the chessboard. Starting with the second square and doubling on each subsequent square gives us: 2, 4, 8, 16, 32, 64, 128, 256, 512, 1024. So, rather conveniently $2^{10} = 1024$; this is the number of grains on the 11th square of the board (11th rather than 10th, because we started on square 2). We can call this a thousand and represent it by the letter 'k' (i.e. $2^{10} \sim 1000 = k$). We can now continue piling up grains on each square, doubling in units of k.

After ten more doublings, we reach: $2^{10} \times k = k^2 = M = 2^{20}$, where 'M' represents a million; this is the number of grains on square 21. Ten more doublings gives: $2^{10} \times M = G = 2^{30}$, where 'G' represents a billion; this is the number of grains on square 31. Onwards and upwards: $2^{60} = G^2$, where $G^2$ represents a billion billion; this is the number of grains on square 61. This doubles to $2G^2$ on square 62, $4G^2$ on square 63, and finally $8G^2$, or eight billion billion, on the last square. The sum of all the grains on the board is twice this, giving a grand total of sixteen billion billion.[16]

To simplify the calculation, we approximated $2^{10}$ as a thousand, so we have not found the exact number of grains of wheat, but that matters little when it comes to an exponential explosion. The king is bankrupt whether we use the exact figure or not. The exact figure for the grand total is:

$$2^{64} - 1 = 18,446,744,073,709,551,615$$

According to Alan Guth, the universe underwent just this sort of exponential growth in its first moments. The idea is that if we go back to an almost infinitesimal tenth of a thousandth of a trillionth of a trillionth of a trillionth of a second, or $10^{-39}$ seconds, after the Big Bang, the universe was doubling in size every $10^{-39}$ seconds. It is thought to have doubled in size about 60 times, which parallels the chess board story quite nicely.[17] After 60 doublings, the universe would have inflated by a factor of a billion billion but, if we check our watch, the time is now just $60 \times 10^{-39}$ seconds after the Big Bang. The universe has blown up out of all proportion, but we are still within the first $10^{-37}$ seconds of the beginning. At this point, inflation is turned off and the universe expands at a constant rate. For example, after ten billion years, the universe had ten times the diameter that it had after one billion years.

Guth suggested that his inflationary model would explain the flatness problem by enlarging the universe well beyond the horizon that we can see. It would also solve the uniform temperature issue because, in his inflationary model, the temperature could have equalized when the universe was just a mote in God's eye, before it underwent its exponential expansion. So is there any evidence for inflation?

Inflation is a theory of what happened in the first instant of creation. For several decades, it appeared as though it might belong to the sort of cosmological speculation that could never receive any observational backing. In March 2014, however, there was some incredible news from a team of American scientists who are operating a telescope based at the South Pole. This experiment is known as BICEP2 (Background Imaging of Cosmic Extragalactic Polarization 2). It is a relatively small telescope (around 30 cm) that is observing the deep universe beyond our galaxy from Antarctica. The telescope is cooled to just four degrees above absolute zero, so that it can observe the cosmic microwave background.

## *Put Your Polaroid Glasses On Now!*

The light that we receive from the Sun is randomly polarised, which means that the light waves are oscillating by the same amount in every direction. In other words, the light is unpolarised. Polaroid filters are formed of needle-like crystals that are aligned and embedded in a plastic film. The crystal needles will block light waves that are oscillating in the direction that is perpendicular to their alignment, and will transmit the light waves that are oscillating parallel to their alignment. The electromagnetic wave in Figure 41 on page 147 is shown in a single polarisation. The oscillating electric field (shown as the darker arrows) defines the plane of polarisation.

Just as visible light can be decomposed into two polarisations, so can microwaves. BICEP2 has been specifically designed to examine the polarisation of the cosmic microwave background. The results announced by the BICEP team show that the microwaves are, indeed, polarised. The big question is: how did this polarisation arise?

Theorists predicted the observed polarisation pattern. They believe that these polarised microwaves are the signature of inflation. More specifically, they believe that gravitational waves would have been generated during the inflationary epoch. The stretching and squeezing of space produced by these gravitational waves in this first instant would have distorted the material within the universe and left its imprint on the radiation that was emitted. In short, these distortions would lead to differences in the amount of light polarised in different directions. They are the frozen relics of shockwaves in the fabric of space, magnified by the exponential inflationary expansion of the early universe. Figure 69 on page 223 shows the effect of a gravitational wave on a collection

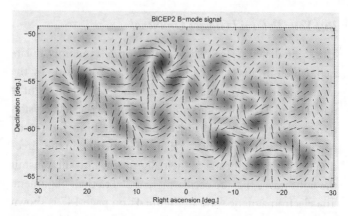

**Figure 101** A map produced by BICEP2 of the cosmic microwave background polarisations in a region of sky in the southern hemisphere. The lines indicate the direction and degree of polarisation.

of test particles arranged in a circle. As it passes by, the gravitational wave alternately stretches and squeezes space in perpendicular directions.

The results from BICEP2 are consistent with an inflationary epoch that took place less than a trillionth of a trillionth of a trillionth of a second after the Big Bang. Extraordinary claims require extraordinary evidence. Like all scientific discoveries, this one will require corroboration from other experiments.

Several other teams are currently exploring the microwave background. The BICEP2 telescope is looking at a relatively small region of sky. The Planck satellite is analysing the cosmic microwave background over the whole sky. The Planck team is due to report in October 2014, and its results will be eagerly awaited. If everything pans out, then further analysis of the microwave background promises the possibility of extracting even more information about what was going on immediately after the Big Bang.

The exploration of the earliest moments of the universe is no longer a distant dream. It might soon be possible to distinguish between the different approaches to quantum gravity. Perhaps, we might even be able to test string theory and other potential Theories of Everything.

We are close to finally cracking the cosmic code by revealing the magical symmetries within the fundamental laws of nature. We could be on the verge of discovering the secrets of the first instant of creation and finding out how it all began.

# BANG!

# NOTES

**INTRODUCTION**

1. http://www.youtube.com/watch?v=5C5_dOEyAfk

**1 THE COSMIC PUZZLE**

1. Richard Foster, *Patterns of Thought: The Hidden Meaning of the Great Pavement of Westminster Abbey* (Jonathan Cape, 1991).

2. Richard Foster, *Patterns of Thought: The Hidden Meaning of the Great Pavement of Westminster Abbey* (Jonathan Cape, 1991), Chapter 5: The Inscription.

3. The emphasis on the number three in the rhyme may also derive from Aristotle, who wrote in the opening section of *On the Heavens*:

   'A magnitude if divisible one way is a line, if two ways a surface, and if three a body. Beyond these there is no other magnitude, because the three dimensions are all that there are, and that which is divisible in three directions is divisible in all. For, as the Pythagoreans say, the world and all that is in it is determined by the number three, since beginning and middle and end give the number of an 'all', and the number they give is the triad. And so, having taken these three from nature as (so to speak) laws of it, we make further use of the number three in the worship of the Gods.'

   Translated by J. L. Stocks,
   http://classics.mit.edu/Aristotle/heavens.1.i.html

4. Following the philosopher Empedocles.

5. Bertrand Russell, *A History of Western Philosophy*, Chapter XXIII

6. Within the framework of the Hierarchic Universe, all spheres of knowledge were incorporated into a grand unified theology. In the realm of biology, the hierarchy took the form of the Great Chain of Being. Every organism, from the lowliest worm to the higher mammals, had its God-given place in the order of things. The pinnacle of the terrestrial hierarchy was, of course, man himself but, even within the human species, every grade of person – peasant, merchant, priest, lord – took their place in a linear procession. The king stood at the very tip of the spire, the instrument of God's will on Earth. The hierarchy continued beyond human beings, through the various ranks of angels in their allotted heavenly spheres, onwards to its ultimate omniscient terminus

– God – and downwards, from the lowliest human to the higher animals and on to the most primitive creatures. Thus, Mankind, with its divine intellect trapped in its sensuously brutish body, held the intermediate station halfway between the worm and God. Even the vermian end of the hierarchy was extended to inanimate matter, through symbolic correspondences and sympathies such as those between precious stones and the planets.

7. The late medieval church had an overwhelming grip on the whole of European society. The Christian world view of that time was so alien to our own, in this age of science, that it is very hard to imagine how its educated citizens must have thought. Their world was interpreted in terms of symbolism, and the main function of the objects within it was considered to be to symbolically represent the entire range of religious mysteries. In this climate, scientific discoveries could not occur. If a phenomenon is not important in itself, but only in so far as it is a metaphor for a deeper mystery, it is not going to be critically analysed to uncover its own inner workings. The belief in mystical and symbolic correspondences between objects also precludes the observation of genuine causal relationships. The cosmogony of the medieval church was clearly never envisaged as a model of the real universe, but that was not the criterion by which it would have been judged. The physical world was not seen as being important.

8. http://everything2.com/title/Dante%2527s+use+of+threes+in+the+Inferno

9. Dante Alighieri, *Paradise*, Canto XXXIII 133, translated by Dorothy L. Sayers (Penguin, 1949).

10. In Book XI of *The Republic*, Plato offers a poetic description of the cosmos. He suggests that the planets form concentric circles, with the Earth motionless at the centre. These planetary orbs are depicted as eight whorls wound around the diamond shaft of the Spindle of Necessity. Moving outwards from the centre, the whorls represent the orbits of the Moon, the Sun, each of the planets and the fixed stars. The motion of the planets on these eight circles produces eight notes of constant pitch, composing a single scale. Outside the last sphere, Plato imagined the three Fates – Lachesis, Clotho and Atropos, daughters of Necessity – bethroned equidistant from the centre, singing of the past, present and future respectively, while giving the occasional twirl to the spindle.

11. This is because it takes Venus 224.7 days to orbit the Sun, which means that, in eight years, Venus orbits the Sun almost exactly thirteen times. Therefore, after eight years the positions of the Earth and Venus in their orbit will have returned to almost exactly the same positions.

12. NASA Catalogue of Solar Eclipses: http://eclipse.gsfc.nasa.gov/SEsaros/SEsaros139.html

13. Every third eclipse in a saros cycle will be visible from the same general region of the globe. Taking every third eclipse in a saros cycle produces the Callippic cycle, which is three times as long as the saros cycle, i.e. 54 years 34 days.

14. Mark Littmann, Ken Willcox and Fred Espenak, *Totality: Eclipses of the Sun* (Oxford University Press 2009), p.48, gives the date of the eclipse predicted by Thales.

15. 'When, in the sixth year they encountered one another, it so fell out that, after they had joined battle, the day suddenly turned into night. This transformation of day into night was foretold to the Ionians by Thales of Miletus.' Herodotus – *The Histories* I, 74.

16. This story in Herodotus may have been the inspiration behind a very similar incident that occurs in Mark Twain's novel *A Connecticut Yankee in King Arthur's Court*.

17. Half a saros interval prior to a solar eclipse, i.e. 9 years 5.5 days, a lunar eclipse occurs with similar properties to the solar eclipse. Thales may have known of the solar eclipse of 18th May, 603 BC, which would have been visible in the Middle East, and also the lunar eclipse of 24th May, 594 BC.

18. Jo Marchant, *Decoding the Heavens: Solving the Mystery of the World's First Computer* (Windmill, 2009).

19. Geologists had already questioned Biblical chronology. Charles Lyell who wrote *Principles of Geology* (1830–33) promoted the notion that geology was best understood in terms of gradual processes such as the deposition of sediment and the slow erosion of mountain chains. These processes would require millions of years; far more than Biblical chronology would allow. Darwin was convinced by Lyell's arguments and this was an important step towards the development of his theory of evolution by natural selection. The publication of Darwin's *On the Origin of Species* in 1859 generated a furious debate that forced the Church, and society as a whole, to address the issue of the age of the Earth.

20. The night sky is like a huge sphere, and astronomers indicate the positions of stars by their coordinates on this sphere. This is very like the mapping of places on Earth by their longitude and latitude. Any place can be located by providing two angles that determine the position with respect to two circles around the Earth – one being the equator and the other being, quite arbitrarily, the Greenwich meridian (a meridian is a circle passing through the North and South Poles, so the Greenwich meridian is the circle that passes through the North and South Poles

and Greenwich). Greenwich is defined to be zero longitude. The point at which the Greenwich meridian crosses the equator is defined to be the origin of the coordinate system – in other words, the point which has coordinates (0° longitude, 0° latitude). To specify the position of any other place on Earth, we give an angle representing the longitude of the place and an angle representing the latitude of the place. To find a place on the globe from its longitude and latitude, we start at the origin of the coordinate system and move around the equator an angle corresponding to the longitude, which can be any angle between zero and 360°, then we move around a meridian northwards or southwards by an angle corresponding to the latitude. Latitude is specified by an angle between –90° and +90° or, alternatively, by an angle between 0° and 90° south or an angle between 0° and 90° north. Astronomers specify the position of a star in very much the same way, by projecting this coordinate system onto the sphere of the heavens, so the position of any star or other object is determined by two angles. The apparent distance in the night sky between any two celestial objects is given as an angle, which would be the angle by which the celestial globe would need to be turned along an arc joining the positions of the two objects to bring them together.

21. We can think of a star as sitting in the centre of an enormous circle with the Earth positioned on the circumference of the circle. To determine the distance to the star we must work out the radius of this circle, which is the circumference divided by $2\pi$. As the Earth orbits the Sun, its position changes. In January, it will be at one point on the circumference. Six months later, it will have reached a slightly different position on the circumference. The two viewpoints of the star are the ends of one edge of a polygon inscribed within the circle. The length of this edge is the diameter of the Earth's orbit (or twice the distance to the Sun). Imagine that the star's position shifts by one degree or 1/360th of a circle. Then this polygon is a 360-gon. The polygon very closely approximates a circle, as it has so many sides, and its perimeter is almost the same as the circumference of the circle. So, for a star whose position shifts by one degree during the course of a year, 360 times the diameter of the Earth's orbit is a very good approximation to the circumference of the circle with the star at the centre. If we approximate $2\pi$ as 6, which is close enough for our purposes, then the distance to the star is about 360/6 = 60 times the diameter of the Earth's orbit.

22. The size of the retrograde loops for each planet is partially due to parallax but, as the planets are moving in the same direction as the Earth, the loops are not as big as they would be if the planets were stationary relative to the Earth. The sizes of the retrograde loops are approximately as follows: Jupiter: 10°, Saturn: 6°, Uranus: 4°, Neptune: 3°.

23. 2 × 313.6 mas (milli arc seconds) to be precise:
    http://en.wikipedia.org/wiki/61_Cygni

24. The modern figure is 11.4 light years.

25. It is possible to estimate the distance to closer astronomical objects, such as the Moon or a comet, by using the Earth's diameter as the baseline and taking measurements as the Earth rotates during the course of a single night. The size of the Earth's diameter has been known since ancient times.

26. Michael J. Crowe, *Theories of the World from Antiquity to the Copernican Revolution* (Dover 2001).

## 2  THE SECRET OF THE UNIVERSE

1. Max Caspar, *Kepler* (Dover, 1993), p.59.

2. More precisely, Jupiter's orbital period is 11.86 years and Saturn's orbital period is 29.46 years.

3. J.V. Field, *Kepler's Geometrical Cosmology* (Athlone, 1988)

4. Malcolm Longair, *Theoretical Concepts in Physics* (Cambridge University Press, 2003), p.26. According to Malcolm Longair, Kepler's polyhedral model fits the planetary orbits to within a 5% accuracy.

5. Arthur Koestler, *The Sleepwalkers* (Penguin, 1959) p.271

6. A detailed account of this incident was recorded by Pierre Gassendi in 1654. According to Gassendi:

   'On the 10th December 1566, there was a dance at Lucas Bacmeister's house in the connection to a wedding. Lucas Bacmeister was a professor of theology at the university of Rostock, where Tycho studied. Among the guests were Tycho Brahe and another Danish nobleman, Manderup Parsberg. They started an argument and they separated in anger. The 27th of December, this argument started again, and in the evening of the 29th of December a duel was held. It was around 7 in the evening and in darkness. Parsberg gives Tycho a cut over his nose that took away almost the front part of his nose. Tycho had an artificial nose made, not from wax, but from an alloy of gold and silver, and put it on so skillfully, that it looked like a real nose Wilhelm Janszoon Blaeu, who spent time with Tycho for nearly two years, also said that Tycho used to carry a small box with a paste or glue, with which he often would put on the nose.'

   http://www.nada.kth.se/~fred/tycho/nose.html

7. See Nicholas Mee, *Higgs Force: Cosmic Symmetry Shattered* (Quantum Wave, 2012).

8. N.M. Swerdlow, *Astronomy in the Renaissance* in Christopher Walker (ed.), Astronomy Before the Telescope, (British Museum Press, 1999), p.210.

9. Malcolm Longair, *Theoretical Concepts in Physics* (Cambridge University Press, 2003), p.23.

10. http://www.biblicalscholarship.net/geoking.htm

11. Malcolm Longair, *Theoretical Concepts in Physics* (Cambridge University Press, 2003), p.23.

12. By returning the Earth to a stationary position at the centre of the universe, Tycho had removed the need to assume that the stars must lie at an enormous distance in an essentially infinite universe.

13. http://www.cosmosmagazine.com/news/3864/16th-century-astronomer-exhumed-solve-death

14. William Shakespeare, *Hamlet*, I, v

15. Joshua Gilder and Anne-Lee Gilder, *Heavenly Intrigue: Johannes Kepler, Tycho Brahe, and the Murder Behind one of History's Greatest Scientific Discoveries* (Doubleday, 2004).

16. http://www.spiegel.de/international/europe/0,1518,601729-2,00.html

17. A good place to look is the website *Heavens Above* (www.heavens-above.com). This website provides information about all the planets, the positions of bright comets and much else besides.

18. Nicholas Mee, *Higgs Force: Cosmic Symmetry Shattered* (Quantum Wave, 2012).

19. Which is longer – summer or winter? If you live in Britain, you may well feel that winter is definitely longer than summer. However, in the northern hemisphere, summer is actually over five and a half days longer than winter. The year can be divided into four quarters by the equinoxes and the solstices. The equinoxes are the days on which the Sun is directly overhead at the equator, which means that, at this time of year, the day is divided in half, with the period of daytime equalling the period of night-time. This is the origin of the name 'equinox' (equal night). The solstices are the days on which the Sun is overhead at the tropics of Cancer or Capricorn, its furthest excursion northwards or southwards respectively. These are the days on which the apparent journey of the Sun northwards or southwards stops before the Sun begins its return to the other hemisphere. Hence, the name 'solstice' which means stationary Sun.

Officially, the seasons are designated as the periods between these four marker days. The Earth is closest to the Sun on January 3 and the Earth moves faster around its orbit when it is closer to the Sun. This means that the period of time between the winter solstice (December 21) and the spring equinox (March 21) is shorter than the period of time between the summer solstice (June 21) and the autumn equinox (September 21). http://en.wikipedia.org/wiki/File:SeasonDuration.png

20. One complete rotation of the Earth takes around 23 hours and 56 minutes. This is the time that it takes for a star that is due south in the sky to return to the same position due south. On average, it takes 24 hours for the Sun to return to the same position in the sky. The extra four minutes are due to the motion of the Earth around its orbit. In a year, these four minutes add up to one complete rotation. Thus, in a year – the time taken to complete one orbit – the Earth rotates on its axis 366¼ times.

21. More precisely, he determined it to be 1°50' (one degree and 50 minutes).

22. Julian Barbour, *The Discovery of Dynamics* (Oxford University Press, 2001).

23. *Selections from Kepler's Astronomia Nova: A Science Classics Module for Humanities Studies*, selected, translated and annotated by William H. Donahue (Green Lion Press, 2008), p.256.

24. Quoted in Max Caspar, *Kepler* (Dover, 1993), p.128.

25. Quoted in Max Caspar, *Kepler* (Dover, 1993), p.128.

26. The orbit that Kepler had determined for the Earth was a circle, with the Sun off-set from the centre of the circle. This is a very good approximation for the Earth's orbit, as the eccentricity of the Earth's orbit is small. Kepler would later show that, like Mars, the Earth's orbit is actually elliptical.

27. In 1604, Kepler published *Astronomiae Pars Optica* (*The Optical Part of Astronomy*).

28. The trajectory of Mars through space could now be described quite simply. All that was required to specify it precisely were the size of the orbit, the eccentricity of the orbit and the direction of the axis of the ellipse, corresponding to the direction from the Sun towards the position of the closest Martian approach to the Sun and represented by a point on the celestial sphere.

29. In Ptolemy's model, the Earth was situated on one side of the centre of a planet's orbit and the equant point was at an equal distance on the opposite side of the centre. The same construction in the Keplerian system would put the Sun at one focus of the elliptical orbit and the equant point at the other focus. To a good approximation, first order in

the eccentricity, the angular velocity of a planet is constant when viewed from the second focus of the ellipse. This means that the equant point really does provide a fairly accurate way to model the motion of the planets, and this is why the Ptolemaic system worked as well as it did.

30. The orbits of the planets are ellipses, as Kepler discovered. Strictly speaking it is the semi-major axis of the planet's elliptical orbit that should be used in the harmonic law, not the radius of the orbit.

31. Mensus eram coelos, nunc Terrae metior umbras.
Mens coelestis erat, corporis umbra jacet.

KGW 19 393.
http://www-history.mcs.st-and.ac.uk/Quotations/Kepler.html

## 3  THE MAGIC SPYGLASS

1. Galileo's *The Starry Messenger*

2. Strictly speaking, this is only true for small oscillations of the pendulum.

3. If Galileo was observing a swinging chandelier in a cathedral, perhaps during a rather tedious sermon, this may be significant because, in that case, the pendulum would have been very long and the amplitude of the oscillations would probably have been quite small, so this property would have held to a very good approximation.

4. Julian Barbour, *The Discovery of Dynamics* (Oxford University Press, 2001), p.356.

5. Galileo did not quite have the same concept of inertia as Newton. He believed that the motion of the ball would not be a straight line, but would follow the surface of the Earth, i.e. it would be circular.

6. The passage continues:

'In jumping, you will pass on the floor the same spaces as before, nor will you make larger jumps toward the stern than toward the prow even though the ship is moving quite rapidly, despite the fact that during the time that you are in the air the floor under you will be going in a direction opposite to your jump. In throwing something to your companion, you will need no more force to get it to him whether he is in the direction of the bow or the stern, with yourself situated opposite. The droplets will fall as before into the vessel beneath without dropping toward the stern, although while the drops are in the air the ship runs many spans. The fish in their water will swim toward the front of their bowl with no more effort than toward the back, and will go with equal ease to bait placed anywhere around the edges of the bowl. Finally, the butterflies and flies will continue their flights indifferently toward every side, nor will it ever happen that they are concentrated toward the stern, as if tired out from keeping up with the course of the ship, from which they will have been separated during long intervals by keeping themselves in the air. And if smoke is made by burning some incense, it will be seen going up in the form of a little cloud, remaining still and moving no more toward one side than the other. The cause of all these correspondences of effects is the fact that the ship's motion is common to all the things contained in it, and to the air also. That is why I said you should be below decks; for if this took place above in the open air, which would not follow the course of the ship, more or less noticeable differences would be seen in some of the effects noted.'

*Dialogue Concerning the Two Chief World Systems*, translated by Stillman Drake (University of California Press, 1953), pp. 186–187.

7. Julian Barbour, *The Discovery of Dynamics* (Oxford University Press, 2001), p.371.

8. This law can be represented as: $s = \frac{1}{2} at^2$, where $s$ is distance, $a$ is the acceleration due to gravity and $t$ is time.

9. The force of gravity is assumed to be constant when showing that the path of a projectile is a parabola. This is a good approximation if the path remains close to the surface of the Earth. If the force of gravity is assumed to be an inverse square law, then the calculation would show that the path of the projectile is along an arc of a very eccentric ellipse, with a focus at the centre of the Earth.

10. *The Essential Galileo*, edited and translated by Maurice A. Finocchiaro (Hackett, 2008), p.314 line 20.

11. The full passage from Milton's *Areopagitica* reads:
And lest some should persuade ye, Lords and Commons, that these arguments of learned men's discouragement at this your Order are mere flourishes, and not real, I could recount what I have seen and heard in other countries, where this kind of inquisition tyrannises; when I have sat among their learned men, for that honour I had, and been counted happy to be born in such a place of philosophic freedom, as they supposed England was, while themselves did nothing but bemoan the servile condition into which learning amongst them was brought; that this was it which had damped the glory of Italian wits; that nothing had been there written now these many years but flattery and fustian. There it was that I found and visited the famous Galileo, grown old a prisoner to the Inquisition, for thinking in astronomy otherwise than the Franciscan and Dominican licensers thought.

12. All the planetary orbits in the solar system lie in the same plane (or nearly so). This plane also contains the Sun's equator and, when projected onto the sky, it is called the ecliptic. The paths of the planets across the sky always lie near to this circle. Although the planetary orbits all lie close to the ecliptic, their alignment is not perfect. The orbits are tilted slightly with respect to each other. The orbit of Venus is inside the Earth's orbit and it is inclined at an angle of around three and a half degrees relative to the Earth's orbit around the Sun. This means that, as viewed from Earth, on almost all occasions when Venus overtakes the Earth on its inner track around the Sun, it passes well above or well below the Sun's disc (the apparent diameter of the Sun's disc is about half a degree).

13. The Julian calendar was still in use in Britain at this time. All the dates that are quoted from the 17th century were those in use at the time. The date of the transit according to the Gregorian calendar was 4 December, 1639.

14. http://eclipse.gsfc.nasa.gov/transit/catalog/VenusCatalog.html

15. 8.85 years, to be precise.

16. http://en.wikipedia.org/wiki/Lunar_precession

17. Peter Aughton, *The Transit of Venus: The Brief, Brilliant Life of Jeremiah Horrocks Father of British Astronomy* (Phoenix, 2004), p.122.

18. Peter Aughton, *The Transit of Venus: The Brief, Brilliant Life of Jeremiah Horrocks Father of British Astronomy* (Phoenix, 2004), p.128.

19. Peter Aughton, *The Transit of Venus: The Brief, Brilliant Life of Jeremiah Horrocks Father of British Astronomy* (Phoenix, 2004), p.119.

20. This passage from one of Crabtree's letters is quoted on page 174 of *The Transit of Venus* by Peter Aughton.

21. This quote is not original to Newton, but it is found in a private letter from Newton to Robert Hooke and is considered by some to be a jibe at Hooke's expense, as Hooke was a short and hunched figure.

## 4   VOYAGING THROUGH STRANGE SEAS OF THOUGHT

1. Richard S. Westfall, *Never At Rest: A Biography of Newton* (Cambridge University Press, 1980), pp. 402–403.

2. Newton gave this account to De Moivre long after the event. At the time of the meeting, Halley had not yet received his doctorate and Newton had not been awarded his knighthood.

3. Quoted in Richard S. Westfall, *Never At Rest: A Biography of Newton* (Cambridge University Press, 1980), p.143.

4. The other two are arguably the discovery of mathematical proof by the Ancient Greeks and algebra.

5. Galileo believed that inertial motion would follow the curvature of the Earth, so it was only approximately in a straight line.

6. Another example is a rocket. When a rocket is propelled upwards by the explosive expansion of the gases in its combustion chamber, the upwards force that acts upon the rocket is exactly equal to the downwards force on the exhaust gases that it emits.

7. Newton's Third Law can be expressed equivalently as the Law of Conservation of Momentum.

8. It was clear to Newton that gravity acts throughout the solar system. The Sun has its system of planets and the Earth is orbited by the Moon. Jupiter is orbited by the four moons discovered by Galileo, and more recently five satellites of Saturn had been discovered: Titan in 1655 by Christiaan Huygens, and Rhea, Dione, Tethys and Iapetus in 1671–1672 by Giovanni Cassini. The force of gravity appeared to diminish with distance from the giant planets in exactly same way as it diminished with distance from the Sun. This was clear because each satellite system obeys its own version of Kepler's Third Law. The square of the period of the satellites of Jupiter grows as the cube of the radius of their orbit, and similarly for the satellites of Saturn, but with a different constant of proportionality. This was a great clue. It showed that the force of gravity operates in the same way everywhere it was possible to look.

9. The Sun's gravitational pull on the Earth is proportional to the mass of the Sun. The universal law of gravity implies that the Earth pulls on the Sun, just as the Sun pulls on the Earth. This is in accordance with Newton's Third Law of Motion, which requires that forces arise in equal and opposite pairs (so rather than the Earth orbiting the Sun, it is more accurate to say that the Sun and the Earth revolve around their common centre of mass). The mass of the Sun is vastly greater than the mass of the Earth, so their centre of mass is close to the centre of the Sun.

10. The area of the regions in the shell that pull on the object is proportion to the square of the distance to these regions. If the force diminishes as the inverse square of distance, there is a complete cancellation.

11. The volume of the sphere beneath us is proportional to the cube of the distance to the centre. If the density is uniform, then the mass of this sphere is also proportional to the cube of the distance to the centre. The gravitational force is inversely proportional to the square of the

distance to the centre. Therefore, assuming uniform density, the force is proportional to the distance from the centre. At the centre, there will be no gravitational force on us; all the material forming the Earth will be further from the centre than we are. The gravitational attraction of all the material around us will cancel out.

12. If the Earth had uniform density, we would undergo simple harmonic motion.

13. As the Moon orbits the Earth once a month, it crosses the meridian due south in the sky every 24 hours and 50 minutes, which means that the time between high tides is around 12 hours and 25 minutes.

14. In addition to being stretched in the direction towards the Moon, the Earth is squeezed in the plane perpendicular to this direction. This is best understood in terms of Einstein's theory, which is presented in a later chapter. It means that low tides are lower than they would otherwise be.

15. http://www.ams.org/samplings/feature-column/fcarc-tidesiii2

16. http://www.westminster-abbey.org/our-history/people/sir-isaac-newton

17. http://www.e-ir.info/2011/08/24/the-industrial-revolution-and-a-newtonian-culture/

18. C. Bekar and R. Lipsey, *Science, Institutions and the Industrial Revolution* (October 2002).

19. BEDFM 1974.27.1570

20. In 1750, Michell showed that the magnetic force exerted by each pole of a magnet decreases with the square of the distance.

21. William Herschel was influenced by Michell's work on double stars. After Michell's death, Herschel purchased his ten-foot telescope. Although it was no longer in working condition, Herschel used it as a model for a telescope that he constructed himself.

22. http://www.amnh.org/education/resources/rfl/web/essaybooks/cosmic/cs_michell.html

23. http://www.astronomyedinburgh.org/publications/journals/39/black-holes.html

24. In 1774, the Astronomer Royal, Nevil Maskelyne, led an expedition to determine the strength of gravity by measuring the deflection of a pendulum due to the gravitational attraction of an isolated Scottish mountain known as Schiehallion. The experiment was carried out with great care and included a systematic survey of the mountain to ascertain its volume. The result produced a value for Newton's gravitational constant (or equivalently, the mass of the Earth) with an accuracy of around 20%.

25. Philip Ball, *Elegant Solutions: Ten Beautiful Experiments in Chemistry* (Royal Society of Chemistry, 2005), p.26.

26. This could be deduced from Kepler's Third Law of Planetary Motion, which relates the size of the orbit to its period.

27. Tom Standage, *The Neptune File* (Penguin, 2001).

28. Tom Standage, *The Neptune File* (Penguin, 2001), p.60.

29. Tom Standage, *The Neptune File* (Penguin, 2001), p.108.

30. Clifford M. Will, *Was Einstein Right?* (Oxford University Press, 1986), p.91. (These are modern figures and are more accurate than those used by Le Verrier.)

## 5  THE GREAT OCEAN OF TRUTH

1. Nicholas Mee, *Higgs Force: Cosmic Symmetry Shattered* (Quantum Wave, 2012).

2. For example, Russell's teapot.

3. Galileo's understanding of inertia was not quite correct. He did not realise that an object will continue in a straight line unless acted on by a force, as stated in Newton's First Law. He believed the motion of an unperturbed body would be circular – it would revolve around the Earth. Descartes was probably the first to correctly define inertial motion.

4. A. Einstein, *On the Electrodynamics of Moving Bodies*, June 30, 1905.

5. A. Einstein, *On the Electrodynamics of Moving Bodies*, June 30, 1905.

6. A. Einstein, *On the Electrodynamics of Moving Bodies*, June 30, 1905.

7. The experiment by Rossi and Hall was performed at an elevation of 3,230 metres on Mount Evans, which is near Echo Lake, Colorado.

8. The full relativistic formula is: Inertial mass $= m(1 - v^2/c^2)^{\frac{1}{2}}$. At velocities that are low compared to the speed of light, $v/c$ is much less than one. The formula can be expanded in powers of $v/c$ to give: Inertial mass $= m + \frac{1}{2} m(v/c)^2 + \dots$, where only the first two terms have been retained. The next term is multiplied by $(v/c)^4$, which is tiny except at velocities approaching the speed of light.

9  H.G. Wells, *The Time Machine*, p.1 (Heinemann, 1895).

10 'Space And Time', a translation of an address delivered at the 80th Assembly of German Natural Scientists and Physicians, at Cologne, 21 Sep 1908. In: H.A. Lorentz, H. Weyl, H. Minkowski, et al.,

*The Principle of Relativity: A Collection of Original Memoirs on the Special and General Theory of Relativity*, p.74 (Dover, 1952).

11  An example of this approach is the liquid drop model of the nucleus developed by Niels Bohr.

12  Einstein's letter to Ehrenfest in 1916. Gino Segre, *Faust in Copenhagen: A Struggle for the Soul of Physics and the Birth of the Nuclear Age*, p.175 (Pimlico, 2008).

## 6  LET'S DO THE TIME WARP AGAIN

1.  Leon Battista Alberti's treatise, '*Della Pittura*'.

2.  Quoted in P. Davis and R. Hersh, *The Mathematical Experience* (Boston, 1981).

3.  Lobachevsky never accepted that Gauss had independently pre-empted his great discovery, but it is certainly true.

4.  It is negative because +1 multiplied by −1 is equal to −1. Positive curvature arises when the centres of curvature are both in the same direction.

5.  James B. Hartle, *Gravity: An Introduction to Einstein's General Relativity* (Addison Wesley, 2003), p.15.

6.  This was first proved by the French mathematician Henri Poincare. The hyperbolic disc is sometimes known as the Poincare disc.

7.  This is the stress-energy tensor.

8.  This is the Einstein tensor.

9.  Abraham Pais, *Subtle is the Lord: The Science and the Life of Albert Einstein* (Oxford University Press, 1982), p.253.

10. Letter from K Schwarzschild to A Einstein, dated 22 December 1915, in *The Collected Papers of Albert Einstein*, vol.8a, doc. No.169.

11. Eisenstaedt, 'The Early Interpretation of the Schwarzschild Solution,' in D. Howard and J. Stachel (eds), *Einstein and the History of General Relativity: Einstein Studies*, Vol. 1, pp. 213–234 (Boston: Birkhauser, 1989).

12. I. R. Kenyon, *General Relativity* (Oxford University Press, 1990), p.17.

13. James B. Hartle, *Gravity: An Introduction to Einstein's General Relativity* (Addison Wesley, 2003), p.124.

14. http://www.astronomy.ohio-state.edu/~pogge/Ast162/Unit5/gps.html

15. The Earth is solid and so resists being stretched and squeezed by the distortion of space. The oceans are free to flow, so the distortion of space raises the tides.

16. Wolfgang Rindler, *Relativity: Special, General and Cosmological* (Oxford University Press, 2001), p.231.


## 7   A BRIEF HISTORY OF BLACK HOLES

1. Michael White and John Gribbin, *Stephen Hawking: A Life in Science* (Penguin, 1991), p.131.

2. Remarkably, white dwarfs are supported by nothing more than the exclusion principle. The electrons within the white dwarf must all exist in their own separate quantum state, and this produces a huge resistance to their being squeezed any closer together. This is called 'electron degeneracy pressure'.

3. The easiest white dwarf to see with a telescope is a member of a triple star system known to astronomers as *omicron 2 Eridani*. This star system is a close stellar neighbour at about 16 light years distance. It is also known by the name Keid, which is derived from the Arabic for broken eggshell. The main star, which is visible to the naked eye, is orbited by a binary that requires a telescope to be seen. The binary consists of a white dwarf and an even fainter red dwarf. (The red dwarf is a ordinary low-mass star that is generating energy by converting hydrogen into helium.) According to Gene Roddenberry, the creator of *Star Trek*, Spock's home planet Vulcan orbits the star Keid A. http://en.wikipedia.org/wiki/Vulcan_(Star_Trek)

4. Like white dwarfs, neutron stars are supported by the exclusion principle. This time it is their component neutrons that resist being squeezed any closer together. Neutrons have almost two thousand times the mass of electrons, and it is their greater mass that means that neutron degeneracy pressure is able to support matter at these incredible densities.

5. Jocelyn Bell Burnell, *Little Green Men, White Dwarfs or Pulsars?* Presented as an after-dinner speech with the title 'Petit Four' at the Eighth Texas Symposium on Relativistic Astrophysics and published in *Annals of the New York Academy of Science*, vol. 302, pages 685–689, Dec. 1977.

6. Mitchell Begelman and Martin Rees, *Gravity's Fatal Attraction: Black Holes in the Universe*, Second Edition (Cambridge University Press, 2010).

7. Spacetime is an incredibly stiff medium. It would take a pressure of $10^{43}$ N per metre squared to warp spacetime into a shape with a radius of curvature of one metre (I. R. Kenyon, *General Relativity* (Oxford University Press, 1990), p.124).

8. However, there is not necessarily anything unusual about the structure of space in the region of the event horizon.

9. http://heasarc.nasa.gov/docs/uhuru/uhuru.html

10. http://www.nasa.gov/mission_pages/chandra/news/cygnusx1.html

11. Quoted in Mitchell Begelman and Martin Rees, *Gravity's Fatal Attraction: Black Holes in the Universe*, Second Edition, (Cambridge University Press, 2010), p. 224.

12. C. P. Snow's address continues:

    'I now believe that if I had asked an even simpler question – such as, What do you mean by mass, or acceleration, which is the scientific equivalent of saying, Can you read? – not more than one in ten of the highly educated would have felt that I was speaking the same language. So the great edifice of modern physics goes up, and the majority of the cleverest people in the western world have about as much insight into it as their neolithic ancestors would have had.'

13. The First Law was actually formulated after the Second Law. But it is logically the first.

14. Photons cannot be confined within a black hole if their wavelength is comparable to the radius of the event horizon. If M is the mass of the black hole, $c$ is the speed of light and G is Newton's constant, then the Schwarzschild radius of the black hole is $2GM/c^2$. If $\lambda$ is the typical wavelength of a photon in the Hawking radiation, then:

    $\lambda \sim 2GM/c^2$

    If a black body emits photons with a typical wavelength $\lambda$, then its temperature is:

    $T \sim E_{photon}/k = (hc/\lambda)(1/k)$

    where $k$ is Boltzmann's constant. The Hawking temperature of the black hole is therefore:

    $T_H \sim hc^3/2kGM.$

    Hawking's more precise quantum field theoretic derivation gives:

    $T_H = hc^3/8\pi kGM.$

15. This is much closer in scale to a 610 metre (2,000 foot) British mountain rather than a Himalayan peak.

16. Mitchell Begelman and Martin Rees, *Gravity's Fatal Attraction: Black Holes in the Universe*, Second Edition (Cambridge University Press) p.267.

17. The Kerr solution describes rotating black holes. In this case the singularity actually forms a ring of infinite density rather than a point.

18. John Archibald Wheeler with Kenneth Ford, *Geons, Black Holes & Quantum Foam: A Life in Physics* (Norton, 2000) p.247.

19. Ben Allanach, *Particle Hunting at the LHC* (Plus, 2009). http://plus.maths.org/content/particle-hunting-lhc

## 8 RINGING THE CHANGES

1. John Fauvel, Raymond Flood and Robin Wilson (eds.) *Music and Mathematics: From Pythagoras to Fractals*, Chapter 7, *Ringing the Changes: bells and mathematics*, by Dermot Roaf and Arthur White, (Oxford University Press, 2003).

2   $5040 = 7!$

3   It may come as a surprise, but the variation in the *angular* motion of the planet is not a consequence of the pull towards the Sun. It is completely determined by the conservation of angular momentum (with a bit of reflection, we can see that this must be the case, as the gravitational pull of the Sun is directed towards the Sun and not around the circumference of the orbit). As the gravitational force acting on the planet is always directed towards the Sun, it is only the radial motion of the planet (i.e. the motion towards and away from the Sun) that is affected by the gravitational force between the planet and the Sun.

4   If the extra dimension were a closed loop, as suggested by Klein, this would also explain why electric charge only exists in multiples of a fundamental unit – the charge on the electron. (It would be determined by the number of times the particle's wave is wrapped around the loop. The charge would be quantised, like the energy levels of an electron in a hydrogen atom.)

5. Walter Isaacson, *Einstein: His Life and Universe* (Simon and Schuster, 2007), p. 543.

6. Satyendra Nath Bose: http://www-history.mcs.st-andrews.ac.uk/Biographies/Bose.html

7. Spin is measured as a multiple of Planck's constant, which has the same units as angular momentum.

8. The weak force is unified with the electromagnetic force in the electroweak theory of Glashow, Weinberg and Salam. This is a Yang-Mills theory, based on the group $SU(2) \times U(1)$. $SU(2)$ is closely related to the symmetry group of a sphere, which is called $SO(3)$.

9. The Higgs mechanism breaks the symmetry group $SU(2) \times U(1)$ to the $U(1)$ of electromagnetism. This $U(1)$ is not the $U(1)$ in the original group $SU(2) \times U(1)$. It is partially embedded within the $SU(2)$ of this group.

10. A much fuller description of the standard model and the Higgs mechanism are given in my previous book *Higgs Force*.

11. Gravitational lensing can also be used to calculate the mass of the galaxy cluster that is bending the light from more distant galaxies. This also suggests that galaxy clusters contain several times as much matter as their luminosity would suggest.

12. In the first couple of minutes after the Big Bang, the temperature and density of the universe were sufficiently high to generate nuclear fusion reactions that created nuclei of deuterium (heavy hydrogen), helium and traces of other elements. Calculations based on our understanding of the immediate aftermath of the Big Bang match the observed abundances of these isotopes very well. This is one of the great successes of cosmology and is one pillar of evidence for the Big Bang. However, if the density of ordinary matter was much higher in the early universe, this match between observation and theory would be lost.

13. The eight gluons of QCD and the four electroweak exchange bosons.

## 9   THE ENDLESS KNOT

1. If a knot can be cut in two places, so that the four loose ends can be connected together to produce two other knots, then the original knot is a compound knot. For instance, if we follow this procedure with a granny knot, we can produce two trefoil knots. Granny knots are therefore compound knots. The prime knots are those that cannot be decomposed in this way into other knots. In the same way that all whole numbers can be factorised into products of prime numbers, so all knots are constructed from the prime knots.

2. Donald H. Perkins, *Introduction to High Energy Physics*, Second Edition (Addison-Wesley, 1982), p.175.

3. The regular honeycombs give another example (a honeycomb is a collection of polytopes that fill space without leaving any gaps). There is a cubic honeycomb in any number of dimensions. For instance, it is possible to divide a line into line segments, a two-dimensional plane into the square tessellation, three dimensions into the honeycomb of cubes and so on. This gives us an infinite family of cubic honeycombs. There are just four exceptional regular honeycombs: in two dimensions, the equilateral triangle and regular hexagon tessellations; and in four dimensions, there is a honeycombs of cross polytopes and a honeycomb of 24-cells.

4. They would be situated at the vertices of an eight-dimensional polytope known as Gosset's polytope. A polytope is a higher-dimensional equivalent of a polyhedron.

5. Consideration of a simple toy model universe will help us to see the world as string theorists see it. Imagine a universe that has just two spatial dimensions and that, at the origin of the universe, these two dimensions form an open-ended cylinder. In this universe, one of the two spatial dimensions is a line segment, while the other spatial dimension forms a circle.

   Now imagine that one of the two dimensions undergoes an enormous expansion, while the second dimension remains the same size. This might be the equivalent of the Big Bang in our toy model. If the space that forms the line segment expands and the circular dimension remains unchanged, then the result is a very long, thin tube. When the line segment becomes much longer than the diameter of the circular dimension, the universe will appear to be one-dimensional. Any hypothetical creatures that live in this universe would be able to move back and forth along the line, but would be completely unaware of the second spatial dimension that forms a tiny circle. Macroscopically, the universe would look one-dimensional, but in reality it is two-dimensional and the second 'hidden' dimension forms a tiny circle (at each point along the macroscopic dimension, there is a tiny perpendicular circle).

   An alternative scenario would be that the Big Bang in our model universe would cause the circular dimension to expand while leaving the other dimension unchanged. In this case, the universe would again appear to be one-dimension to its hypothetical inhabitants, but it would now be circular. At each point of the macroscopic circle, there would be a tiny perpendicular line segment that is too small for the inhabitants to be aware of it.

6. Nothing special has happened to the hidden dimensions – they have just remained close in size to the Planck scale, which is the natural scale for quantum gravity, whereas the other three spatial dimensions have undergone an enormous expansion, so it might be more appropriate to refer to the three macroscopic spatial dimensions as *expandified*.

7. Shing-Tung Yau and Steve Nadis, *The Shape of Inner Space: String Theory and the Geometry of the Universe's Hidden Dimensions* (Basic, 2010).

8. Calabi-Yau manifolds satisfy Einstein's equations in a vacuum.

9. These polyhedra are known as convex polyhedra.

10. The technical name for the number of handles is the genus of the surface. The genus of a sphere is 0. The genus of a torus is 1.

11. Note that adding handles transforms the original surface into a new surface with a different topology. This is why topological invariants such as the Euler number are changed in the process.

12. For this reason, the cube and octahedron share the same symmetry group. Similarly, the icosahedron and the dodecahedron share the same symmetry group. The same sort of duality relationship also holds between the regular tessellations. The hexagonal tessellation is dual to the equilateral triangle tessellation. The tessellation of squares is self-dual.

13. Strictly speaking, the dual polyhedra should be scaled in size so that they intersect at the midpoints of their edges, rather than the vertex of one being at the middle of the face of the other.

14. The usual methods of particle physics work fine for calculating the effect of scattering particles, etc. It is extremely difficult to solve the equations of quantum field theory and, with the exception of a few special cases, exact solutions have not been found. The usual strategy followed by physicists is to begin with a very simple situation where the solution is known – such as empty space with nothing happening – and then approach the solution to the problem in hand as a series of steps. For many purposes, this approach works extremely well. In particular, it works for forces that are not too strong, so that there is a weak interaction between particles. This is fine when considering a particle such as an electron scattering off another electron; however, quantum field theories contain many riches that will not show up in this approach. When strong forces are in operation, new phenomena may appear that are missed by this sort of analysis. These phenomena include the binding of two or more particles to form new particles, the confinement of particles as though they were in a bag, the existence of vortices and other complex structures. The search for mathematical techniques to tackle these issues is one of the biggest problems in physics.

15. Katrin Becker, Melanie Becker and John H. Schwarz, *String Theory and M-Theory: A Modern Introduction* (Cambridge University Press, 2007).

16. However, the journey is far from complete. There is much about string theory that remains to be understood. This is true both of the mathematical structure of the theory and of its relationship to the world that we observe. In attempts to make contact with the standard models of particle physics and cosmology, we typically return to the old idea of Kaluza-Klein compactifications. Is this the right approach? Or are we missing some important and subtle conceptual ingredient? Or is the existence of this remarkable mathematical structure called string theory merely a red herring that has nothing to do with the real world?

David Tong, *String Theory, Part III Mathematics Course*, Cambridge University (2009).

## 10 ACROSS THE UNIVERSE

1. Mitchell Begelman and Martin Rees, *Gravity's Fatal Attraction: Black Holes in the Universe*, Second Edition (Cambridge University Press, 2010), p.111.

2. For information about progress towards the development of nuclear fusion power, see the ITER website: https://www.iter.org/

3. After a star has collapsed, it will be spinning much faster, due to conservation of angular momentum. It is therefore natural to expect that white dwarfs and neutron stars will be spinning very rapidly. This is readily confirmed in the case of neutron stars, because we can detect the pulsars that they generate. As black holes are even smaller than neutron stars, we would expect them to be spinning even faster. Furthermore, the black hole's spin is expected to increase as it accumulates more material from its swirling accretion disc. It is becoming possible to analyse the X-rays from the accretion disc of distant supermassive black holes to determine their rate of spin, and the early evidence suggests that typically they are spinning at close to the maximum rate allowed by general relativity.

4. Mitchell Begelman and Martin Rees, *Gravity's Fatal Attraction: Black Holes in the Universe*, Second Edition (Cambridge University Press, 2010), p.119.

5. http://en.wikipedia.org/wiki/Messier_87

6. The galaxy appears to be embedded within a sphere of dark matter that has a fairly uniform distribution. Within a uniform spherical mass, the period of the orbits should be the same, irrespective of the radius of the orbit – just like a conical pendulum. There is observational evidence to suggest that the rotation rate is constant in the outer reaches of a galaxy. If this held true to the centre of the galaxy, then it would mean that the stars at the centre would be moving much more slowly than the stars that are further out.

7. Fulvio Melia, *The Black Hole at the Centre of the Galaxy*, (Princeton University Press, 2003), p.40.

8. A. M. Ghez et al, *Measuring Distance and Properties of the Milky Way's Central Supermassive Black Hole with Stellar Orbits.*

9. At its closest, SO-2 approaches to about 18 billion kilometres from the black hole. By comparison, the distance from Neptune to the Sun is about 4.5 billion kilometres.

10. Analysis of the orbits of this pair of stars will shed further light on the characteristics of the supermassive black hole and could even enable new tests for general relativity to be carried out. Physicsworld.com,

4 October 2012: *Star Seen Whizzing Around Supermassive Black Hole*, http://physicsworld.com/cws/article/news/2012/oct/04/star-seen-whizzing-around-supermassive-black-hole

11. The angular resolution of the HST is 0.05 arcseconds. The Schwarzschild radius of the black hole at the centre of the galaxy is 10 micro-arcseconds.

12. http://www.eventhorizontelescope.org/docs/Doeleman_event_horizon_CGT_CFP.pdf

13. The universe is, of course, not flat like a pancake or the galaxy. The 3D space that forms the universe is flat in the sense that, on the largest scale, its geometry is best described by Euclidean geometry. Clusters of galaxies form gravitational lenses, but these are like little dimples within what is essentially flat space.

14. Dante Alighieri, *The Divine Comedy 3: Paradise* (trans. Dorothy L Sayers, Penguin, 1962). In this canto, Dante reaches the primum mobile. Dante is comparing the vast hierarchy of the angelic host to the grains of wheat on a chess board, as set out in the doubling problem.

15. Clifford A. Pickover, *The Math Book: From Pythagoras to the 57th dimension, 250 Milestones in the History of Mathematics* (Sterling, 2009).

16. The exact total of grains of wheat on the chess board can be calculated as follows. If this total is called S, then

$$S = 1 + 2 + 4 + ..... + 2^{62} + 2^{63} .$$

We can multiply both sides of this sum by 2, to give:

$$2S = 2 + 4 + 8 + ..... + 2^{63} + 2^{64} .$$

Now, all the terms in these two sums are identical except the first term in the first sum and the last term in the second sum. If we subtract the sum corresponding to S from the sum corresponding to 2S, this gives:

$$2S - S = 2^{64} - 1 .$$

Therefore, the total number of grains of wheat on the chess board is:
$$S = 2^{64} - 1 .$$

17. Steven Weinberg, *Cosmology* (Oxford University Press, 2008), p.212.

# Further Reading

I have written a number of articles about fundamental physics for my blog which can be found on the Quantum Wave website at www.quantumwavepublishing.com.

The following books are highly recommended sources of information about gravity and some of the other topics mentioned in this book.

Nicholas Mee, *Higgs Force: Cosmic Symmetry Shattered* (Quantum Wave, 2012).
*Gravity: Cracking the Cosmic Code* is intended as a companion to my first book *Higgs Force*. If you enjoyed reading this book, I am sure that you will find *Higgs Force* equally rewarding.

Jo Marchant, *Decoding the Heavens: Solving the Mystery of the World's First Computer* (Windmill, 2009).
*Decoding the Heavens* is an account of the discovery of the Antikythera mechanism and the painstaking detective work that has revealed how it worked and enabled its reconstruction.

Peter Aughton, *The Transit of Venus: The Brief, Brilliant Life of Jeremiah Horrocks, Father of British Astronomy* (Phoenix, 2004).
This is a great biography of one of the neglected figures of British science, who deserves to be much better known.

Julian Barbour, *The Discovery of Dynamics* (Oxford University Press, 2001).
Barbour describes the historical development of dynamics, from antiquity up to the time of Newton. The book contains valuable insights into the work of Hipparchus, Ptolemy, Copernicus, Kepler, Galileo and Newton, including many significant details that are overlooked in most other books.

Richard S. Westfall, *Never At Rest: A Biography of Newton* (Cambridge University Press, 1980).
*Never At Rest* is the definitive scientific biography of Newton. It is a work on an epic scale, as befits an account of Newton's life and work.

Walter Isaacson, *Einstein: His Life and Universe* (Simon and Schuster, 2007).
This is a very readable biography of Einstein that balances information about his personal life with good explanations of his scientific work.

Lee Smolin, *Three Road to Quantum Gravity: A New Understanding of Space, Time and the Universe* (Phoenix, 2000).
Smolin is an outspoken critic of the excesses of string theory. In this book, he presents string theory as one of a number of approaches to quantum gravity that are currently under investigation.

Mitchell Begelman and Martin Rees, *Gravity's Fatal Attraction: Black Holes in the Universe* (Cambridge University Press, 2010).
This is a wonderful account of the astrophysics of black holes and the observational evidence for their existence.

Alan H. Guth, *The Inflationary Universe: The Quest for a New Theory of Cosmic Origins* (Vintage, 1998).
Guth is the architect of the idea of an inflationary expansion of the extremely early universe. This is a very accessible account of inflation written for the non-specialist reader.

# Credits

Chapter 2 includes material originally written for an article published as *Venus in the Face of the Sun* in the June 2012 issue of History Today.

Chapters 7 and 10 include material originally written for articles on Nicholas Mee's blog on the Quantum Wave website.

The Quintic Hypersurface illustration was produced for the 'Intersections: Henry Moore and Stringed Surfaces' exhibition which was held from April to June 2012 at The Royal Society, London.

All images in the book were designed and created by Nicholas Mee and are © Nicholas Mee, with the exception of the images listed below.

Front Cover Illustration: Cygnus X-1 © NASA/CXC/M.Weiss.

**PLATES**

Exploded Computer model of the Antikythera Mechanism © 2012 Tony Freeth, Images First Ltd.

Kelvin's Tide Machine
© Science Museum/Science & Society Picture Library

Supernova 1993J exploding (artist's impression) European Space Agency and Justyn R. Maund (University of Cambridge).

Cygnus X-1 (artist's impression) © NASA/CXC/M.Weiss.

Immortality © Nicholas Mee and John Robinson.

Gordian Knot © Nicholas Mee and John Robinson.

Projection of the $E_8$ weight lattice © J. Gregory Moxness.

Torus knot formed of golden beads wrapped around a torus
© Nicholas Mee.

Quintic Hypersurface © Nicholas Mee.

Stellar Orbits Around SgrA*
© Keck/UCLA Galactic Center Group.

## FIGURES

The first coat of wax being applied to the surface of
Westminster Abbey's Cosmati pavement.
© The Dean and Chapter of Westminster Abbey.

Uraniborg, Ven © 2005 Google, © 2006 Europa Technologies,
Image © 2006 DigitalGlobe.

LRG 3-757 © HST, NASA/ESA.

Gravitational Lensing Cluster Abell 2218 © NASA/ESA.

Archimedean Polyhedra – image created by Robert Austin
using Stella software: www.software3d.com/Stella.php.

Andromeda Galaxy © HST, NASA.

Radio Galaxy Cygnus A © NRAO/AUI.

Sagittarius and the Galactic Centre
© ESA, NASA & Akira Fujii.

Map of the CMB © NASA/WMAP Science Team.

B-Mode Signal Map © BICEP Team.

## Acknowledgments

Completing *Higgs Force* was a Sisyphean task, so thanks again to everyone who helped to bring my first book to fruition.

Since writing *Higgs Force*, I have built up my blog on the Quantum Wave website. Thank you to everyone who has registered for the Quantum Wave newsletters, and thanks for all the very encouraging comments about the blog articles. This feedback has been very valuable and made the writing process much easier and more enjoyable.

I have also had numerous interesting and useful discussions at the various astronomy events and other book signing events that I have attended since the publication of *Higgs Force*. Thank you to John Eastwood for all his help at numerous book signing events and thank you to Pat Williams for all her help in arranging signing events and promoting my work.

Thank you to Allan Chapman for a very helpful discussion about Jeremiah Horrocks at Astrofest 2014. Also, thank you to Heidi Chapman for an engaging conversation about the tides.

Enormous thanks to Juliet Smith for her unceasing encouragement and assistance with bringing another publishing project to a successful conclusion. Thank you to everyone else involved in the production of *Gravity* including Brian Asbury, Sarah McCall, Cathryn Pritchard and Sally Coleman.

Many thanks to everyone who read drafts of various parts of *Gravity*, especially Karen Day, Nick Manton and Juliet Smith.

Special thanks to Debra Nightingale for reading several drafts of the book and for all her perceptive comments. Thank you for ensuring that all my arguments are clear and water-tight.

Thank you to Angie for her continued backing of my various projects. And above all, thank you to my parents, for their invaluable and enthusiastic support.

# Index

# Higgs Force
## Cosmic Symmetry Shattered

he award-winning *Higgs Force: Cosmic Symmetry Shattered* tells the incredible
ory of the most important scientific discovery of the past 50 years. It begins with
e ideas of the Greek philosophers over two thousand years ago, and takes us on a
urney through many of the most important scientific discoveries in history before
inging us right up to date with the discovery of the Higgs particle in July 2012.

delightfully readable and accessible account of the search
r the force which ensures that there is something rather
an nothing in the Universe.'
hn Gribbin,
strophysicist and Science Author

remarkable story told with lucidity and verve.'
nathan Evans, Lecturer in Physics,
ambridge University

jood reading for anyone interested in what today's
ysicists are excited about.'
e CERN Courier, July 2012

liggs Force takes a new approach to contemporary
ysics, and makes notoriously difficult material accessible
d approachable, very readable and entertaining.'
ny Mann, President of the British Society
r the History of Mathematics

**HIGGS FORCE**
Cosmic Symmetry Shattered

The story of the greatest scientific
discovery for 50 years

Nicholas Mee

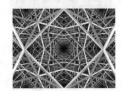

Virtual Image, 184 Reddish Road, South Reddish, Stockport SK5 7HS

email@virtualimage.co.uk      Tel: 0161 480 1915      Fax: 0161 612 2965

# www.virtualimage.co.uk

VIRTUAL
IMAGE

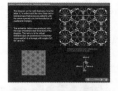

# Quantum Wave Publishing

Nicholas Mee's blog is packed with cutting edge news from the world of science. It is hosted by the Quantum Wave website at: www.quantumwavepublishing.com. Quantum Wave is a new publisher specializing in high quality popular science books, eBooks and multimedia.

Black Holes: Big Ones, Small Ones,
(and now Middle-Sized Ones)
Most of the Universe is Missing!
Rocket Science
Bosons, Lasers and Superfluids
Snowflakes are Dancing!
Higgs Boson - update from CERN
Fermions, Atoms and Neutron Stars
The Great Comet of 2013
Mirror Mirror on the Wall
Steam Powered Computing
A Few Fractals
Symbolic Sculpture
Super Symmetry!
A Faustian Pact and the Chamber of Secrets
Inspirational Games
Quantum Waves and the Rosetta Stone
What on Earth is a Boson?
Twinkle, Twinkle Little Star
From Olympic Fireworks to Cosmic Ones
Quantum Wave: From Radar to Quasar
Mathematical Sculptures

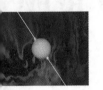

# www.quantumwavepublishing.com

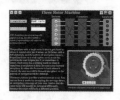
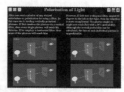